P O Box 569
Swindon SN2 2YP

customers@english-heritage.org.uk

www.english-heritage.org.uk

☎ 0870 333 1181
(non-geographic call rates apply)

🖷 01793 414926

MINICOM
Minicom text telephone for
the deaf or hard of hearing
0800 015 0516

   #EnglishHeritage

OPENING TIMES

All dates shown run from 1 April 2014 to 29 March 2015

All information is correct at the time of going to press. Due to unforeseen circumstances, some opening times may change. Please call Customer Services or check our website before you travel to any of our properties.

At some of our properties, visitors cannot be admitted less than one hour before closing time. Please call in advance to confirm individual policies.

Where properties have key keepers, please contact them before setting off. For those open at 'any reasonable time', please visit during daylight hours for safety reasons and to avoid causing a disturbance.

🇹 Properties showing this symbol may be closed at certain times for private events. Please call in advance to check.

Some of our smaller staffed properties may close between 1pm and 2pm. Please call Customer Services for more information.

Don't forget to check opening times online before you visit, **www.english-heritage.org.uk/daysout/properties**

If you're a history lover, like me, nothing beats being in a place where you can really connect with the past.

I'm happy to say that this year, there's an outstanding selection of places where we can all experience England's story: from the Neolithic at our new exhibition and transformed landscape at Stonehenge, to the magnificence of the 18th century at Kenwood, now restored to the original Robert Adam paint scheme.

For families, there's also great fun to be had at the refurbished nurseries at Audley End and at the Swiss Cottage at Osborne, where you can experience a Royal Victorian Childhood through our new interactive displays.

I'm looking forward to stepping onto the new viewing platforms at Kenilworth Castle to experience the view that Queen Elizabeth I saw from the rooms that Robert Dudley built to woo her in the 1570s. The re-created Tudor garden there is a must too – now in its fifth year!

On a more sombre note, as part of our commemoration of the start of the First World War, there are events at many sites including Wrest Park, Dover Castle and Scarborough Castle and we'll also be giving listed status to over 2500 war memorials.

And as ever, we have a packed events programme, so I do hope that you will find inspiration to visit. You can also find out more about what's on near you on our website or follow us on Twitter and Facebook.

As we move towards becoming an independent charity our Members are more important than ever, as visitors, volunteers and donors. Thank you for all your support.

Simon Thurley
Chief Executive

INSPIRE ME

DAYS OUT IN 2014

With hundreds of years of history to discover at English Heritage sites across the country, it's no surprise that there are plenty of tales to tell. From hidden gems to fascinating collections, seasonal garden highlights to hands-on children's activities, there is plenty to see and do for all the family throughout the year. Here are a few ideas to get you started.

Don't forget to visit the website for more ideas and inspiration for great days out
english-heritage.org.uk/daysout/inspireme

COME RAIN OR SHINE

Entertain the kids no matter what the weather.

Fun in the sun or rain for the little adventurers, at one of our many events created just for kids. Put on your wet weather gear and burn off some energy at one of the many fun events!

BATTLE HISTORY

With a fun audio tour and touch screen displays, **1066 Battle of Hastings Abbey and Battlefield's** indoor Discovery Centre is perfect for keeping children entertained.

RIVALRY, SUSPICION AND THE COLD WAR

Spend a day inside the atmospheric **York Cold War Bunker**, built to monitor nuclear explosions in the Yorkshire region.

GO UNDERGROUND

There's no better way of escaping the weather than by heading underground, and a visit to Norfolk's **Grime's Graves** – prehistoric flint mine. (Note: no under 5's)

FOUNTAINS, FOLLIES AND FANCIES

Our gardens are hiding plenty of strange quirks and surprises!

A TUDOR JOKE!

The Elizabethan Garden at **Kenilworth Castle** hides a rather odd surprise for visitors. Based on an eye-witness account of the original garden, the fountain in the recreated garden contains a 'water joke'. Water jets have been carefully placed so as to surprise unwary visitors – so keep your wits about you if you get up close!

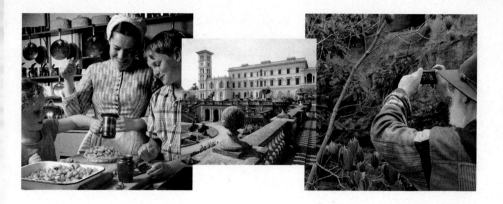

TAKING TEA

During the 18th and 19th centuries, a garden wasn't complete without somewhere to indulge in a spot of tea. At **Audley End**, Robert Adam's elegant Tea House Bridge served this purpose.

A ROYAL PLAY AREA

Osborne, a country escape for Queen Victoria, Prince Albert and their growing family. Visitors today can see where the children played in the great gardens.

AS SEEN ON SCREEN

Top five English Heritage properties on film.

WOLVESEY CASTLE, HAMPSHIRE

Les Misérables (2012), *starring Hugh Jackman, Russell Crowe and Anne Hathaway.*

ELTHAM PALACE AND GARDENS, LONDON

Brideshead Revisited (2008), *starring Emma Thompson and Ben Whishaw.*

CASTLE ACRE PRIORY, NORFOLK

Glorious 39 (2009), *starring Bill Nighy, David Tennant and Christopher Lee.*

DOVER CASTLE, KENT

The Other Boleyn Girl (2008), *starring Scarlett Johansson and Natalie Portman.*

GOODRICH CASTLE, HEREFORDSHIRE

Merlin (2009–present), *starring Colin Morgan.*

Step into E

PREHISTORY
BEFORE AD 43

The earliest known humans came to England nearly a million years ago. But continuous settlement began only after the end of the last Ice Age, some 12,000 years ago.

THE FIRST FARMERS

Nomadic 'hunter-gatherer' people left few visible traces, but with the arrival of farming in the Neolithic (New Stone Age) period, people began constructing monuments. Among the earliest are ritual enclosures like *Windmill Hill* and communal tombs like *West Kennet Long Barrow*.

MONUMENTS AND METAL-WORKING

Circular earthwork 'henges' appear from about 3000 BC, when *Stonehenge* was begun. The later Neolithic and early Bronze Ages saw massive stone circles like *Castlerigg Stone Circle* and *Avebury Stone Circle* raised, sometimes becoming elements of 'ritual landscapes' like that including mysterious *Silbury Hill*. *Grime's Graves* flint mines were in use by 2600 BC: but before *Stonehenge* was completed in about 2000 BC, the working of bronze was known in England.

ROUND BARROWS, VILLAGES AND HILL FORTS

Individual burials in Bronze Age 'round barrows' (like *Flowerdown Barrows*) meanwhile replaced communal tombs. From about 1500 BC landscapes were divided up by great field systems, with dwellings grouped into villages such as *Grimspound* and *Chysauster Ancient Village*. New iron-working technology from around 750 BC coincided with the spread of hill forts like *Maiden Castle*. Then town-like tribal power-centres such as *Lexden Earthworks* developed – a process interrupted by the Roman Conquest.

Among the 56 prehistoric sites in English Heritage's care are:
Avebury Stone Circle | Castlerigg Stone Circle | Chysauster Ancient Village | Grime's Graves | Lexden Earthworks | Maiden Castle | Silbury Hill | Stonehenge | Stanwick Iron Age Fortifications | West Kennet Long Barrow | Windmill Hill

L to R: Stonehenge, Chysauster Ancient Village, Maiden Castle.

c.950,000 years ago	c.12,000 years ago	c.4000– 2500 BC	c.3000 BC	c.2500– 750 BC	from c.750 BC	AD 43
Earliest human activity in England	Continuous human settlement begins	Neolithic period (First Farmers)	Stonehenge begun	Bronze Age	Iron Age	Roman Conquest begins

CONQUEST

Though Julius Caesar raided Britain in 55 and 54 BC, full-scale conquest began when Roman forces landed near *Richborough Roman Fort* in AD 43. Despite resistance by Boudica (Boadicea) and others, Roman armies had reached northern Scotland by AD 84, before eventually retiring to the permanent frontier of *Hadrian's Wall*. Incomparably the most impressive Roman monument in Britain, the Wall's defensive system includes major forts like *Birdoswald*, *Chesters* and *Housesteads*.

CIVILISATION

Away from the frontiers, Roman Britain was for long periods peaceful and prosperous. 'Country houses' like *Lullingstone Roman Villa* flourished, bath-houses and amphitheatres were built, and many towns were founded – including large *Silchester* and *Wroxeter* and smaller *Aldborough* and *Corbridge* – often at existing British tribal centres. Most were later walled against increasing external threats.

THE SAXON SHORE

Towards the end of the 3rd century, attacks by seaborne Germanic raiders prompted the creation of 'Saxon Shore' coastal fortifications like *Burgh Castle*: further trouble saw the system strengthened in the next century, and *Pevensey Castle* added. Garrisons were by now mainly British-born, and little distinguished 'Romans' from 'Britons' when imperial rule petered out. There was no clearly definable end to Roman Britain.

Among the 52 Roman sites in English Heritage's care are:
Birdoswald Roman Fort | Burgh Castle | Chesters Roman Fort
Corbridge Roman Town | Hadrian's Wall | Housesteads
Roman Fort | Lullingstone Roman Villa | Pevensey Castle
Richborough Roman Fort and Amphitheatre | Wroxeter
Roman City

ROMANS
AD 43–C.410

Roman Britain lasted for over three and a half centuries, leaving an indelible mark on the nation's landscape. English Heritage's Roman sites reflect the era from its violent beginning to its obscure close.

L to R: Lullingstone Roman Villa, Hadrian's Wall, Chesters Roman Fort – Relief of Minerva and Aesculapius.

AD 43	AD 84	AD 122	c.AD 260–360	c.AD 410–425
Roman Conquest begins	Furthest extent of Roman rule in Britain	Hadrian's Wall begun	Saxon Shore defences built	Imperial rule by Rome fades

DARK AGES

C.400–1066

Called 'dark' only because its history is sparsely documented, the momentous era between the end of Roman Britain and the Norman Conquest saw the gradual emergence of the English nation.

THE ENGLISH CONQUEST

Post-Roman Britain was assailed by sea-borne Germanic peoples – Angles, Saxons, Jutes and Frisians. Though delayed by Romano-British resistance (perhaps inspired by a fabled 'Arthur') these 'Anglo-Saxon' invaders conquered most of lowland England by the mid-600s, establishing several independent kingdoms. Tantalising hints about this shadowy period come from sites like *Birdoswald Roman Fort, Tintagel Castle* and *Wroxeter Roman City*.

CHRISTIAN CULTURE BLOSSOMS

Increasingly called 'English', the pagan conquerors were converted to Christianity by missionaries from Rome and Ireland. Christian culture blossomed: *Lindisfarne Priory* produced its illuminated Gospels, while Bede's writings at *St Paul's Monastery, Jarrow* fostered the concept of an English nation. The architecture and craftsmanship of *St Peter's Church, Barton-Upon-Humber* and *Sandbach Crosses* likewise reflect the English Church's vitality.

THE VIKING THREAT

Towards the end of the 8th century, soon after *Offa's Dyke* defined its western boundary, England's development was imperilled as Viking raids became invasions. King Alfred of Wessex turned the tide, and his descendants reconquered Viking-held lands: his grandson Aethelstan became the first ruler of a unified English state. But Danish pressure was revived by King Cnut, and it was a weakened England which faced the Normans in 1066.

Among the 19 sites within this period in English Heritage's care are: 1066 Battle of Hastings, Abbey and Battlefield Lindisfarne Priory | Lydford Castle and Saxon Town Offa's Dyke | St Augustine's Abbey | St Paul's Monastery, Jarrow | St Peter's Church, Barton-upon-Humber | Sandbach Crosses | Tintagel Castle | Whitby Abbey

L to R: Sandbach Crosses, Lindisfarne Priory, St Peter's Church – Barton-upon-Humber.

c.410–25	c.550–c.650	597–625	787–89	871–900	927	1066
End of Imperial Roman rule in Britain	Anglo-Saxons conquer lowland England	Principal Christian missions	Viking raids begin	Alfred the Great reigns	Aethelstan becomes first king of all England	Norman Conquest begins

THE LAND FILLED WITH CASTLES

Earthwork and timber 'motte and bailey' castles were the instruments and symbols of the Norman Conquest: many, like *Clifford's Tower* and *Totnes Castle*, were later refortified in stone. The great stone keeps of the Norman and Angevin kings and their barons formed the core of major early fortresses like *Dover Castle*, *Conisbrough Castle* and *Richmond Castle*, before the focus shifted to many-towered enclosure walls with powerful gatehouses, as at *Framlingham Castle* and *Goodrich Castle*. Equipped with halls, chapels and many domestic buildings, some strongholds like *Beeston Castle* or *Kenilworth Castle* were immense in scale. More compact fortresses – including *Farleigh Hungerford Castle* and *Nunney Castle* – developed towards the end of the era, some (like *Berry Pomeroy* and *Kirby Muxloe* castles) equipped for artillery defence.

TOWN AND COUNTRY

Only a tiny minority of medieval people lived in castles. English Heritage's collection also includes lightly fortified or undefended manor houses like *Stokesay Castle* or *Old Soar Manor*, and urban houses like Southampton's *Medieval Merchant's House*. Country life is represented by *Wharram Percy Deserted Medieval Village* and farm buildings like imposing *Harmondsworth Great Barn*.

OASES OF PEACE

Whether in castle, town or country, medieval life was dominated by the Church: in the 14th century about one in fifteen Englishmen were clergy of some kind. English Heritage cares for parish churches like *St Mary's Kempley* with its wonderful wall-paintings, and bishops' mansions including *Lincoln Medieval Bishops Palace:* and the evocative remains of many monasteries, from big, prosperous *Castle Acre Priory* to tiny *Mattersey Priory*.

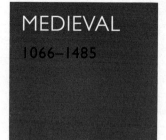

MEDIEVAL
1066–1485

Nearly half of all English Heritage sites date from the 'medieval' centuries between the battles of Hastings in 1066 and Bosworth in 1485. Their variety mirrors the era's developing character.

L to R: The Battle of Hastings, St Mary's Church Kempley, Dover Castle.

1066	1066–1154	1215	1154–1485	1277–1307
Norman Conquest	Norman Kings	Magna Carta	Angevin/ Plantagenet Kings	Edward I's wars in Wales and Scotland

MEDIEVAL
CONTINUED
1066–1485

Each reflects the characteristics of the monastic order which inhabited it: 'mainstream' Benedictines at *Binham Priory* and *Whitby Abbey*; solitude-seeking Cistercians at *Furness Abbey* and *Rievaulx Abbey*; decoration-loving Cluniacs at *Wenlock Priory*; Augustinian canons at lovely *Lanercost Priory*; hermit-like Carthusians at *Mount Grace Priory* or the urban friars of Gloucester's *Blackfriars* and *Greyfriars*.

MEMORIES OF CONFLICT
Many of English Heritage's medieval sites, by contrast, recall the foreign or internal wars of medieval England. Some – like *Carlisle Castle* – guarded land borders against Scots or Welsh, or like *Carisbrooke Castle* and *Dartmouth Castle*, defended coasts against sea-borne invasion and raiding. Others, including *Rochester Castle*, endured conflicts between monarchs and barons, or like *Dunstanburgh Castle* or *Warkworth Castle*, witnessed the dynastic Wars of the Roses, ended by the Battle of Bosworth which began the Tudor age.

Among the 202 sites within this period in English Heritage's care are: Beeston Castle | Carisbrooke Castle | Carlisle Castle Castle Acre Priory | Clifford's Tower | Conisbrough Castle Dover Castle | Eleanor Cross, Geddington | Framlingham Castle | Goodrich Castle | Harmondsworth Great Barn Kenilworth Castle | Lanercost Priory | Middleham Castle Mount Grace Priory | Old Sarum | Rievaulx Abbey | St Mary's Church, Kempley | Scarborough Castle | Stokesay Castle

L to R: Hailes Abbey, Conisbrough Castle, Rievaulx Abbey.

1337–1453	1349	1381	1455–85	1476–77
Hundred Years War with France	Black Death	Peasants' Revolt	Wars of the Roses	First books printed in England

THE TRIUMPH OF MONARCHY

Ending the Wars of the Roses, Henry VII curtailed aristocratic power and castle-building, and his successors strengthened the grip of monarchy. Henceforth fortresses would be raised only by the crown, most notably Henry VIII's coastal artillery forts – the first co-ordinated system of national defence – including *Deal Castle*, *Pendennis Castle* and *Portland Castle*.

RELIGIOUS UPHEAVALS

Henry's new-style forts defended England against European Catholic reaction to the religious changes he initiated: English Heritage's outstanding collection of monastic ruins bear witness to his Dissolution of the Monasteries. After swinging from Edward VI's radical Protestantism to Mary's revived Catholicism, the nation settled down to religious compromise under Queen Elizabeth.

THE FLOWERING OF ENGLISH CULTURE

Elizabeth's long and glorious reign witnessed the expansion of English sea power (reinforced by her defeat of the Spanish Armada) and the flowering of English culture epitomised by Shakespeare. It also saw the burgeoning of the great English country house: some were converted monasteries or adapted medieval fortresses like *Kenilworth Castle and Elizabethan Garden*, but most were built from new, like *Kirby Hall*. All these developments expressed a new-found English self-confidence.

Among the 50 sites within this period in English Heritage's care are: Deal Castle | Hailes Abbey | Hardwick Old Hall Kenilworth Castle and Elizabethan Garden | Kirby Hall Norham Castle | Pendennis Castle | Rushton Triangular Lodge Titchfield Abbey | Tynemouth Priory and Castle

TUDORS
1485–1603

The pivot of medieval and modern history, the Tudor era saw strong royal government established; England transformed from a Catholic to a Protestant nation; and the flowering of a distinctively English culture.

L to R: Queen Elizabeth I, Rushton Triangular Lodge, Framlingham Castle.

1485	1509–47	1536–40	1532–59	1558–1603	1588	1564–1616
Battle of Bosworth	Henry VIII reigns	Dissolution of the Monasteries	Religious changes	Elizabeth I reigns	Spanish Armada	Shakespeare living

STUARTS
1603–1714

Following a long peace, the intense political and religious conflicts of the Stuart era transformed England's government. Developments in architecture and living standards are also reflected in this era's English Heritage sites.

GRACIOUS LIVING
The earlier ('Jacobean') part of the period saw many lavish mansions like *Audley End House* and *Bolsover Castle* built, and fine interiors created in more modest dwellings like *Bessie Surtees House* and *Great Yarmouth Row Houses*.

THE ENGLISH REVOLUTION
The Civil Wars between Charles I and Parliament (1642–51) brought much devastation; epic sieges of *Pendennis Castle* and many other places; and (after his imprisonment at *Carisbrooke Castle*) the king's execution and the creation (1649–53) of the Commonwealth, the only republic in English history. Young Charles II narrowly escaped capture near *Boscobel House*.

RESTORATION AND NEW STYLES
Epitomised by Pepys's diary, the reign of the restored Charles II brought continuing scientific advances, but also plague and fire in London and humiliating Dutch attack, provoking the building of defences like *Tilbury Fort*. The 'English Baroque' style of Christopher Wren and *Abingdon County Hall* came increasingly into fashion towards the end of the period.

ENGLAND AND BRITAIN
The era's long-simmering religious disputes were addressed in 1689, after the Catholic James II was deposed by the Protestant William and Mary. Under Queen Anne, the Acts of Union with Scotland made England part of 'Great Britain'.

Among the 39 sites within this period in English Heritage's care are: Abingdon County Hall | Audley End House and Gardens | Berry Pomeroy Castle | Bolsover Castle Boscobel House and the Royal Oak | Carisbrooke Castle Great Yarmouth Row Houses | Langley Chapel Pendennis Castle | Tilbury Fort

L to R: Boscobel House, Audley End House and Gardens, Tilbury Fort.

1603–25	1642–51	1649–60	1660–69	1688	1706–07
James I (Jacobean period)	Civil Wars	Commonwealth and Cromwell's Protectorate	Pepys's diary written	James II deposed	Acts of Union with Scotland

ELEGANT MANSIONS

English Heritage's outstanding collection of Georgian and Regency mansions reflect the period's progression of fashionable styles, from the Palladian of *Chiswick House* via Robert Adam's *Kenwood* to the 'Regency' Greek Revival of *Belsay Hall* and *The Grange at Northington*. Extravagant or tasteful interiors (as at *Marble Hill House*) were matched by formal or 'landscaped' gardens – an English gift to the world – often adorned (as at *Audley End House* and *Wrest Park*) with charming garden architecture.

INDUSTRIAL REVOLUTION

The wealth which financed these mansions was increasingly founded on England's pioneering Industrial Revolution, itself founded on entrepreneurial enterprise and new developments like canals, the 'factory system' and steam power. The *Iron Bridge* was the world's first of its kind, and the world's first steam trains ran in England in 1825.

WAR AND EMPIRE

International trade boomed alongside an expanding empire, particularly in India and the Americas. Yet as *Dover Castle* and *Dymchurch Martello Tower* demonstrate, Britain's growing military and especially naval power did not go unchallenged, notably during the long wars with Revolutionary and Napoleonic France. Wellington, the greatest military hero of these wars, is remembered at *Apsley House*, *Walmer Castle* and *Wellington Arch*.

Among the 42 sites within this period in English Heritage's care are: Apsley House | Belsay Hall, Castle and Gardens Chiswick House | Derwentcote Steel Furnace | Iron Bridge Kenwood | Marble Hill House | The Grange at Northington Wellington Arch | Wrest Park

GEORGIANS
1714–1837

An age of contrasts, counterpointing elegant aristocratic mansions with grimy, overcrowded mills, the Georgian era saw Britain become the world's first industrial nation, at the hub of a rapidly growing empire.

L to R: Kenwood, Marble Hill House, Wrest Park.

1715 & 1745/6	1756–63	1779	1793–1815	1811–20	1825
Jacobite Risings	'Seven Years War' expands British Empire	Industrial Revolution: Iron Bridge completed	Napoleonic Wars	Regency period	First public steam railway opens

VICTORIANS
1837–1901

The long reign of Queen Victoria saw Britain at the zenith of her international power and status, and the greatest manufacturing nation in the world.

L to R: Down House, Osborne, Stott Park Bobbin Mill.

MASTERS AND SERVANTS
The Queen's strong personality is reflected at *Osborne*. Her wealthier subjects also continued to build great mansions like *Brodsworth Hall* and *Witley Court,* operated by armies of servants – as *Audley End's* kitchens, Nursery Wing and stables demonstrate.

A HIVE OF INDUSTRY
J.W. Evans Silver Factory and *Stott Park Bobbin Mill* recall Victorian England as a hive of manufacturing industry: rural life was also transformed by machinery, as seen in English Heritage's collection of windmills.

DOUBT AND CERTAINTY
The publication of Charles Darwin's ideas on evolution (matured and written at *Down House*) shook Victorian religious certainty, but did not stem the period's flood of chapel and church building – the latter almost always in the ubiquitous 'Gothic Revival' style. *St Mary's Church, Studley Royal* is a flamboyant example.

AN IMPERIAL POWER
Despite the 1860s French invasion scare which produced new fortifications like *Fort Brockhurst* and the updating of older defences like *Dartmouth Castle*, Britannia's fleets continued to rule the waves and her armies to fight far-flung colonial wars. The Indian Mutiny of 1857 and the Boer War of 1899–1902 dented 'Imperial' confidence, but at the Queen's death the British Empire was still rapidly expanding.

Among the 30 sites within this period in English Heritage's care are: Audley End House | Brodsworth Hall The Home of Charles Darwin, Down House | Fort Brockhurst J.W. Evans Silver Factory | Osborne | St Mary's Church, Studley Royal | Sibsey Trader Windmill | Stott Park Bobbin Mill Witley Court

1837	1854–56	1859	1895	1897	1901
Accession of Queen Victoria	Crimean War	Darwin's 'Origin of Species' published	First motor cars in England	Victoria's Diamond Jubilee	Death of Queen Victoria

TWO WORLD WARS – AND A THIRD?

The First World War, with its terrible carnage, and the Second World War – whose far greater impact on civilian life is underlined at *Great Yarmouth Row Houses* – are both reflected in English Heritage properties. Old fortresses like *Portland Castle* were updated for new types of warfare, and the *Secret Wartime Tunnels* beneath *Dover Castle* played a crucial role in saving the nation in 1940. The dead of both wars are remembered by the London war memorials cared for by English Heritage, including the poignant *Royal Artillery Memorial* at Hyde Park Corner. But *York Cold War Bunker* is a chilling reminder that the threat of even greater mass destruction remained ever-present.

SOCIAL TRANSFORMATION

Both World Wars transformed the social structure of England: *Brodsworth Hall* tracks the decline of the country house and its servant-dependent lifestyle – though remodelled *Eltham Palace* displays the stylish living still enjoyed by the millionaire few.

AN ONGOING REVOLUTION

The post-Second World War creation of the Welfare State made life easier for the many. The advent of radio and TV and more recently of affordable computer technology fostered a still greater (and still continuing) revolution in lifestyles.

MODERN
1901–PRESENT

During a century of rapidly-developing technologies, the two World Wars which dominate the modern age of British history acted as catalysts for previously unimaginable social changes.

English Heritage cares for 23 sites with major features of this period – including the following – and several London war memorials: Brodsworth Hall and Gardens | Calshot Castle Dover Castle (Secret Wartime Tunnels) | Eltham Palace Great Yarmouth Row Houses | Portland Castle Royal Garrison Church | Tynemouth Priory and Castle York Cold War Bunker

L to R: Dover Castle, Eltham Palace and Gardens, Brodsworth Hall.

1914–18	1922	1936	1939–45	1948	1946–1989	1981 Personal computers and
First World War	First BBC radio broadcast	Regular TV broadcasting begins	Second World War	National Health Service established	Cold War	1990 mobile phones widely available

MEMBERSHIP AND EVENTS

Thank you for supporting English Heritage – your membership really does make a difference to our work and helps protect more than 400 historic properties, ranging from castles to grand palaces, inspiring abbeys to lavish gardens. We look forward to welcoming you on your next visit soon.

DON'T FORGET YOUR MEMBERSHIP ENTITLES YOU TO:

- Free, unlimited entry to all our sites.
- Free entry for up to six accompanied children (under 19) within your family group per member.
- Free or reduced price admission to over 100 associated attractions.
- Your free handbook (RRP £10.95) to help you get the most out of your visits.
- Our award-winning exclusive Members' Magazine – packed with ideas, inspiration and news.
- Access to exclusive Members' events and behind the scenes tours.

READ ALL ABOUT IT

Our superb magazine is packed with inspiration and ideas for making the most of your membership, including a full list of our events. What's more, it's completely FREE to members and is delivered direct to you, so look out for it. You can also be the first to hear about special events and the latest news by signing up to receive our regular e-newsletter. Go to **english-heritage.org.uk/newsletter**

MORE VALUE, MORE PROPERTIES

Your English Heritage membership card opens doors to many other associated attractions and properties – often at no extra cost. Check details in this handbook or visit **english-heritage.org.uk/members** to see offers and check terms and conditions.

EVENTS

Every year we offer a whole host of fantastic days out. There's something for everyone, from live action spectaculars to ghost tours, arts and crafts fairs, talks, tours, exhibitions and children's quests and trails.

If you have a passion for history, or are just looking for a great day out, we recommend you visit at least one of our unmissable event weekends: St George's Day Festival at Wrest Park (26-27 Apr); World War II Weekend at Dover Castle (24-26 May); and the fantastic History Live! weekend (19-20 Jul). **www.historylive.com**

MEMBERS' EVENTS

There is so much more to our properties than you might think, and as a member you have access to behind-the-scenes tours guided by our experts, who will share their unique knowledge and insight with you. We have over 100 members-only events throughout the year, across the country.

See page 332 for more information, or visit **english-heritage.org.uk/events**

SHARE YOUR EXPERIENCE

Tell other members about your visit to one of our properties. Post your message and photos on **flickr.com/groups/ englishheritagedaysout** and subscribe to our YouTube channel to check our latest videos **youtube.com/user/ englishheritagefilm**

Give the Gift of Membership
call us now on
0870 333 1181
see page 355 for full details

flickr You Tube

VISITING OUR PROPERTIES

Goodrich Castle

Please read our Planning Your Visit section on pages 325-27. Each property has a full list of symbols to help you assess its suitability for your visit and plan your perfect day.
You can also find details of our Access For All policy and *Access Guide* on page 328. Please remember to check the latest opening times and events information on our website at www.english-heritage.org.uk/daysout or call us on 0870 333 1181.

LONDON

Kenwood

Keep up to date with
events, news and offers
www.english-heritage.
org.uk/newsletter

Apsley House

Enfield

Barnet

Harrow

Haringey

Waltham
Forest

Redbridge

Havering

Hillingdon

Brent

Islington

Camden

Hackney

Barking
and
Dagenham

Westminster

City of
London

Tower
Hamlets

Newham

Ealing

Kensington

Hammersmith

10

11

13

12

8

9

Greenwich

Hounslow

5

Southwark

3

Bexley

Wandsworth

Lambeth

Lewisham

2

7

Richmond
upon
Thames

6

Merton

Kingston
upon
Thames

Bromley

Sutton

Croydon

Details of local public transport information in England are available from Traveline
www.traveline.org.uk or call 0871 200 2233.

Remember to check opening times before you visit any of our properties
www.english-heritage.org.uk/daysout

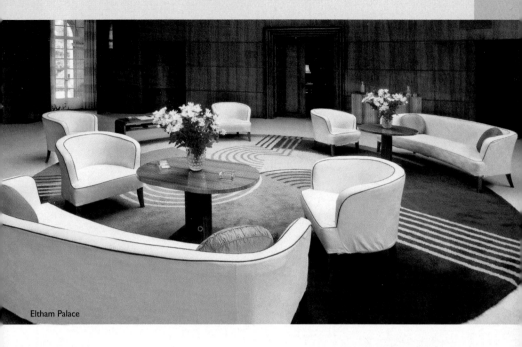

Eltham Palace

PROPERTIES

HIGHLIGHTS FOR 2014/15 IN **LONDON**

p.32

Eltham Palace & Gardens: experience the glamour of 1930s society.

p.34

Kenwood: enjoy the vividly refurbished interiors and new family activities.

p.39

Ranger's House: wonder at glittering jewellery and fabulous art collections.

p.40

Wellington Arch: see the fascinating new exhibitions and enjoy the panoramic views.

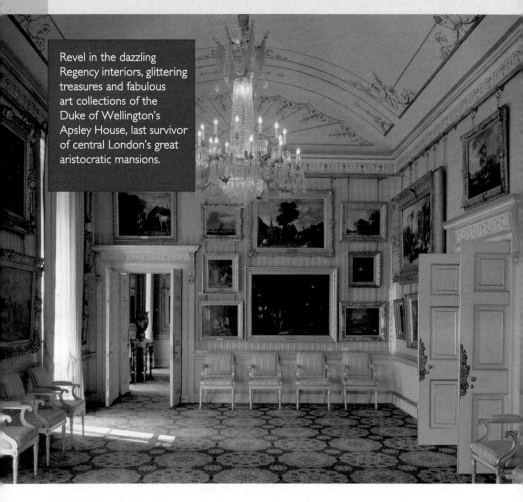

Revel in the dazzling Regency interiors, glittering treasures and fabulous art collections of the Duke of Wellington's Apsley House, last survivor of central London's great aristocratic mansions.

VISIT US

Address: Apsley House, 149 Piccadilly, Hyde Park Corner, London

Direction: 149 Piccadilly, Hyde Park Corner

Train: Victoria ½ mile

Bus: From surrounding areas

Tube: Hyde Park Corner

Tel: 020 7499 5676

NON-MEMBERS

Apsley House

Adult	£6.90
Concession	£6.20
Child	£4.10

Joint ticket with Wellington Arch

Adult	£8.90
Concession	£8.00
Child	£5.30
Family	£23.10

OPENING TIMES

1 Apr-2 Nov, Wed-Sun & Bank Hols	11am-5pm
3 Nov-21 Mar, Sat-Sun	10am-4pm
24-26 Dec, 31 Dec-1 Jan	Closed

Last admission 30 mins before closing

ACQ.1947

Disabled access very limited. Please phone property for information.

MAP Page 338 (4E)
OS Map 176, 161/173: TQ284799

Don't miss our 15-minute Walk and Talk Gallery Tours which take place twice daily throughout the year.

Apsley House, home of the first Duke of Wellington and his descendants, stands right in the heart of London at Hyde Park Corner. For over 200 years, this great metropolitan mansion has been known colloquially as 'Number 1 London', because it was the first house encountered after passing the tollgates at the top of Knightsbridge.

Apsley House was originally designed and built by Robert Adam between 1771 and 1778 for Baron Apsley – from whom it takes its name. It passed to the Wellesley family in 1807, being first owned by Richard and then his younger brother Arthur Wellesley – the Duke of Wellington.

Wellington is most famous for defeating Napoleon at the Battle of Waterloo in 1815, but this was only the culmination of a brilliant military career. He was also a major politician, becoming Prime Minister in 1828.

Remodelled by Benjamin Wyatt to reflect the Duke's rising status, Apsley House's dazzling interiors are magnificent examples of the Regency style. They provided the perfect backdrop for entertaining, particularly at the annual Waterloo Banquets which commemorate the great victory.

Inside Apsley House you will see many aspects of the first Duke's life and work, including his outstanding art collection. Paintings by many famous artists hang throughout the first floor rooms, including a number that were recovered from the baggage of Joseph Bonaparte after the Battle of Vitoria in 1813. Later the collection was gifted to Wellington by the King of Spain. A colossal nude statue of Napoleon by Canova dominates the stairwell at the centre of the house.

Throughout his military career, the Duke was presented with a vast collection of silver plate and fine porcelain as trophies from grateful nations. Many of these can be seen in the Plate and China Room. Wellington's victories are also celebrated in the fine British craftsmanship of the magnificent Wellington Shield, designed by Thomas Stothard, and the impressive candelabra presented by the Merchants and Bankers of the City of London.

When the seventh Duke of Wellington gave the house to the nation in 1947, the family retained the private rooms, which they still use today. This makes Apsley House not only the last surviving great aristocratic London town house open to the public, but also the only property managed by English Heritage in which the original owner's family still live.

NEW FOR 2014

Step into a new look for the entrance hall and experience the grandeur of this fine town house with its new displays.

CHANDOS MAUSOLEUM (ST LAWRENCE'S CHURCH)
LITTLE STANMORE
HA8 6RB

© CCT

Chandos Mausoleum was added to early 18th-century St Lawrence's Church (church not part of CCT's estate) in 1736. The Mausoleum contains a magnificent monument by master carver Grinling Gibbons and the walls and ceiling are lavishly decorated. There are also hatchments in the ante-room.

Owned and managed by The Churches Conservation Trust.

OPENING TIMES

Summer, Sun	2pm-5pm
Winter, Sun	2pm-4pm

For other times please call 020 8952 0019 to enquire

VISIT US

Train: Mill Hill Broadway 1¾ miles

Bus: TfL bus services 79, 186 & 340 all pass the site

Tube: Canons Park

Within 1 hour of Apsley House, Wellington Arch, Kenwood, Chapter House and Pyx Chamber and Jewel Tower

MAP Page 338 (3E)
OS Map 176, 173: TQ186913

CHAPTER HOUSE AND PYX CHAMBER
WESTMINSTER ABBEY – SW1P 3PA

Built by the royal masons in 1250, the Chapter House of Westminster Abbey was used from the 13th to the 16th century by Benedictine monks for their daily meetings. It was also sometimes used as a meeting place of the King's Great Council and the Commons, predecessors of today's Parliament.

A beautiful octagonal building with a vaulted ceiling and delicate central column, it offers rarely seen examples of medieval sculpture, an original floor of glazed tiles and spectacular wall paintings. The 11th-century Pyx Chamber also has a medieval tiled floor, and was used as a monastic and royal treasury. It contains a 13th-century stone altar which survived the Reformation.

During 2009/10, English Heritage funded a major programme of conservation repairs to the external fabric of the Chapter House. This included repairs to the roof, gutters, stonework on the elevations and flying buttresses, and repairs to the lead light glazing – thus preserving this highly important building for future generations.

Chapter House free to EH members. Under the care and management of the Dean and Chapter of Westminster.
www.westminster-abbey.org

OPENING TIMES

1 Apr-29 Mar, Mon-Sat & Bank Hols	10.30am-6pm or dusk (whichever is earlier)
Good Fri, 24-26 Dec & 1 Jan	Closed

May be closed at short notice on state and religious occasions

VISIT US

Direction: Through the cloister from Dean's Yard if you only want to visit the Chapter House. Turn into Dean's Yard off Broad Sanctuary. Turn left along the square and go through the entrance-way into the cloister

Please show your EH membership card to the Marshal at the gate

Train: Victoria and Charing Cross both ¾ mile, Waterloo 1 mile

Bus: From surrounding areas

Tube: Westminster and St James' Park stations both ¼ mile

Tel: 020 7654 4900

ACQ.1872 Chapter House
ACQ.1901 Pyx Chamber

MAP Page 339 (4F)
OS Map 176/177, 161/173: TQ299795

CHISWICK HOUSE AND GARDENS
SEE FEATURE OPPOSITE

☎ Available for corporate
and private hire –
contact Chiswick House
and Gardens Trust
020 8742 2762

⚑ Licensed for civil
wedding ceremonies

VISIT US

Direction: Burlington Lane

Train: Chiswick ½ mile

Bus: TfL 190, E3

Tube: Turnham Green 1 mile then bus E3

Tel: 020 8995 0508

NON-MEMBERS

Adult	£6.10
Concession	£5.50
Child	£3.70
Family	£15.90

Members may be charged for special events

OPENING TIMES

1 Apr-30 Sep, Sun-Wed & Bank Hols	10am-6pm
1 Oct-2 Nov, Sun-Wed	10am-5pm
3 Nov-29 Mar	Closed

Last admission 30 mins before closing

Disabled access (ground floor; wheelchair stair-climber to first floor, please call to confirm use prior to visit).

Dogs on leads (restricted areas only).

Parking (charged – off westbound A4).

No photography allowed inside the house.

MAP Page 338 (4E)
OS Map 176, 161: TQ210775

Chiswick House is among the most glorious examples of 18th-century British architecture. The third Earl of Burlington, who designed this noble Roman-style Palladian villa, drew inspiration from his 'grand tours' of Italy. The sumptuous interiors, created by William Kent, display a rich collection of Old Master paintings which complement the beautiful painted and gilded ceilings, and show the diversity of Burlington's collections.

Chiswick House Gardens are a site of international importance, both as the birthplace of the English Landscape Movement, and as the setting for one of the most beautiful houses in London. Spreading over 65 acres, they have inspired countless designed landscapes, from Blenheim Palace to Central Park in New York. Highlights of a £12m restoration include the planting of over 1600 trees, including trees propagated from the original 18th-century cedars of Lebanon; the opening up of historic views from the Classic Bridge; and the complete refurbishment of the 19th-century conservatory, housing an internationally important collection of camellias – possibly the oldest collection outside China and Japan.

Complete your day by visiting the acclaimed modern airy café. For more information including events and activities, visit www.chgt.org.uk

Chiswick House Gardens are managed by Chiswick House and Gardens Trust in partnership with English Heritage, which manages and maintains Chiswick House itself.

Don't miss the Camellia Festival, held here in March, where you can discover Chiswick's glorious camellias in the restored conservatory and enjoy spectacular new spring flower displays in the 19th-century Italian Garden. Details can be found at www.chgt.org.uk. Pre-booking is advised.

🎞 *The Golden Compass.*

A unique combination of an astonishing top-of-the-range 1930s millionaire's Art Deco mansion with a medieval and Tudor royal palace and beautiful gardens.

VISIT US

Address: Court Yard, Eltham, Greenwich, London

Direction: Off Court Rd SE9, Jct 3 on the M25, then A20 to Eltham

Train: Eltham and Mottingham, both ½ mile

Bus: TfL bus services 124,126, 160 or 161 and then a short walk

Tel: 020 8294 2548

NON-MEMBERS

House and Gardens

Adult	£10.20
Concession	£9.20
Child	£6.10
Family	£26.50

Members may be charged for special events

Gardens (during winter only)

Adult	£6.40
Concession	£5.80
Child	£3.80

OPENING TIMES

1 Apr-30 Sep, Sun-Thu & Bank Hols	10am-6pm
1-26 Oct, Sun-Thu	10am-5pm
27-31 Oct, daily	10am-5pm
1 Nov-15 Feb, Sun	10am-4pm
16-20 Feb, daily	10am-4pm
21 Feb-29 Mar, Sun	10am-4pm
29 Mar, 17-18 Apr, 24-26 Dec, 31 Dec-1 Jan	Closed

Due to conservation works taking place in Spring 2014, please check the website prior to visiting in April to ensure that all areas of the house are fully open

Events on Sat 10 May and Sat 13 Sep for Art Deco Fair, and Sat 21 Jun for Joust

Members may be charged for special events

Disabled access (and parking via Court Yard entrance).

A car parking charge of £2 per day applies which will be refunded on admission. Please note on Bank Holiday weekends and selected special events the charge will not be refunded.

Pushchairs and large rucksacks need to be left at reception.

No photography allowed inside the house.

MAP Page 339 (4F)
OS Map 177, 162: TQ424740

The Gathering Storm; Bright Young Things; Brideshead Revisited; Shanghai; Revolver; Madonna's WE.

⊤ Available for corporate and private hire

⬛ Licensed for civil wedding ceremonies

When millionaires Stephen and Virginia Courtauld built their 1930s Art Deco mansion adjoining the Great Hall of medieval Eltham Palace, they created a masterpiece of 20th-century design.

Completed in 1936, the red brick exterior of the house was built in sympathy with the Great Hall. But the interior remains a glamorous 1930s showpiece, an eclectic mix of Art Deco, ultra-smart ocean-liner style and cutting-edge Swedish design.

The dining room is a tour de force, with pink leather upholstered chairs, bird's-eye maple veneered walls, a shimmering aluminium-leaf ceiling and black-and-silver doors portraying animals and birds.

Even more exotic is Virginia Courtauld's vaulted bathroom, complete with onyx bath and sink and gold-plated bath taps. Luxury also emanates from the centrally-heated sleeping quarters of the Courtaulds' pet ring-tailed lemur, Mah-Jongg. Equipped with all the latest modern conveniences, the house featured underfloor heating, a centralised vacuum cleaner and a built-in audio system.

Upstairs is a display of discoveries from the Courtauld era, including original furniture and family photographs. Visitors can also enjoy a restored original 10-minute Courtauld home movie, giving an intimate glimpse of their family life. A display celebrating the Royal Army Education Corps' (RAEC) post-Second World War association with Eltham Palace highlights a further chapter in its fascinating history. It includes a recreation of an officer's bedroom of the 1960s, together with exhibition panels and a photograph album telling the story of the RAEC's time here.

The medieval palace presents a striking contrast to the opulent 1930s house. The Great Hall, with its stunning hammerbeam roof, was built for Edward IV in the 1470s, and Henry VIII spent much of his childhood here.

The palace's 19 acres of beautiful gardens feature both 20th-century and medieval elements. These include a moat, spanned by a medieval bridge, a stunning herbaceous border and plenty of picnic areas. Striking at any time of year, garden highlights include the spring bulbs and the wisteria cascading over the classical pergola in summer.

Eltham Palace hosts a range of events throughout the year, including the popular Art Deco fairs in May and September and the Eltham Joust in June. Look out for details in your exclusive Members' Magazine or on our website.

NEW FOR 2014

A fantastic new play area for children and new interpretation in the tennis pavilion.

With vividly re-presented Robert Adam interiors and collections as well as much improved facilities for visitors and an interactive family activities base, newly-refurbished Kenwood has even more to offer.

VISIT US

Address: Kenwood, Hampstead

Direction: Hampstead Lane, NW3

Train: Gospel Oak or Hampstead Heath

Bus: TfL 210 (also bus H3 passes within a short walk)

Tube: Golders Green or Archway then bus 210

Tel: 020 8348 1286

OPENING TIMES

House

1 Apr-29 Mar, daily	10am-5pm
24-26 Dec, 31 Dec-1 Jan	Closed

Brewhouse Café

1 Apr-2 Nov, daily	9am-6pm
3 Nov-29 Mar, daily	9am-4pm
24-25 Dec & 31 Dec	Closed

Garden Shop

1 Apr-29 Mar, daily	10am-4pm
24-25 Dec & 31 Dec	Closed

Estate open from 8am to dusk (see park entrance for closing time)

Entry to the House and grounds is free; donations welcome.

Pre-booked group tours available

Disabled access (lift to all floors for visitors with a disability or mobility problems; toilets).

Dogs on leads (restricted areas only).

Café open, daily.

Parking (Charge applies. Disabled bays. Mobility service available on request).

New guidebook.

MAP Page 338 (3E)
OS Map 176, 173: TQ271874

⊤ Available for corporate and private hire

⚑ Licensed for civil wedding ceremonies

Kenwood, one of the finest of all English Heritage's great houses, is open again. An intensive five-year programme of repair, conservation and re-presentation has given it a new lease of life.

New features include a re-presentation of the wonderful Adam interiors; the re-display of the outstanding Iveagh Collection of paintings; imaginative new interpretation for visitors of all ages; and the opening of the restored ornamental Dairy, set in Kenwood's Humphry Repton landscaped parkland. Chairs and a lift now also make viewing Kenwood's splendours a more relaxed and comfortable experience.

Crowning Hampstead Heath, Kenwood was remodelled by Robert Adam between 1764 and 1779 into a majestic villa for a great judge, the first Earl of Mansfield, and later extended for his nephew. Time and weather had taken their toll on the mansion, necessitating major conservation work to its roof and walls to secure Kenwood and its precious contents for generations to come. Now its dignified exteriors have been returned to their 1790s colours and finishes.

Kenwood's principal art collection, including paintings by Rembrandt, Vermeer, Turner, Reynolds, Gainsborough and Constable, was bequeathed to the nation with the mansion and grounds by brewing magnate Edward Guinness, Earl of Iveagh, in 1927. It has been re-displayed and interpreted in rooms refurbished – as the donor wished – 'as a fine example of the artistic home of an 18th-century gentleman'. Chairs for visitors' use encourage leisurely viewing.

A lift to their first floor setting also makes the Suffolk Collection of Tudor and Stuart portraits more accessible. This includes an unrivalled array of full length paintings of extravagantly-dressed Jacobean ladies and gentlemen, painted by William Larkin in 1610-19.

Most striking of all Kenwood's glories, however, is its suite of magnificent and internationally important Robert Adam rooms: Entrance Hall, Great Stair, Ante-Room, and his masterpiece, the Great Library. Following detailed archaeological and documentary research, these amazing rooms have now been redecorated as they originally appeared over two centuries ago. Even their beautifully made original deal floors are now revealed to view.

A new introduction to the house and grounds, and those who lived and worked here, includes an interactive 'dolls-house' model of the mansion and an audio visual display. Dido Belle, Lord Mansfield's mixed-race great-niece, is one of the many people and features of Kenwood which the new interpretation brings to life. 'Growing Space', an activity base in the Orangery for families, features areas where they can look at themes connected with Kenwood and select equipment to explore the house together.

Kenwood's 112 acres of leafy parkland, landscaped by Humphry Repton, is beloved by locals and visitors alike for its fine views over London, its sculptures and its meandering woodland paths. The conserved ornamental 18th-century Dairy, which once both supplied the mansion with fresh produce and allowed the ladies of the house to take tea or fashionably play at dairymaids, re-opens to visitors with re-instated decorative interiors. (Open 1st Sunday of the month only).

A free multimedia tour for your phone can be downloaded from our website.

🎬 Notting Hill; Mansfield Park; Scenes of a Sexual Nature; Venus

COOMBE CONDUIT
KINGSTON-UPON-THAMES
KT2 7HE

These two brick-walled chambers, connected by an underground passage, were once part of a system which collected water from nearby springs and channelled it to Hampton Court Palace.

Managed by the Kingston-upon-Thames Society.

OPENING TIMES
1 Apr-30 Sep,
every 2nd Sun   2pm-4pm

VISIT US
Direction: Coombe Lane on the corner of Lord Chancellor Walk

Train: Norbiton ¾ mile or Raynes Park 1 mile then bus 57

Bus: TfL 57

Tube: Wimbledon then bus 57

Tel: 020 8541 3108/020 8942 7387

www.kingstonuponthamessociety.co.uk

ACQ.1978

MAP Page 338 (4E)
OS Map 176, 161: TQ204698

HARMONDSWORTH GREAT BARN
HILLINGDON – UB7 0AQ

Medieval timber-framed barn built in 1426-27 by Winchester College. The Great Barn is one of the largest ever known to have been built in England, and one of the most complete and unaltered pre-Dissolution buildings in Britain.

Managed by the Friends of the Great Barn of Harmondsworth.

A free virtual tour and podcast are available on our website **english-heritage.org.uk/harmondsworth-barn**

OPENING TIMES
Please check the website for latest opening times. Due to a major conservation project, we will only be open on the following dates

---

HARMONDSWORTH GREAT BARN

April, 2nd Sun only	11am-4pm
May-Sep, every 2nd Sun only	10am-5pm
Oct, 2nd Sun only	11am-4pm
1 Nov-29 Mar	Closed

VISIT US
Direction: Located in High Street, Harmondsworth Village

Train: West Drayton 2 miles

Bus: TfL U3 and 350

Tube: Heathrow Terminals 1, 2, 3 – 2 miles

Tel: 0870 333 1181

ACQ.2012

MAP Page 338 (4E)
OS Map 176, 160: TQ056778

THE HOME OF CHARLES DARWIN, DOWN HOUSE
SEE FEATURE – PAGE 64

ELTHAM PALACE AND GARDENS
SEE FEATURE – PAGE 32

JEWEL TOWER
SEE FEATURE OPPOSITE

KENWOOD
SEE FEATURE – PAGE 34

LONDON WALL
TOWER HILL – EC3N 4DJ

This is the best-preserved remnant of the Roman wall which once formed part of the eastern defences of Roman Londinium. Built c. AD 200, the wall defined the shape and size of London for over a millennium.

OPENING TIMES
Any reasonable daylight hours

VISIT US
Direction: Located outside Tower Hill Underground station, EC3

Train: Fenchurch Street ¼ mile or London Bridge 1 mile

Bus: From surrounding areas

LONDON WALL

Tube: Tower Hill

DLR: Tower Gateway

ACQ.1953

MAP Page 339 (3F)
OS Map 176/177, 173: TQ336807

MARBLE HILL HOUSE
SEE FEATURE – PAGE 38

RANGER'S HOUSE – THE WERNHER COLLECTION
SEE FEATURE – PAGE 39

WELLINGTON ARCH
SEE FEATURE – PAGE 40

WINCHESTER PALACE
SOUTHWARK – SE1 9DG

Part of the great hall of Winchester Palace, built in the early 13th century as the London house of the Bishops of Winchester, including the striking rose window which adorns the west gable. Most of the palace was destroyed by fire in 1814.

OPENING TIMES
Any reasonable daylight hours

VISIT US
Direction: Next to Southwark Cathedral and the Golden Hinde replica ship; corner of Clink St and Stoney St, SE1

Train/Tube: London Bridge ¼ mile

Bus: From surrounding areas

ACQ.1967

MAP Page 339 (4F)
OS Map 176/177, 173: TQ325803

VISIT US

Direction: Located on Abingdon Street, opposite the southern end of the Houses of Parliament (Victoria Tower)

Train: Victoria and Charing Cross ¾ mile, Waterloo 1 mile

Bus: From surrounding areas

Tube: St James's Park and Westminster ¼ mile

Tel: 020 7222 2219

NON-MEMBERS

Adult	£4.00
Concession	£3.60
Child	£2.40

OPENING TIMES

1 Apr-30 Sep, daily & Bank Hols	10am-6pm
1 Oct-2 Nov, daily	10am-5pm
3 Nov-29 Mar, Sat-Sun	10am-4pm
24-26 Dec, 31 Dec-1 Jan	Closed

Last admission 30 mins before closing

Light refreshments available.

Disabled access (limited).

MAP Page 339 (4F)
OS Map 176/177, 161/173: TQ301793

Tucked away between the Houses of Parliament and Westminster Abbey, the Jewel Tower is an easily overlooked but precious fragment of English history, built in c.1365 as the 'King's Privy Wardrobe' to house Edward III's personal treasury. The sole survivor of the private royal quarters within the great medieval Palace of Westminster, it is also the only part of the palace complex which survived the disastrous fire of 1834 and is regularly open to the public. Displaying finely carved medieval vaulted roofs, it later housed the House of Lords records and then the National Weights and Measures Office.

Recently installed displays on all three floors highlight the tower's history and changing roles over the centuries. Features include a model of the 'lost' medieval palace of Westminster, replicas of precious objects, and room settings helping you experience the lives of a medieval treasury official and an 18th-century clerk.

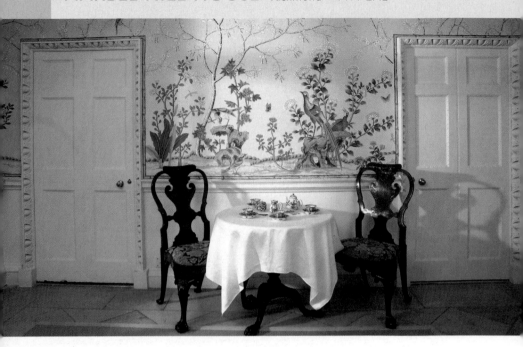

VISIT US

Direction: Richmond Road, Twickenham, London

Train: St Margaret's or Twickenham

Bus: TfL 33, 490, H22, R68, R70

Tube: Richmond 1 mile

Tel: 020 8892 5115

NON-MEMBERS

Adult	£5.90
Concession	£5.30
Child	£3.50
Family	£15.30

OPENING TIMES

1 Apr-3 Nov

Sat	10.30am and 12pm
Sun	10.30am, 12pm, 2.15pm and 3.30pm

Entry by guided tours only.
Tours last around 1½ hours

Park

All year, daily	7am-dusk

Café

1 Apr-2 Nov, daily	10am-5pm
3 Nov-29 Mar, daily	10am-4pm
24-25 Dec & 1 Jan	Closed

ACQ.1986

Café (Coach House Café, open all year).

Disabled access (exterior & ground floor only; toilets).

Parking charge.

No photography allowed inside the house.

MAP Page 338 (4E)
OS Map 176, 161: TQ173736

A lovely Palladian villa still set in 66 acres of riverside parkland, Marble Hill House is the last complete survivor of the elegant villas which bordered the Thames between Richmond and Hampton Court in the 18th century. It was begun in 1724 for Henrietta Howard, Countess of Suffolk, a remarkable 18th-century woman of letters, who was also the mistress of King George II and friend of some of the cleverest men in England. The house and gardens were planned by a coterie of fashionable connoisseurs, including the poet Alexander Pope.

The interiors of the house have been exquisitely restored and recreated, and there is also a fine collection of early Georgian paintings, including portraits of Mrs Howard and her circle. Marble Hill was intended as an Arcadian retreat from crowded 18th-century London, and there can be few places in England which better recall the atmosphere of Georgian fashionable life.

Nanny MacPhee 2: The Big Bang

Available for corporate and private hire

Licensed for civil wedding ceremonies

Please note: No photography in the house.

VISIT US

Address: Chesterfield Walk, Blackheath, London

Direction: Ranger's House is on Chesterfield Walk and overlooks the junction of General Wolfe Road and Shooters Hill Road

DLR: Deptford Bridge then bus 53

Train: Blackheath ¾ mile

Bus: TfL 53, 386

River: Greenwich Pier

Tel: 020 8294 2548

NON-MEMBERS

Adult	£6.90
Concession	£6.20
Child	£4.10

OPENING TIMES

1 Apr-1 Oct,
Sun-Wed   11am and 2pm
Entry by guided tours only.
Tours last around 1½ hours

ACQ.1986 🏛 🍴 🔔 🚶 ⛲ 🖼 P
♿ OVP

Toilets (including disabled).

MAP Page 339 (4F)
OS Map 177, 161/162: TQ388769

Ranger's House is an elegant Georgian villa built in 1723, which became the official residence of the 'Ranger of Greenwich Park'. From 1815 this post was held by Princess Sophia Matilda, niece of George III. It remained an aristocratic and then royal home until 1902. Today it houses the Wernher Collection – an astounding display of medieval and Renaissance works of art, all purchased by the diamond magnate, Sir Julius Wernher (1850-1912).

Arranged within the panelled interiors of this graceful mansion, the Wernher Collection presents a glittering spectacle. Nearly 700 works of art are on display, including early religious paintings and Dutch Old Masters, minute carved Gothic ivories, fine Renaissance bronzes and silver treasures. Together they proclaim the genius of medieval craftsmen, and the unparalleled quality of Renaissance decorative arts.

Entrance is by guided tour only (included in the entrance fee), providing a detailed insight into the history of the Collection.

🍴 Available for corporate and private hire

🔔 Licensed for civil wedding ceremonies

Take the lift within this famous landmark to two floors of changing top-class exhibitions, and wonderful views over Royal London from the balconies.

VISIT US

Address: Wellington Arch, Apsley Way, Hyde Park Corner, London

Direction: Hyde Park Corner, W1J

Train: Victoria ½ mile

Bus: From surrounding areas

Tube: Hyde Park Corner, adjacent

Tel: 020 7930 2726

NON-MEMBERS

Adult	£4.20
Concession	£3.80
Child	£2.50

Joint ticket with Apsley House

Adult	£8.90
Concession	£8.00
Child	£5.30
Family	£23.10

OPENING TIMES

1 Apr-30 Sep, daily	10am-6pm
1 Oct-2 Nov, daily	10am-5pm
3 Nov-29 Mar, daily	10am-4pm
24-26 Dec, 31 Dec-1 Jan	Closed

Last admission 30 mins before closing

The property may close to install new exhibitions. Please call in advance for details

ACQ.1999 🛡 E f 🖼 Y 🖺 ♿
⚠ OVP

MAP Page 338 (4E)
OS Map 176, 161/173: TQ284798

 Available for corporate and private hire

Set in the heart of the capital at Hyde Park Corner, Wellington Arch is one of London's most famous and striking landmarks. It is crowned by the largest bronze sculpture in Europe, depicting the Angel of Peace descending on the 'Quadriga' – or four-horsed chariot – of War.

Despite its air of immovably changeless grandeur, the appearance and the siting of Wellington Arch have altered since it was designed by the architect Decimus Burton and erected in 1825-27. Intended as a grand outer entrance to

Buckingham Palace, it was originally aligned with the Hyde Park Screen, and later took on the role of a victory arch proclaiming Wellington's triumph over Napoleon. In 1846 a colossal equestrian bronze statue of Wellington was added to the top, sparking furious controversy. By 1883, however, the original siting of the Arch was causing serious traffic bottlenecks: so it was moved stone by stone some 20 metres to its current position, the present great bronze sculpture being then substituted for the Wellington statue. Its balconies offer glorious panoramas over the Royal Parks and the Houses of Parliament, as well as unique views of the Household Cavalry, passing beneath to and from the Changing of the Guard at Horse Guards Parade.

The Arch is also now home to the Quadriga Gallery, which hosts changing displays showcasing the best of English Heritage's work.

NEW FOR 2014 AT THE QUADRIGA GALLERY

6 FEB-6 JUL
Carscapes: How the Motor Car Reshaped England

The motor car transformed English towns and countryside, changing our working and living patterns and our townscapes to carscapes. The exhibition explores how our motoring heritage developed its own art and architecture, with dramatic aerial photographs showing the grandeur of motorway design. It answers a very modern question: how do people and traffic co-exist?

The exhibition launches a new English Heritage publication, *England's Motoring Heritage from the Air*, by John Minnis.

16 JUL-30 NOV
We Will Remember Them: London's Great War Memorials

2014 sees the start of the Great War commemorations. This exhibition focuses on the London First World War memorials cared for by English Heritage. These include the Royal Artillery Memorial and the Machine Gun Corps Memorial, both immediately adjacent to Wellington Arch. It also highlights memorials to individuals, for example Edith Cavell, the nurse shot for assisting British soldiers to escape: and the most iconic memorial in Britain – the Cenotaph. The display explores artists' designs, and the history of the First World War memorial.

Permanent displays interpret the history of the Arch itself: further special exhibitions will be mounted in late 2014-early 2015. Call site for details.

Please note that during changeovers of exhibitions Wellington Arch may temporarily close to the public. Please telephone in advance or visit our website for up-to-date information.

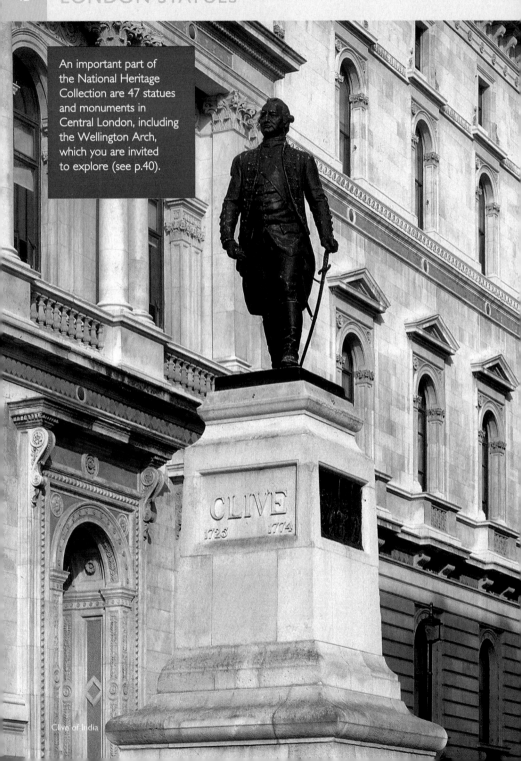

An important part of the National Heritage Collection are 47 statues and monuments in Central London, including the Wellington Arch, which you are invited to explore (see p.40).

CLIVE
1725   1774

Clive of India

Statues provide a fascinating insight into the preoccupations of the period. Many of them are associated with wars and military campaigns, such as the Napoleonic Wars, the Boer War and the two World Wars – including the Cenotaph in Whitehall (below).

Others represent Royal figures such as Charles I (1633) and Edward VII (1921).

A leaflet giving more information about the intriguing history of 20th-century war memorials in London is available from Customer Services (tel 0870 333 1181).

The Capital's Monuments

Viscount Alanbrooke Whitehall, SW1	**Duke of Kent** Crescent Gardens (locked), Portland Place, W1
Queen Anne Queen Anne's Gate, SW1	**Baron Lawrence** Waterloo Place, SW1
Belgian War Memorial Victoria Embankment	**Machine Gun Corps** Apsley Way, W1
Simon Bolivar Belgrave Square, SW1	**Montgomery** Whitehall, SW1
Duke of Cambridge Whitehall, SW1	**Lord Napier of Magdala** Queen's Gate, SW7
Colin Campbell Waterloo Place, SW1	
Carabiniers Memorial Chelsea Embankment, SW3	**Marble Arch** W1
Edith Cavell St Martin's Place, WC2	**Florence Nightingale** Waterloo Place, SW1
Cenotaph Whitehall, SW1	**Samuel Plimsoll** Victoria Embankment
King Charles I Whitehall, SW1	
Queen Charlotte Queen Square, WC1	**Lord Portal** Victoria Embankment
Clive of India King Charles St, SW1	**Sir Walter Raleigh** Old Royal Naval College, Greenwich, SE10
Christopher Columbus Belgrave Square, SW1	
Crimea Memorial Waterloo Place, SW1	**Royal Artillery Memorial** Apsley Way, W1
Thomas Cubitt St George's Drive, Pimlico, SW1	**General de San Martin** Belgrave Square, SW1
Lord Curzon Carlton House Terrace, SW1	**Captain Scott** Waterloo Place, SW1
Duke of Devonshire Whitehall, SW1	**Viscount Slim** Whitehall, SW1
Edward VII Waterloo Place, SW1	**Lord Trenchard** Victoria Embankment
General Eisenhower Grosvenor Square, W1	**George Washington** Trafalgar Square, WC2
Sir John Franklin Waterloo Place, SW1	**Duke of Wellington** Apsley Way, W1
General de Gaulle Carlton Gardens, SW1	
King George II Golden Square, W1	**Wellington Arch and Quadriga** Apsley Way, W1
King George III Cockspur St, SW1	**King William III** St James's Square, SW1
General Gordon Victoria Embankment	
Earl Haig Whitehall, SW1	
Sir Arthur Harris St Clement Danes, WC2	
Lord Herbert Waterloo Place, SW1	
King James II National Gallery, Trafalgar Square, WC2	

Cenotaph, Whitehall

DISCOUNTED ATTRACTIONS:

Use your membership to get exclusive discounts at these independent attractions in London. Please remember to show your card as proof of membership.

BENJAMIN FRANKLIN HOUSE
London WC2N 5NF

The world's only remaining home of US Founding Father Benjamin Franklin, featuring a unique 'Historical Experience'.

www.benjaminfranklinhouse.org
Tel. 020 7925 1405

CHURCHILL WAR ROOMS
London SW1A 2AQ

Visit Churchill War Rooms to discover the original Cabinet War Rooms, the underground headquarters that sheltered Churchill and his wartime government during the Blitz.

www.iwm.org.uk
Tel. 020 7930 6961

CRAVEN COTTAGE (STADIUM)
London SW6

A unique piece of London's heritage – step through the listed turnstiles of our 19th-century Premier League football ground.

www.fulhamfc.com/visit
Tel. 0843 208 1234 (option 4)

ENGLISH HERITAGE PROPERTY GUIDEBOOKS

Want to know more about a property near you?

www.english-heritage shop.org.uk

DANSON HOUSE
Kent DA6 8HL

A beautiful Georgian villa with sumptuous interiors, built for pleasure and entertaining. Enjoy this superb example of 18th-century architecture with its elegant interiors.

www.dansonhouse.org.uk
Tel. 020 8303 6699

DULWICH PICTURE GALLERY
London SE21 7AD

Dulwich Picture Gallery, England's first public gallery, was founded in 1811. A masterpiece of Regency architecture by Sir John Soane.

www.dulwichpicturegallery.org.uk
Tel. 020 8693 5254

LONDON

Discount applies to:

| KEY | **#** MEMBERS | OVP OVP HOLDERS | **†∳?** NO. OF MEMBER'S CHILDREN |

Terms and conditions may apply, so make sure you check the individual pages on our website or call the individual property for more details.

#

HMS BELFAST
London SE1 2JH
HMS *Belfast* tells the stories of life on board this warship during the Second World War and beyond. Explore all nine decks and join in the action in the Gun Turret Experience.
www.iwm.org.uk
Tel. 020 7940 6300

#

LONDON CANAL MUSEUM
London N1 9RT
The museum tells the story of London's fascinating canals, their people, horses, and trades, in a former warehouse where ice from Norway was once stored in underground wells.
www.canalmuseum.org.uk
Tel. 020 7713 0836

 # †∳3

LONDON TRANSPORT MUSEUM
London WC2E 7BB
Lively and interactive galleries depict the past, present and future of transport in London, and how it shaped the culture and lives of its people.
www.ltmuseum.co.uk
Tel. 020 7565 7298

OVP

STRAWBERRY HILL HOUSE
London TW1 4ST
Horace Walpole's 'little gothic castle' is a fairytale castle by the Thames. Now restored to its former glory, visiting Strawberry Hill is a truly theatrical experience.
www.strawberryhillhouse.org.uk
Tel. 020 8744 1241

GIVE THE GIFT OF MEMBERSHIP
Give friends and family the opportunity to enjoy these fantastic discounts too!

- Free entry to over 400 historic properties
- Kids go free (up to six per adult in a family group)
- Free or discounted entry to hundreds of events
- Free handbook worth £10.95
- Exclusive Members' Magazine

See page 355 for full details.

SOUTH EAST

Dover Castle

Keep up to date with events, news and offers www.english-heritage.org.uk/newsletter

1066 Battle of Hastings, Abbey & Battlefield

Banbury
Milton Keynes
50 46
Buckingham
Oxfordshire **Buckinghamshire**
49
47
48 Oxford
45
High Wycombe
52 51
Reading Windsor
1 **Berkshire**
Newbury
14 Woking
Basingstoke Guildford **Surrey**
Hampshire 53
54
4 7
Winchester 17
Crawley
2
Southampton **West Sussex**
11 15 59
10 16 58 Lewes
3 12 Chichester Brighton
Cowes 5 Portsmouth
8 64 62 6 Worthing
61 9
Newport 13
60
63 **Isle of Wight**

30 34
42
22 41 Gillingham
24 28 26 23 29 35 36 33 37
31 39 Maidstone Canterbury 32
Tonbridge 40 **Kent** 19 43
18 Ashford 38 20 44
25 Folkestone 27 Dover
21
East Sussex
56
55
57 Hastings

Details of local public transport information in England are available from Traveline
www.traveline.org.uk or call 0871 200 2233.

HIGHLIGHTS FOR 2014/15 IN THE **SOUTH EAST**

p.64

p.58

p.88

Home of Charles Darwin, Down House: explore the world-changing ideas of Charles Darwin in his family house and gardens.

Dover Castle: great medieval fortress and 1940 hotspot, with 900 years of history.

Osborne: step back in time and share the experience and atmosphere of a royal Victorian childhood.

PROPERTIES

BERKSHIRE
1 Donnington Castle

HAMPSHIRE
2 Bishop's Waltham Palace
3 Calshot Castle
4 Flowerdown Barrows
5 Fort Brockhurst
6 Fort Cumberland
7 The Grange at Northington
8 Hurst Castle
9 King James's and Landport Gates
10 Medieval Merchant's House
11 Netley Abbey
12 Portchester Castle
13 Royal Garrison Church
14 Silchester Roman City Walls and Amphitheatre
15 Southwick Priory
16 Titchfield Abbey
17 Wolvesey Castle (Old Bishop's Palace)

KENT
18 Bayham Old Abbey
19 Deal Castle
20 Dover Castle
21 Dymchurch Martello Tower
22 Eynsford Castle

23 Faversham Stone Chapel (Our Lady of Elverton)
24 The Home of Charles Darwin, Down House
25 Horne's Place Chapel
26 Kit's Coty House and Little Kit's Coty House
27 Knights Templar Church
28 Lullingstone Roman Villa
29 Maison Dieu
30 Milton Chantry
31 Old Soar Manor
32 Reculver Towers and Roman Fort
33 Richborough Roman Fort and Amphitheatre
34 Rochester Castle
35 St Augustine's Abbey
36 St Augustine's Abbey Conduit House
37 St Augustine's Cross
38 St John's Commandery
39 St Leonard's Tower
40 Sutton Valence Castle
41 Temple Manor
42 Upnor Castle
43 Walmer Castle and Gardens
44 Western Heights, Dover

OXFORDSHIRE
45 Abingdon County Hall Museum
46 Deddington Castle
47 Minster Lovell Hall and Dovecote
48 North Hinksey Conduit House
49 North Leigh Roman Villa
50 Rollright Stones
51 Uffington Castle, White Horse and Dragon Hill
52 Wayland's Smithy

SURREY
53 Farnham Castle Keep
54 Waverley Abbey

EAST SUSSEX
55 1066 Battle of Hastings, Abbey and Battlefield
56 Camber Castle
57 Pevensey Castle

WEST SUSSEX
58 Boxgrove Priory
59 Bramber Castle

ISLE OF WIGHT – see page 84
60 Appuldurcombe House
61 Carisbrooke Castle
62 Osborne
63 St Catherine's Oratory
64 Yarmouth Castle

Remember to check opening times before you visit any of our properties
www.english-heritage.org.uk/daysout

BERKSHIRE

DONNINGTON CASTLE
WEST BERKSHIRE

The striking, twin-towered, 14th-century gatehouse of this castle, later the focus of a Civil War siege and battle, survives amid impressive earthworks.

OPENING TIMES
Any reasonable daylight hours; exterior viewing only

Car park open daily	7am-7pm

VISIT US
Direction: 1 mile N of Newbury, off B4494

Train: Newbury 1¼ miles

Bus: Newbury & District services 4, 6, 6A, 107 & Go-Ride services 5 & 5A

Disabled access (steep slopes within grounds).

MAP Page 338 (4C)
OS Map 174, 158: SU461692

ST BARTHOLOMEW'S CHURCH, LOWER BASILDON
BERKSHIRE – RG8 9NH

© James Davies

This striking 700-year-old flint and brick church stands in a pretty churchyard near a beautiful stretch of the Thames. Inside it is simple and serene, with ornate roof timbers and memorials to past parishioners. Jethro Tull is buried here.

Owned and managed by The Churches Conservation Trust.

ST BARTHOLOMEW'S CHURCH, LOWER BASILDON

OPENING TIMES
Keyholder nearby

VISIT US
Train: Pangbourne 2 miles

Bus: Thames Travel services 132 & 133

30 mins from Donnington Castle

MAP Page 338 (4C)
OS Map 175, 159/171: SU612793

ST THOMAS' CHURCH, EAST SHEFFORD
BERKSHIRE – RG17 7EF

© CCT Cameron Newham

This simple little church stands in an idyllic spot beside a water meadow. Its village has long since vanished, but the spirit of the villagers shines through in the church's simple craftsmanship, glorious medieval wall paintings and fabulous tombs, giving an intriguing glimpse into 15th-century fashion.

Owned and managed by The Churches Conservation Trust.

OPENING TIMES
Open daily during daylight hours

VISIT US
Train: Nearest ⊇ Kintbury 5 miles

Bus: Newbury & District service 4

15 mins from Donnington Castle

MAP Page 338 (4B)
OS Map 174, 158: SU391747

HAMPSHIRE

BISHOP'S WALTHAM PALACE
HAMPSHIRE – SO32 1DH

The ruins of a medieval palace (and its later additions) used by the bishops and senior clergy of Winchester as they travelled through their diocese. Winchester was the richest diocese in England, and its properties were grandiose and extravagantly appointed. Much of what can be seen today is the work of William Wykeham, who was bishop from 1367. The ground floor of the farmhouse adapted from the palace's lodging range is occupied by the Bishop's Waltham Town Museum, which exhibits local artefacts.

Other palaces of the bishops of Winchester include Farnham Castle Keep (p.78) and Wolvesey Castle (Old Bishop's Palace) (p.56).

NEW FOR 2014
New interpretative panels and downloadable audio guide.

OPENING TIMES
Grounds

1 Apr-30 Sep, daily	10am-6pm
1 Oct-29 Mar, Sat & Sun	10am-4pm

Farmhouse Museum

1 May-30 Sep, Sat & Sun	2pm-4pm

VISIT US
Direction: In Bishop's Waltham

Train: Botley 3½ miles

Bus: Brijan bus 7, 8, 17; Stagecoach bus 69

Tel: 01489 892460

Disabled access (grounds only).
Dogs on leads (restricted areas only).

MAP Page 338 (6C)
OS Map 185, 119: SU552174

CALSHOT CASTLE
HAMPSHIRE – SO45 1BR

This artillery fort, built by Henry VIII to defend the sea passage to Southampton, later saw service in both World Wars.

Managed by Hampshire County Council.

NON-MEMBERS
Adult	£3.00
Concession	£2.10
Child	£2.10
Family	£7.60

OPENING TIMES
1 Apr-30 Sep, daily	10.30am-4.30pm
Castle closed 30 minutes during lunchtime period	
1 Oct-29 Mar	Closed

VISIT US
Direction: On spit, 2 miles SE of Fawley, off B3053

Bus: Solent Blue Line Bluestar 8 passes within 1 mile

Tel: 023 8089 2023; when castle is closed, please call 023 8089 2077

ACQ.1964

Disabled access (Keep: ground floor only; toilets).

MAP Page 338 (6C)
OS Map 196, OL22/OL29/119: SU489025

FLOWERDOWN BARROWS
HAMPSHIRE

FLOWERDOWN BARROWS

Three Bronze Age burial mounds, including two bowl barrows, and the largest and finest disc barrow in Hampshire.

OPENING TIMES
Any reasonable daylight hours

VISIT US
Direction: Off B3049, out of Winchester to Littleton; at crossroads in centre of village

Train: Winchester 2 miles

Bus: Stagecoach in Hampshire 7, 68

ACQ.1972

MAP Page 338 (5C)
OS Map 185, 132: SU459320

FORT BROCKHURST
HAMPSHIRE – PO12 4DS

© Skyscan Balloon Photography

One of a number of forts built in the 1850s and 1860s to protect Portsmouth and its vital harbour against a French invasion. Largely unaltered, the parade ground, gun ramps and moated keep can all be viewed.

FORT BROCKHURST

The fort currently stores a treasure trove of objects from English Heritage's extensive reserve collections. Objects on display have been excavated from sites in the South East and South West. They include stonework, textiles, jewellery and furniture from many periods, as well as rarely-seen treasures on tour from stores in the North and East. The Collections Access Centre offers pre-booked adult and school groups a hands-on experience of English Heritage's rich and varied collections of artefacts, under the guidance of a curator, conservator or trained educator.

Portchester Castle – which acted as a prison during the Napoleonic Wars – is nearby (see p.55).

OPENING TIMES
1 Apr-30 Sep	11am-3pm
on the second Sat of every month	

Gosport's Big Day Out and Heritage Open Days (check website)

VISIT US
Direction: Off A32, in Gunner's Way, Elson; on N side of Gosport

Train: Fareham 3 miles

Bus: First E1, E2, 9A, 10 & 11 – Gosport Ferry links with Portsmouth & Southsea)

Tel: 023 9258 1059

ACQ.1963

Disabled access (grounds and ground floor only).

Dogs on leads (restricted areas only).

MAP Page 338 (6C)
OS Map 196, OL29/119: SU596021

FORT CUMBERLAND
HAMPSHIRE – PO4 9LD

Perhaps England's most impressive piece of 18th-century defensive architecture, Fort Cumberland was reconstructed in pentagonal form by the Duke of Richmond between 1785 and 1810, and designed to protect Langstone Harbour. Southsea beach is nearby.

OPENING TIMES
The fort opens for pre-booked group guided tours and Heritage Open Days

Call 023 9285 6700 for opening details

VISIT US
Direction: In Portsmouth's Eastney district on the estuary approach, via Henderson Rd off Eastney Rd, or from the Esplanade

Train: Fratton 2 miles

Bus: First 15 (Mon-Sat), 16 (Sun only)

Tel: 023 9285 6700

ACQ.1975 ⚠

MAP Page 338 (6C)
OS Map 196, 119/120: SZ683993

THE GRANGE AT NORTHINGTON
HAMPSHIRE

Set like a lakeside temple in a landscaped park, the Grange at Northington is the foremost example of the Greek Revival style in England. Created between 1804 and 1809 when William Wilkins encased an earlier house in Classical facades. Most striking is the temple front supported on eight gigantic columns. It provides a stunning backdrop for the opera evenings which take place here in the summer; call 01962 868600 for details.

🎬 The 1999 film, *Onegin*, with Ralph Fiennes.

OPENING TIMES
Exterior only:

1 Apr-31 May, daily	10am-6pm
1 Jun-31 Jul, daily	9am-12pm
1 Aug-30 Sep, daily	10am-6pm
1 Oct-29 Mar, daily	10am-4pm

Closes early for opera evenings in June and July

24-26 Dec & 1 Jan	Closed

VISIT US
Direction: Located 4 miles N of New Alresford, off B3046 along a farm track – 450 metres (493 yards)

Train: Winchester 8 miles

Bus: Nearest bus service is Velvet Bus 67 to Itchen Abbas or Mervyns Coaches 95, 96 to Lunways Inn then 3 mile walk

Tel: 0870 333 1181

ACQ.1975 🐕 ♿ P 🏕 ♿ ⚠
Disabled access (with assistance, steep steps to terrace).

MAP Page 338 (5C)
OS Map 185, 132: SU562362

HOLY TRINITY CHURCH, PRIVETT
HAMPSHIRE – GU34 3PE

© Christopher Dalton

HOLY TRINITY CHURCH, PRIVETT

The spire of Holy Trinity is visible for miles around in this idyllic corner of Hampshire. It is extraordinary to find such a lavishly decorated church in a rural location. Magnificent stonework and dazzling stained glass blend beautifully with the colourful marble mosaiced floors.

Owned and managed by The Churches Conservation Trust.

OPENING TIMES
Open daily   10am-3pm

VISIT US
Train: Petersfield 4¾ miles

Bus: Velvet service 67 is closest service. Alight West Meon Hut (approx. 2½ miles walk)

30 mins from Wolvesey Castle

MAP Page 338 (5C)
OS Map 186, 132: SU677270

HURST CASTLE
HAMPSHIRE – SO41 0TP

One of the most advanced of the artillery fortresses built by Henry VIII: used as a prison for eminent 17th-century captives, including King Charles I, and later strengthened during the 19th and 20th centuries. It commands the narrow entrance to the Solent.

Managed by Hurst Castle Services.

HURST CASTLE

NON-MEMBERS

Adult	£4.50
Concession	£4.20
Child	£2.60

OPENING TIMES

1 Apr-30 Sep, daily	10.30am-5.30pm
1 Oct-2 Nov, daily	10.30am-4pm
3 Nov-29 Mar	Closed

Occasionally open in winter at weekends – please ring 01590 624500

VISIT US

Direction: 1½ mile walk on shingle spit from Milford-on-Sea. Best approached by ferry from Keyhaven – call 01590 642500 for ferry details and fares

Train: Lymington Town 6½ miles

Bus: More X1 to Milford-on-Sea to within 2½ miles, or 1 mile to ferry

Tel: 01590 642344

ACQ.1933 🐕 ▢ 🚻 ♿ ☕ ⚠

Dogs on leads (restricted areas only).

Tearoom/restaurant (Castle Café, not managed by EH. Open Apr-May weekends only, Jun-Sep daily).

Parking (charge payable, at Milford seafront or Keyhaven).

MAP Page 338 (7B)
OS Map 196, OL22/OL29: SZ318897

KING JAMES'S AND LANDPORT GATES, PORTSMOUTH
HAMPSHIRE – PO1 2EJ

Two ornamental gateways, once part of Portsmouth's defences, King James's Gate

KING JAMES'S AND LANDPORT GATES, PORTSMOUTH

(of 1687) has been moved, but Landport Gate (1760), once the principal entrance to Portsmouth and possibly based on a design by Nicholas Hawksmoor, remains in its original position.

OPENING TIMES

Any reasonable daylight hours; exterior viewing only

VISIT US

Direction: King James's Gate forms the entrance to United Services Recreation Ground (officers), Burnaby Rd; Landport Gate as above, men's entrance on St George's Road

Train: Portsmouth Harbour ¼ mile

Bus: First services 1, 8, 15, 16 and Stagecoach service 23 and 700 pass Landport Gate. First services 7, 8, 15, 19 and Stagecoach 23 pass within a short walk of King James's Gate

ACQ.1930 🐕

MAP Page 338 (6C)
OS Map 196, OL29/119
King James's Gate: SZ636999
Landport Gate: SZ634998

MEDIEVAL MERCHANT'S HOUSE, SOUTHAMPTON
HAMPSHIRE – SO1 0AT

John Fortin, a merchant who traded with Bordeaux, started building this house c. 1290.

MEDIEVAL MERCHANT'S HOUSE

A residence and place of business, it stood on one of the busiest streets in medieval Southampton. Now restored to its mid-14th-century appearance by the removal of later additions, it is equipped with replica period furnishings. It stands near the medieval town wall, built to defend Southampton against seaborne attacks. Netley Abbey (p.54), Calshot Castle (p.51) and Hurst Castle (p.52) are all within reasonable travelling distance.

NON-MEMBERS

Adult	£4.00
Concession	£3.60
Child	£2.40

OPENING TIMES

1 Apr-30 Sep, Sun only	12pm-5pm
1 Oct-29 Mar	Closed

VISIT US

Direction: 58 French St, ¼ mile S of city centre, just off Castle Way (between High St and Bugle St)

Train: Southampton ¾ mile

Bus: Unilink U1, U6 & First 1, 2, 2A, 3, 6 all stop very close by

Tel: 023 8022 1503

Local Tourist Information
Southampton: 02380 833333

ACQ.1973 ▢ 🚻 ♿ 🚫🐕 ♿ OVP

Disabled access (two steps). Ground floor only.

MAP Page 338 (6B)
OS Map 196, OL22: SU419112

NETLEY ABBEY
HAMPSHIRE – SO31 5FB

The most complete surviving Cistercian monastery in southern England, with almost all the walls of its 13th-century church still standing, along with many monastic buildings. After the Dissolution, the buildings were converted into the mansion house of Sir William Paulet. Even in ruins, the abbey continued to be influential, inspiring Romantic writers and poets. A free downloadable audio tour is available from the English Heritage website.

OPENING TIMES
1 Apr–30 Sep, daily	10am–6pm
1 Oct–29 Mar, Sat–Sun	10am–4pm
24–26 Dec, 31 Dec–1 Jan	Closed

VISIT US
Direction: In Netley; 4 miles SE of Southampton, facing Southampton Water

Train: Netley 1 mile

Bus: First service 6

Tel: 0870 333 1181

ACQ.1922 🦅 🧍 🛗 P ⛽ ⚠

Toilets (nearby, across the road near the estuary).

Gravel car park, limited spaces.

MAP Page 338 (6C)
OS Map 196, OL22: SU453090

PORTCHESTER CASTLE
SEE FEATURE OPPOSITE

ROYAL GARRISON CHURCH, PORTSMOUTH
HAMPSHIRE – PO1 2NJ

Royal Garrison Church was constructed c. 1212 as part

of a hospital complex. Although the nave was badly damaged in a 1941 fire-bomb raid on Portsmouth, the chancel remains roofed and furnished.

Managed by the Friends of the Royal Garrison.

OPENING TIMES
1 Apr–30 Sep, Tue–Sat	11am–4pm
Bank Holidays	Closed
Contact Customer Services regarding access at other times	

VISIT US
Direction: In Portsmouth; on Grand Parade S of High St

Train: Portsmouth Harbour ¾ mile

Bus: First services 1, 16, 19 and Stagecoach 700 pass within a short walk

Tel: 0870 333 1181

ACQ.1970 P 🦅 ♿

Parking (nearby).

MAP Page 338 (6C)
OS Map 196, OL29/119: SZ633992

SILCHESTER ROMAN CITY WALLS AND AMPHITHEATRE
HAMPSHIRE – RG7 2HP

Originally a tribal centre of the Iron Age Atrebates, Silchester became the large and important Roman town of Calleva Atrebatum. Unlike most Roman towns, it was never re-occupied or built over after its abandonment in the 5th century, so archaeological investigations give an unusually complete picture of its development. The complete circuit of its 3rd-century walls, among the best-preserved Roman town defences in England and 2½ km (1½ miles) long, can still be traced, although none of the buildings within them survive above ground. Outside them are the remains of a Roman amphitheatre, which provided

ROYAL GARRISON CHURCH, PORTSMOUTH

SILCHESTER ROMAN CITY WALLS AND AMPHITHEATRE

seating for over 4500 spectators. A free downloadable audio tour is available from the English Heritage website.

OPENING TIMES
Any reasonable daylight hours

Car park	
1 Apr–30 Sep, daily	8am–7pm
1 Oct–29 Mar, daily	8.30am–4pm

VISIT US
Direction: On a minor road, 1 mile E of Silchester

Train: Bramley or Mortimer, both 2¾ miles

Bus: Stagecoach Hampshire 14 to Silchester (within ½ mile). Alternatively Reading Transport service 2/2A to Mortimer then 2 mile walk

ACQ.1965 🦅 P

There is no parking at the Amphitheatre, visitors should park at the main car park for the Roman Town. Prior notice of tall vehicles (i.e. coaches and minibuses) wishing to park in the car park is needed. Car park operated by Hampshire County Council – please contact 0118 970 0132 to open height barrier.

MAP Page 338 (4C)
OS Map 175, 159: SU639624

SOUTHWICK PRIORY
HAMPSHIRE

Remains of a wealthy Augustinian priory, originally founded at Portchester: once a famous place of pilgrimage. Only part of the refectory wall survives.

OPENING TIMES
Any reasonable daylight hours

VISIT US
Direction: Fully accessible through Southwick village, signposted. Please park in car park opposite

Bus: The only public transport is the Southwick Taxishare service 38

ACQ.1970

MAP Page 338 (6C)
OS Map 196, 119: SU629084

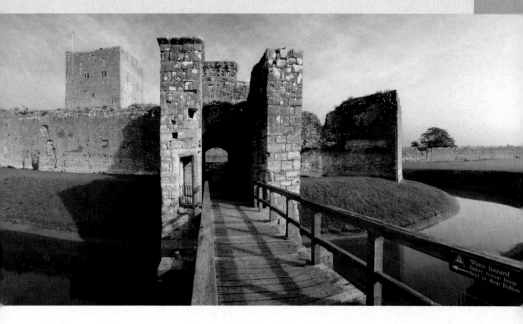

VISIT US

Direction: On the S side of Portchester off A27; Junction 11 on M27

Train: Portchester 1 mile

Bus: First service 3 to within ¼ mile

Tel: 023 9237 8291

NON-MEMBERS

Adult	£5.20
Concession	£4.70
Child	£3.10
Family	£13.50

OPENING TIMES

1 Apr-30 Sep, daily	10am-6pm
1 Oct-2 Nov, daily	10am-5pm
3 Nov-15 Feb, Sat-Sun	10am-4pm
16-20 Feb, daily	10am-4pm
21 Feb-29 Mar, Sat-Sun	10am-4pm
24-26 Dec, 31 Dec-1 Jan	Closed

Disabled access (grounds and lower levels only).

Dogs on leads (outer grounds only).

Toilets (facilities are in the car park, operated by Fareham District Council).

Portchester Castle's commanding location has made it a major factor in the Solent's defences for hundreds of years.

The most impressive and best-preserved of the Roman 'Saxon Shore' forts, Portchester Castle was originally built in the late 3rd century. Covering an area of nearly ten acres, it is the only Roman stronghold in northern Europe whose walls still mainly stand to their full six metre height, complete with most of their original 20 towers. Subsequently housing a Saxon settlement, the huge waterside fortress became a Norman castle in the 12th century, when a formidable tower-keep was built in one corner.

Portchester Castle was in the front line throughout the Hundred Years War, serving as a staging-post for expeditions to France and repelling cross-Channel raids. Richard II transformed part of the castle into a palace in 1396, and Henry V used it as an embarkation point for the Agincourt campaign in 1415. Thereafter it saw little action, but was used to house troops in the Civil War, and prisoners of war during the Dutch and Napoleonic Wars and the Anglo-American War of 1812-14.

An exhibition in the keep interprets the history of the castle and Portchester village, and displays finds excavated on site. The inclusive audio tour explains life in the castle over the centuries, from the point of view of some of the people who worked or were incarcerated there.

MAP Page 338 (6C)
OS Map 196, OL29/119: SU625046

ST MARY'S CHURCH, ITCHEN STOKE
HAMPSHIRE – SO24 0QU

© CCT

Inspired by the Sainte Chapelle (Paris), this dazzling and colourful Victorian jewel overwhelms the senses. Inside is an exhilarating, kaleidoscopic wonderland of pattern and colour from floor to ceiling, with dazzling stained glass, an unusual floor-tile maze and a richly painted roof.

Owned and managed by The Churches Conservation Trust.

OPENING TIMES

Open daily   10am-4pm

VISIT US

Train: Winchester 5¼ miles

Bus: Velvet bus service 67, Stagecoach route 64 (Winchester – Arlesford)

10 mins from The Grange at Northington

MAP Page 338 (5C)
OS Map 185, 132: SU559323

TITCHFIELD ABBEY
HAMPSHIRE – PO15 5RA

The ruins of a 13th-century abbey of Premonstratensian canons, later converted into a Tudor mansion. The church was rebuilt as a grand turreted gatehouse. Information panels tell the story of the monastery and its conversion into a mansion. A free downloadable audio tour is available from the English Heritage website.

OPENING TIMES

1 Apr-30 Sep, daily	10am-5pm
1 Oct-29 Mar, daily	10am-4pm
24-26 Dec & 1 Jan	Closed

VISIT US

Direction: Located ½ mile N of Titchfield, off A27

Train: Fareham 2 miles

Bus: First services 4, X4, 26 & 28. Alight Titchfield by-pass and then use public footpath

Tel: 0870 333 1181

 ACQ.1923

MAP Page 338 (6C)
OS Map 196, 119: SU542067

WOLVESEY CASTLE (OLD BISHOP'S PALACE)
HAMPSHIRE

Wolvesey has been an important residence of the wealthy and powerful bishops of Winchester since Anglo-Saxon times. Standing next to Winchester Cathedral, the extensive surviving ruins of the palace date largely from the 12th-century work of Bishop Henry of Blois. The last great occasion here was on 25 July 1554, when Queen Mary and Philip of Spain held their wedding breakfast in the East Hall. A free downloadable audio tour is available from the English Heritage website.

OPENING TIMES

| 1 Apr-2 Nov, daily | 10am-5pm |
| 3 Nov-29 Mar | Closed |

VISIT US

Direction: ¾ mile SE of Winchester Cathedral, next to the Bishop's Palace; access from College St

Train: Winchester ¾ mile

Bus: From surrounding areas

Tel: 0870 333 1181

 ACQ.1962

MAP Page 338 (5C)
OS Map 185, 132: SU484291

KENT

ALL SAINTS' CHURCH, WALDERSHARE
KENT – CT15 5AT

© CCT Ian Sumner

This pretty church is an ideal resting point for walkers crossing the beautiful North Downs. The south chapel of 1697 contains a touching memorial of life-size marble figures of a husband and wife holding hands. Fantastical monuments, murals and stained glass can be found throughout.

Owned and managed by The Churches Conservation Trust.

OPENING TIMES
Open daily   10.30am-3.30pm

VISIT US
Train: Shepherdswell 3 miles

Bus: Stagecoach services 89 and Regent service 544

10 mins from Dover Castle

MAP Page 339 (5J)
OS Map 179, 138: TR298483

BAYHAM OLD ABBEY
KENT – TN3 8LP

The impressive ruins of an abbey of Premonstratensian 'white canons', on the Kent-Sussex border. They include much of the 13th to 15th-century church, the chapter house and a picturesque 14th-century gatehouse. Now set in a landscape designed by Humphry Repton, the famous landscape gardener who also planned the grounds of Kenwood in London. Rooms in the 'Georgian Gothick' dower house are also open to visitors.

NON-MEMBERS
Adult	£4.50
Concession	£4.10
Child	£2.70

OPENING TIMES
1 Apr-30 Sep, daily	10am-5pm
1 Oct-29 Mar	Closed

VISIT US
Direction: 1¾ miles W of Lamberhurst, off B2169

Train: Frant 4 miles then bus 256

Bus: Autocar 256

Tel: 01892 890381

Local Tourist Information
Tunbridge Wells: 01892 515675

ACQ.1961 ♿ 🐾 🖼 🚹 👥 P 🎁 📷
♿ OVP

Disabled access (grounds only over rough ground and lower floor of Dower House via 4 steps).

MAP Page 339 (5G)
OS Map 188, 136: TQ650365

DEAL CASTLE
SEE FEATURE – PAGE 62

DOVER CASTLE
SEE FEATURE – PAGE 58

DOWN HOUSE – SEE THE HOME OF CHARLES DARWIN
SEE FEATURE – PAGE 64

DYMCHURCH MARTELLO TOWER
KENT – TN29 0NL

One of 103 ingeniously-designed artillery towers built from 1805 at vulnerable points around the south and east coasts to resist threatened Napoleonic invasion. Exterior viewing only.

OPENING TIMES
Interior viewing by appointment only – please call 01304 211067

VISIT US
Direction: Access from Dymchurch High Street

Train: Sandling 7 miles; Dymchurch (Romney, Hythe and Dymchurch Railway) ¾ mile

Bus: Stagecoach in East Kent 'The Wave' services 101, 102 & 105

ACQ.1959 🐾

MAP Page 339 (5H)
OS Map 189, 138: TR102292

DOVER CASTLE Kent – CT16 1HU

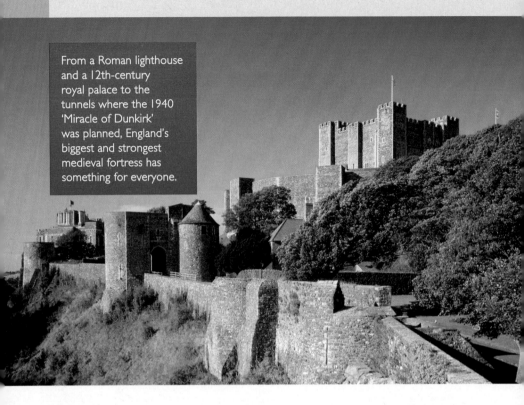

From a Roman lighthouse and a 12th-century royal palace to the tunnels where the 1940 'Miracle of Dunkirk' was planned, England's biggest and strongest medieval fortress has something for everyone.

VISIT US

Address: Dover Castle, Castle Hill, Dover, Kent

Direction: E of Dover town centre

Train: Dover Priory 1½ miles

Bus: Stagecoach in East Kent 15, 15X, 80, 80A, 93

Tel: 01304 211067

Local Tourist Information
Dover: 01304 205108

NON-MEMBERS

Adult	£17.50
Concession	£15.80
Child	£10.50
Family	£45.50

Price includes Secret Wartime Tunnels tour. Additional charges for members and non-members may apply on event days

OPENING TIMES

1 Apr-31 Jul, daily	10am-6pm
1-31 Aug, daily	9.30am-6pm
1-30 Sep, daily	10am-6pm
1 Oct-2 Nov, daily	10am-5pm
3 Nov-15 Feb, Sat-Sun	10am-4pm
16-20 Feb, daily	10am-4pm
21 Feb-29 Mar, Sat-Sun	10am-4pm
24-26 Dec, 31 Dec-1 Jan	Closed

Last admission 1 hour before closing

The Great Tower is free-flow and self-guided. Costumed live interpreters welcome you at the Great Tower on selected days and lifelike hologram characters at all other times. The Secret Wartime Tunnels 'Operation Dynamo' tours are part-guided by site staff, and numbers per tour are limited to 30 people, setting off at approximately 10 minute intervals (tour lasts approximately 50 minutes). Due to the immersive nature of these visits, no independent guiding is allowed in these areas. However, tour leaders of groups of younger visitors must stay with their parties at all times. Access to the

Underground Hospital (separate access from Operation Dynamo) is by guided tour only (limited to 30 people and lasting approximately 20 minutes). Access to Operation Dynamo and Underground Hospital is included in the admission price. At peak times, there may be queues at the popular tunnel experiences. Please ask site staff upon arrival for the best time to visit the tunnels on that specific day. Groups of 11+ are asked to call the site in advance

Please refer to the Dover Castle web page or ring the site directly for information on accessibility. Mobility scooters, wheelchair routes and guides are available on site.

Dogs on leads (restricted areas only).

We advise you to wear comfortable shoes.

MAP Page 339 (5J)
OS Map 179, 138: TR325419

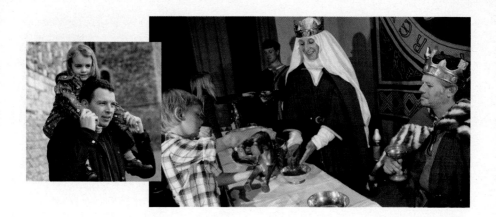

'The Key to England' for over nine centuries, the mighty fortress of Dover Castle displays at its core a dazzling evocation of a medieval royal palace. The Secret Wartime Tunnels in the White Cliffs beneath the castle now host an astonishingly realistic presentation of the 'Miracle of Dunkirk', master-minded here in 1940.

Commanding the shortest sea crossing between England and the continent, Dover Castle boasts a long and immensely eventful history. Its spectacular site atop the famous 'White Cliffs' was probably an Iron Age hill fort, and still houses a Roman lighthouse. The Anglo-Saxon church beside it was probably part of a Saxon fortified settlement, converted soon after 1066 into a Norman earthwork castle. Thereafter Dover Castle was garrisoned uninterruptedly until 1958, a record equalled only by the Tower of London and Windsor Castle. From 1740 its defences were updated in response to every European war involving Britain, and were crucially tested during the darkest days of the Second World War.

Operation Dynamo: Rescue from Dunkirk
At the beginning of the Second World War the network of chalk-cut tunnels deep beneath the castle – begun in 1797 to counter the threat of invasion from Napoleonic France – was recommissioned and further enlarged. Housing a hospital, they crucially also became

Vice Admiral Bertram Ramsay's bomb-proof naval headquarters, where a handful of men and women planned the activities of a determined squadron of Royal Navy ships whose task was to keep the enemy out of the Straits of Dover.

There, at 6:57pm on May 26th 1940, a teleprinter spluttered into life. The words of its brief message – 'Operation Dynamo is to commence' – were meaningless to all but a few. One of the few was Vice Admiral Ramsay, and this was the bad news he had been expecting. The British Army and its French and Belgian allies were trapped at Dunkirk, backs to the sea, fighting for their lives in a shrinking pocket of land. The task of rescuing them demanded rapid planning and round-the-clock working to assemble and send a huge improvised fleet of ships, naval and civilian, large and small, to Dunkirk, under attack from air, sea and land. Over 300,000 soldiers were depending on Ramsay, his HQ staff and the sailors in his ships.

You can now make the adventurous journey into the tunnels up to 26 metres beneath the castle, and immerse yourself in the drama of the daring evacuation that followed. Film presentations and displays vividly recreate

CONTINUED ▶

the outbreak of war in 1939 and the Battle of France in Spring 1940, when allied forces came close to total destruction by the advancing German blitzkrieg. See the pivotal part the Secret Wartime Tunnels played in *Operation Dynamo*. Then, in the very place where it was planned, witness with breathtaking realism the amazing beach rescue operation happening.

You can also take a fascinating guided tour of the (separately accessed) Underground Hospital within the tunnels, and relive the tension as a surgeon battles to save an injured pilot. Find out more about the 'Miracle of Dunkirk', and how it snatched victory from the jaws of defeat, in the Wartime Tunnels Uncovered exhibition, featuring the recorded voices of many who actually took part, from rescued soldiers and skippers of 'Little Ships' to those who welcomed the battered forces home. A guidebook to 'Frontline Fortress Dover' is available in the Secret Wartime Tunnels shop, specialising in 1940s books and material.

The Great Tower

Above ground Dover Castle is essentially the greatest medieval fortress in England, created by King Henry II and his Plantagenet successors. At its heart stands the mighty Great Tower, the grandest and among the last of the keeps raised by the kings of England during the 11th and 12th centuries. Built between 1180 and 1185, this symbol of kingly power was also a palace designed for royal ceremony.

Here, Henry could welcome and impress distinguished visitors to England – particularly noble pilgrims travelling to the new shrine in Canterbury Cathedral of St Thomas Becket.

The entire interior of Henry's Great Tower palace has been recreated as it might have appeared when newly completed. Begin your tour in the exhibition near the foot of the towering keep, where imaginative interactive displays tell the dramatic story of Henry II and his turbulent brood – *A Family at War*. A man of superhuman energy and violent rages, Henry ruled an empire stretching from the Scottish Borders to the Pyrenees, but proved unable to master his own quarrelsome and treacherous family. Children can help European pilgrims reach Becket's shrine at Canterbury and you can 'Ask the Experts' about the recreated rooms, of which a virtual tour is provided for those unable to tour the Great Tower itself.

Ascending the stairs into the Great Tower, meet the first of the many lifelike projected figures which help to guide you round the six great recreated rooms and several lesser chambers of the palace. Among the most spectacular is the King's Hall, dominated by its canopied throne and decked with wall hangings and recreations of contemporary furniture, all brilliantly coloured. The vibrant colours of the Great Tower's interiors, reflecting medieval reality, are indeed the most striking aspect of the re-creation.

The tour continues via the Royal Chapel to the King's Chamber, focussed on the royal bed. Next come the Guests' Bedchamber and the Guest Hall, shown ready for a feast. The cavernous ground floor is fascinatingly set as the fully-equipped royal Kitchen, Brewery and Bakehouse, while the Armoury displays replicas of the weapons used by Henry's household knights. On selected days, you may also encounter costumed live interpreters – including Henry himself – throughout the Great Tower.

A Mighty Fortress

Climb to the Great Tower's roof for panoramic views over the castle's immense complex of fortifications, with busy Dover harbour below. Around his impressive keep Henry built a powerful inner curtain wall, and beyond that an outer curtain wall. These three mutually-supporting lines of defence made Dover the very first 'concentric' fortress in western Europe. Its defences were severely tested during the epic sieges of 1216-17, when the castle resisted ten months of attack. Intrepid visitors can still descend into the 'Medieval Tunnels', burrowed beneath the castle during and after the 1216-17 siege.

The First World War

The cliff-top Admiralty Lookout also played an important role in both World Wars. Inside, a First World War Fire Command Post has been recreated, with displays on the castle's role as a naval signal station. From here the Navy controlled the movements of all ships into and out of the harbour, and could quickly liase with the gunners immediately below.

The First World War naval headquarters in Dover town directed the defence of the Straits, and the famous 'Dover Patrol' of warships: the castle was the headquarters of a garrison of up to 16,000 soldiers. Hence on 21 December 1914 the port attracted the first recorded German air-raid on England – whose single bomb missed the harbour and fell into

the sea. Thereafter Dover was among the first British towns to be equipped with anti-aircraft guns and searchlights, one of them sited on a turret of the castle's Great Tower.

The Stone Hut, built in 1912 for the Royal Garrison Artillery, is now used as an archaeological store. On the first Friday of every month (or by pre-arranged booking), visitors can view changing exhibitions of treasures from across the region, including artefacts from both the Second World War and the Cold War.

All this, and very much more, makes Dover Castle well worth a whole day's exploration.

🎬 *The Other Boleyn Girl*, starring Natalie Portman and Scarlett Johanssen; Zeffirelli's *Hamlet*, starring Mel Gibson; and *To Kill a King*, starring Dougray Scott.

🏠 HOLIDAY COTTAGES AT **DOVER CASTLE**

Peverell's Tower *(see above)* was at one time a prison. Today it sleeps two in liberating comfort.

To stay at the **Sergeant Major's House** is to be surrounded by hundreds of years of history. This elegant and spacious four-storey Georgian building sleeps six. Set just inside the Western Outer Curtain Wall.

DEAL CASTLE KENT – CT14 7BA

EYNSFORD CASTLE
KENT – DA4 0AA

Deal Castle is one of the finest Tudor artillery castles in England. It is among the earliest and most elaborate of a chain of coastal forts, which also includes Calshot, Camber, Walmer and Pendennis Castles. Most were built 'with all speed, and without sparing any cost' between 1539 and 1542 by order of King Henry VIII, who feared an invasion by European Catholic powers. Its squat, rounded bastions were designed to deflect incoming cannon balls, and acted as platforms from which to fire increasingly sophisticated artillery pieces. Deal is also equipped for close-quarter defence, with no less than 145 embrasures for firearms. The fort guarded the sheltered anchorage of 'the Downs' – the stretch of water between the shore and the hazardous Goodwin Sands, a graveyard of ships.

The foreign invasion never materialised, but Deal Castle saw hard fighting during the Civil War (1648). Taken by forces from the rebel Royalist fleet, it was twice besieged by Parliamentarians, and finally surrendered after the bloody repulse of a relief attempt.

Today, it is a fascinating castle to explore, with long, dark passages, battlements and a massive basement in which an absorbing exhibition is housed. A pleasant cycle path links Deal and Walmer Castles along the beachfront.

NON-MEMBERS

Adult	£5.20
Concession	£4.70
Child	£3.10
Family	£13.50

OPENING TIMES

1 Apr-30 Sep, daily	10am-6pm
1 Oct-2 Nov, daily	10am-5pm
3 Nov-29 Mar, Sat-Sun	10am-4pm
24-26 Dec, 31 Dec-1 Jan	Closed

VISIT US
Direction: SW of Deal town centre

Train: Deal ½ mile

Bus: Stagecoach East Kent services 12, 13, 13A, 14, 80A, 82, 82A, 93; Regent Coaches 541, 542, 544

Tel: 01304 372762

Audio tours (also available in Dutch, French and German).

Disabled access (courtyards and ground floor only, parking available).

MAP Page 339 (5J)
OS Map 179, 150: TR378522

The substantial stone walls of a very early Norman 'enclosure castle', begun c. 1085-87 and unusually little altered by later building works. This rare survival stands in an attractive village setting, not far from Lullingstone Roman Villa (p.67).

OPENING TIMES

1 Apr-30 Sep, daily	10am-6pm
1 Oct-29 Mar, daily	10am-4pm
24-26 Dec & 1 Jan	Closed

VISIT US
Direction: In Eynsford, off A225

Train: Eynsford 1 mile

Bus: Arriva bus 478; Go-Coach 421; Nu Venture 405 (Wed)

MAP Page 339 (4F)
OS Map 177, 162: TQ542658

FAVERSHAM STONE CHAPEL (OUR LADY OF ELVERTON)
KENT

FAVERSHAM STONE CHAPEL (OUR LADY OF ELVERTON)

The ruins of the small Anglo-Saxon and medieval chapel of Stone-next-Faversham, incorporating within its fabric the remains of a 4th-century Romano-British pagan mausoleum. It lay close to the probable site of the small Roman town of Durolevum and its Roman cemetery at Ospringe, finds from which can be seen at Maison Dieu (see p.68).

Managed by The Faversham Society.

www.faversham.org/society

OPENING TIMES
Any reasonable daylight hours

VISIT US
Direction: In field immediately N of A2 just W of Ospringe and opposite Faversham Road

Train: Faversham 1½ miles

Bus: Chalkwell 324, Arriva/Chalkwell 333

Tel: 01795 534542

E-mail: ticfaversham@btconnect.com

 ACQ.1972 🐕

MAP Page 339 (4H)
OS Map 178, 149: TQ992613

THE HOME OF CHARLES DARWIN, DOWN HOUSE
SEE FEATURE – PAGE 64

HORNE'S PLACE CHAPEL
KENT

HORNE'S PLACE CHAPEL

A rare survival of a fine domestic chapel, built for William Horne in 1366 and attached to his timber-framed manor house, which was attacked during the Peasants' Revolt of 1381. The house and chapel are privately owned.

OPENING TIMES
By prior arrangement; please call 01304 211067

VISIT US
Direction: 1½ miles N of Appledore

Train: Appledore 2½ miles

Bus: Stagecoach East Kent service 11B (one return weekday journey) & New Enterprise/Kent Coach Tours service 293 (Mon, Thu, Fri only)

ACQ.1950 🐕 P

Parking (nearby).

MAP Page 339 (5H)
OS Map 189, 125: TQ958309

KIT'S COTY HOUSE AND LITTLE KIT'S COTY HOUSE
KENT

© Kelvin Trundle

The remains of two megalithic burial chambers. Impressive Kit's Coty has three uprights and a massive capstone; Little Kit's Coty, alias the Countless Stones, is now a jumble of sarsens.

KIT'S COTY HOUSE AND LITTLE KIT'S COTY HOUSE

NEW FOR 2014
New interpretative panels.

OPENING TIMES
Any reasonable daylight hours

VISIT US
Direction: W of A229, 2 miles N of Maidstone

Train: Aylesford 2½ miles

Bus: Arriva 101 & 142; Nu Venture 150

ACQ.1883 🐕

MAP Page 339 (4G)
OS Map 178/188, 148
Kit's Coty House: TQ745608
Little Kit's Coty House: TQ744604

KNIGHTS TEMPLAR CHURCH, DOVER KENT

The foundations of a small medieval church, traditionally the site of King John's submission to the Papal Legate in 1213.

VISIT US
Direction: On the Western Heights above Dover

Train: Dover Priory ¾ mile

Bus: Stagecoach East Kent service 93 from Dover town centre

Tel: 01304 211067

OPENING TIMES
Any reasonable daylight hours

ACQ.1968 🐕

Dogs on leads (restricted areas only).

MAP Page 339 (5J)
OS Map 179, 138: TR313407

LULLINGSTONE ROMAN VILLA
SEE FEATURE – PAGE 67

The Victorian country house where the world was changed, Down House's advanced but unobtrusive technology helps you experience the lives of Charles Darwin and his family at your own pace.

VISIT US

Address: Down House, Luxted Road, Downe, Kent

Direction: Luxted Rd, Downe; off A21 or A233

Train: Chelsfield 3¾ miles, Orpington 3¾ miles, Bromley South 5½ miles

Bus: TfL bus R8 from Orpington passes; TfL bus 146 from Bromley North & South terminates in Downe village ½ mile from property

Tel: 01689 859119

NON-MEMBERS

Adult	£10.30
Concession	£9.30
Child	£6.20
Family	£26.80

OPENING TIMES

1 Apr-30 Sep, daily & Bank Hols	10am-6pm
1 Oct-2 Nov, daily	10am-5pm
3 Nov-15 Feb, Sat-Sun	10am-4pm
16-20 Feb, daily	10am-4pm
21 Feb-29 Mar, Sat-Sun	10am-4pm
24-26 Dec, 31 Dec-1 Jan	Closed

Last admission 30 mins before closing

ACQ.1996

Audio tour is the multimedia tour.

Parking (plus space for one coach).

MAP Page 339 (4F)
OS Map 177/187,147: TQ431611

Visitors are guided round Darwin's family rooms by a hand-held multimedia tour, narrated by Sir David Attenborough and Andrew Marr. The tour also includes the extensive gardens – Darwin's 'outdoor laboratory' and the place where he made many of his discoveries.

A delightful place to visit in itself, Down House is also a site of outstanding international significance. Here the famous naturalist Charles Darwin lived with his family for forty years; here he worked on his revolutionary theories; and here he wrote *On the Origin of Species by Means of Natural Selection* – the book which shook the Victorian world and has influenced our thinking ever since.

Darwin's work and personality are vividly reflected throughout the house and gardens. The ground floor rooms have been recreated as they appeared when he lived here with his indefatigably supportive wife Emma – a member of the renowned Wedgwood family – and their many children. They include the 'Old Study' where Darwin wrote his most famous books, following a rigid routine despite chronic illness and frequent good-natured interruptions by his children. It still displays his chair, writing desk and many personal items. The family's Drawing Room – with Emma's grand piano – Billiard Room and Dining Room are also on show, likewise mainly furnished with items original to the house.

The video guide includes commentaries by experts, animations, film footage and games for all the family. It is one of many exciting interactive developments at the Home of Charles Darwin introduced to celebrate the 200th anniversary of Darwin's birth and the 150th anniversary of the publication of *On the Origin of Species*.

'Uncovering Origin' Exhibition

An award-winning exhibition on the house's first floor covers Darwin's life, his scientific work, and the controversy which it provoked. It includes many previously unseen objects, with highlights including manuscript pages from the *On the Origin of Species*; Darwin's hat, microscope and notebooks; and a copy of *Das Kapital* inscribed to him by Karl Marx.

Beginning with an introduction to Darwin, his place in Victorian science, and the impact of his theories, the displays continue with his famous five-year voyage aboard the *Beagle* in 1831-36, including a full-scale recreation of his ship's cabin. The notebooks and journals compiled on this round-the-world voyage have been digitised and annotated, allowing visitors to explore them page by page. Further displays highlight *On the Origin of Species*, a book which sold out its first edition immediately and consolidated Darwin's international recognition and notoriety. They also examine how his theories were publicised and defended, principally via letter writing. Visitors can explore some of his key ideas (including his

CONTINUED ►

Stop off at the tearoom, situated in Darwin's kitchen area, for a refreshing break before exploring the grounds.

investigations into the expression of emotions in humans and animals) through hands-on interactives and installations.

The Darwin children's schoolroom celebrates family life at Down House. There is also an education room, available for family learning at weekends, and a resources room for those interested in delving deeper.

Experiments in the Gardens

By no means the stereotypically stern Victorian father, Darwin involved his children in his practical experiments in the extensive grounds of Down House. Visitors too can now follow these via the video guide, beginning with Darwin's 'weed garden' illustrating the struggle for existence in nature.

The sundial amid pretty flowerbeds highlights Emma Darwin's role as a gardener; a surviving mulberry tree recalls family traditions; and a 'lawn experiment' investigates proliferation of plant species. Further afield is the 'worm stone', which Darwin used to measure undermining by earthworms.

The nearby hot-house features some of Darwin's most fascinating experiments, involving carnivorous plants, exotic orchids and climbing species. The curiously-shaped tennis court evokes his family and social life, and in the summer there are working beehives in the laboratory. After a tour of the extensive kitchen gardens, visitors finally reach what is for many a place of pilgrimage: the wooded Sandwalk, Darwin's famous 'thinking path', which he paced five times a day while working out his theories.

Virtual Access

Gain virtual access to Darwin's world through the *Home of Charles Darwin* pages on our website. Features include interactive digital highlights from one of the rarest Darwin manuscript collections in the world, including his *Beagle* notebooks and diary, plus a virtual tour of parts of the house and grounds.

Please note: No photography is allowed inside the house.

Unfortunately picnics are not allowed in the grounds, as they are part of a 'Site of Importance for Nature Conservation', nurturing many important protected species, including fungi.

VISIT US

Direction: ½ mile SW of Eynsford, off J3 of M25, A20 towards West Kingsdown, A225 to Eynsford

Bus: Arriva bus 478; Go-Coach 421; Nu Venture 405 (Wed)

Train: Eynsford 2 miles

Tel: 01322 863467

NON-MEMBERS

Adult	£6.40
Concession	£5.80
Child	£3.80
Family	£16.60

OPENING TIMES

1 Apr-30 Sep, daily	10am-6pm
1 Oct-2 Nov, daily	10am-5pm
3 Nov-15 Feb, Sat-Sun	10am-4pm
16-20 Feb, daily	10am-4pm
21 Feb-29 Mar, Sat-Sun	10am-4pm
24-26 Dec, 31 Dec-1 Jan	Closed

ACQ.1958 ♦ ▮ E ♛ ▣ ⛹ ♿ ✕
P ☐ ♿ ➤ OVP

Parking charges apply to non-members.

Among the most outstanding Roman villa survivals in Britain, Lullingstone Roman Villa has been vividly re-displayed, providing a unique – and all-weather – opportunity to trace Roman domestic life over three centuries.

Set in the attractive surroundings of the Darent Valley, the villa was begun in about AD 100, and developed to suit the tastes and beliefs of successive wealthy owners. These may have included the family of Pertinax, Governor of Britain and later Roman Emperor for just 87 days in AD 193. Additions included a heated bath-suite and a remarkable underground pagan 'cult-room', including a rare painting of three water-nymphs, by far the oldest wall-painting in English Heritage care.

The villa reached its peak of luxury in the mid-4th century, when a big new dining room was added. This still displays spectacular mosaics, including *Europa and the Bull* and *Bellerophon Killing the Chimera*. By now Christians, the owners also created a 'house-church' above the pagan cult-room: the wall-paintings discovered here are among the earliest surviving evidence for Christianity in Britain. Pagan worship may, however, have continued, suggesting a relaxed relationship between the old and new faiths.

All this is appealingly interpreted in the galleries overlooking the fully excavated remains. These display Lullingstone Roman Villa's fascinating and recently-returned collection of Roman artefacts, enlivened by paintings by the award-winning children's illustrator, Jane Ray. Children and other visitors can also play Roman board games, handle original building materials and try on Roman costumes. A specially-commissioned film and light show brings the villa to life, lighting up areas of the remains as the film reveals how they were once used.

MAP Page 339 (4F)
OS Map 177/188, 147/162:
TQ530651

MAISON DIEU
KENT – ME13 8TS

This 13th and 16th-century flint and timber-framed building is virtually all that survives of a much larger complex. It included a 'hospital' for the overnight lodging of pilgrims to Canterbury; a royal suite where many crowned heads stayed on their way to or from the continent; and a school. In layout and appearance it was much like a small monastery. The present building now known as the Maison Dieu is thought to have been a chantry-priest's house. It houses a museum focussing on the Maison Dieu foundation itself and its immediate neighbourhood, and on the extensive finds made during excavations at the main complex and at an important Roman cemetery nearby.

Managed by The Faversham Society.

www.faversham.org/society

NON-MEMBERS

Adult	£2.00
Concession	£1.00
Child	Free
when accompanied by an adult	

OPENING TIMES

5 Apr-2 Nov, Sat-Sun, & Bank Hols	2pm-5pm
3 Nov-29 Mar	Closed
Group visits at other times by appointment	

VISIT US

Direction: On main A2 on W corner of Water Lane in village of Ospringe. Public car park 300yds W

Train: Faversham ¾ mile

Bus: Chalkwell 324, Arriva/Chalkwell 333

Tel: 01795 534542

E-mail: ticfaversham@btconnect.com

ACQ.1947 E ⬇ ⬆ ✂

MAP Page 339 (4H)
OS Map 178, 149: TR003609

MILTON CHANTRY
KENT – DA12 2BH

Mainly encased in brick but still retaining its 14th-century timber roof, this was in turn part of a hospital, a chantry chapel, a public house and a Georgian barracks before its basement became a Second World War gas decontamination chamber. The building, in Gravesham's Heritage Quarter, gives a fascinating insight into the borough's heritage.

Managed by Gravesham Borough Council.

OPENING TIMES

5 Apr-28 Sep, Sat-Sun & Bank Hols	12pm-5pm
29 Sep-29 Mar	Closed
Admission outside these times by appointment	

VISIT US

Direction: In New Tavern Fort Gardens; E of central Gravesend, off A226

Train: Gravesend ¾ mile

Bus: Arriva, Red Route and Nu Venture services pass within a short distance

Tel: 01474 337442

ACQ.1972 🎧 ✂ ⚠

MAP Page 339 (4G)
OS Map 177/178, 162/163: TQ653743

OLD SOAR MANOR
KENT – TN15 0QX

A small but complete portion of a stone manor house built c. 1290. The first floor 'solar' private chamber, with attendant chapel and garderobe, stands over a vaulted undercroft.

Managed by the National Trust on behalf of English Heritage.

OPENING TIMES

1 Apr-30 Sep, Sat-Thu	10am-6pm
1 Oct-29 Mar	Closed

OLD SOAR MANOR

VISIT US

Direction: 1 mile E of Plaxtol

Train: Borough Green and Wrotham 2½ miles

Bus: Autocar 222 Tonbridge – Borough Green; Nu Venture 404 from Sevenoaks. On both alight E end of Plaxtol, then ¾ mile by footpath

Tel: 01732 810378

ACQ.1948 ✂ P
Parking (limited).

MAP Page 339 (5G)
OS Map 188, 147/148: TQ619541

RECULVER TOWERS AND ROMAN FORT
KENT – CT6 6SS

An imposing landmark, the twin 12th-century towers of the ruined church stand amid the remains of an important Roman 'Saxon Shore' fort and a Saxon monastery. Richborough Roman Fort is within easy travelling distance. Download the free audio tour from our website.

Managed by Canterbury City Council.

OPENING TIMES

Any reasonable daylight hours; external viewing only	
Reculver Centre open Sat & Sun 11am-3pm; longer opening hours from Easter and during school holidays – please call 01227 740676 for more information	

VISIT US

Direction: At Reculver, 3 miles E of Herne Bay; signed off Thanet Way A299

Train: Herne Bay 4 miles

Bus: Stagecoach in East Kent 7, 7A, 36

Tel: 01227 740676

ACQ.1925 ✂ 🏛 ⬆ ⬆ P ♿

Disabled access (grounds only – long slope up from car park).

Please note: parking (pay and display). Not managed by English Heritage.

MAP Page 339 (4J)
OS Map 179, 150: TR228693

VISIT US

Direction: At the A256/A257 roundabout, head for Sandwich then turn left onto Richborough Road and proceed for approx. 1 mile

Train: Sandwich 2 miles

Bus: Stagecoach East Kent 87, 88 then walk using Stour Valley Walk/ Saxon Shore Way

Tel: 01304 612013

NON-MEMBERS

Adult	£5.20
Concession	£4.70
Child	£3.10
Family	£13.50

OPENING TIMES

Fort:

1 Apr-30 Sep, daily	10am-6pm
1 Oct-2 Nov, Wed-Sun	10am-5pm
3 Nov-29 Mar, Sat-Sun	10am-4pm
24-26 Dec, 31 Dec-1 Jan	Closed

Amphitheatre: Any reasonable time in daylight hours, access across grazed land from footpath; please call 01304 612013 for details

Dogs on leads (restricted areas only).

Evocatively sited amid the East Kent marshes, Richborough Roman Fort is the most symbolically important of all Roman sites in Britain, witnessing both the beginning and almost the end of Roman rule here. Now landlocked, in AD 43 it overlooked a sheltered channel where the invading Roman forces first came ashore. The line of the Roman foreshore, now two miles inland from the sea, was discovered in 2008 by English Heritage archaeologists digging just outside the fort wall.

The landing was commemorated by a mighty triumphal arch, whose foundations still survive: the arch also provided an impressive gateway for arrivals at what became the port of 'Rutupiae', the province's main point of entry.

By the mid-3rd century, however, Roman Britain was threatened by sea-borne raiders. A fort was therefore hastily created within the port. At first defended by the triple ditches still visible, but soon after by stone walls, this became one of the most important of the 'Saxon Shore' forts. It was also among the last to be regularly occupied: there was still a large Roman population here in the early 5th century.

You can choose to reach the fort as the Romans would have done, by boat. Boats sail from Sandwich, but not every day: please telephone the site to obtain details of the contractor.

MAP Page 339 (4J) OS Map 179, 150
Fort: TR324602
Amphitheatre: TR321598

ROCHESTER CASTLE
KENT – ME1 1SW

Strategically placed astride the London Road, guarding an important crossing of the River Medway, this imposing fortress has a complex history of destruction and rebuilding. Its mighty Norman tower-keep of Kentish ragstone was built c. 1127 by William of Corbeil, Archbishop of Canterbury, with the encouragement of Henry I. Consisting of three floors above a basement, it still stands 113 feet high. Attached is a tall protruding forebuilding, with its own set of defences to pass through before the keep itself could be entered at first floor level.

In 1215, garrisoned by rebel barons, the castle endured an epic siege by King John. Having first undermined the outer wall, John used the fat of 40 pigs to fire a mine under the keep, bringing its southern corner crashing down. Even then the defenders held out within the building, until they were eventually starved out after a resistance of nearly two months.

Rebuilt under Henry III and Edward I, the castle remained a viable fortress in the 15th

ROCHESTER CASTLE

century, but a century later it was decaying. Today it stands as a proud reminder of the history of Rochester, along with the nearby cathedral and Dickensian cobbled streets.

Managed by Medway Council.
www.visitmedway.org

NON-MEMBERS

Adult	£6.00
Concession	£3.80
Child	£3.80
Family	£15.80

OPENING TIMES

1 Apr-30 Sep, daily	10am-6pm
1 Oct-29 Mar, daily	10am-4pm

Last admission 45 mins before closing

24-26 Dec, 1 Jan	Closed

VISIT US

Direction: By Rochester Bridge (A2); junction 1 of M2 and junction 2 of M25

Train: Rochester ½ mile

Bus: Services in Rochester are operated by Arriva and Nu Venture. Alight in Corporation Street within a short distance of the castle

Tel: 01634 332901

ACQ.1965 🎧 🔊 E 🖼 🧍 🔦 ❌ 🗑
⚠ OVP

Audio tours (small charge).

Toilets (in castle grounds).

MAP Page 339 (4G)
OS Map 178, 148/163: TQ741686

ST AUGUSTINE'S ABBEY
KENT – CT1 1TF

This great abbey, marking the rebirth of Christianity in southern England, was founded shortly after AD 597 by St Augustine. Originally created as a burial place for the Anglo-Saxon kings of Kent, it is part of the Canterbury World Heritage Site, along

ST AUGUSTINE'S ABBEY

with the cathedral and St Martin's Church.

The impressive and historically important abbey is situated outside the city walls, but should not be missed by visitors. You can also enjoy the museum and free audio tour.

NON-MEMBERS

Adult	£5.20
Concession	£4.70
Child	£3.10
Family	£13.50

OPENING TIMES

1 Apr-30 Sep, daily	10am-6pm
1 Oct-2 Nov, Wed-Sun	10am-5pm
3 Nov-29 Mar, Sat-Sun	10am-4pm
24-26 Dec, 31 Dec-1 Jan	Closed

VISIT US

Direction: In Canterbury, ¼ mile E of Cathedral Close

Train: Canterbury East and West, both ¾ mile

Bus: From surrounding areas

Tel: 01227 767345

Local Tourist Information
Canterbury: 01227 378100

ACQ.1938 🎧 🦽 🐾 E 🖼 🧍 👕 ✉
📷 ♿ ⚠ OVP

Audio tours.

Disabled access (all site can be viewed, but some steps).

Parking (nearby).

MAP Page 339 (4J)
OS Map 179, 150: TR155578

ST AUGUSTINE'S ABBEY
CONDUIT HOUSE KENT

The Conduit House is part of the monastic waterworks which supplied nearby St Augustine's Abbey.

OPENING TIMES

Any reasonable daylight hours; exterior viewing only

ST AUGUSTINE'S ABBEY
CONDUIT HOUSE

VISIT US
Direction: In King's Park. Approx. 5-10 min walk from St Augustine's Abbey. Please call or ask at the abbey for directions

Train: Canterbury East or West, both ¾ mile

Bus: Stagecoach 13, 13A, 14 or Regent Coaches 649 from George Street City Centre to Canterbury Christ Church University then 10-15 min walk from the Abbey

ACQ.1977

MAP Page 339 (4J)
OS Map 179, 150: TR159580

ST AUGUSTINE'S CROSS
KENT

This 19th-century cross in Saxon style marks what is traditionally believed to be the site of St Augustine's landing on the shores of England in AD 597. Accompanied by 30 followers, Augustine is said to have held a mass here before moving on.

OPENING TIMES
Any reasonable daylight hours

VISIT US
Direction: 2 miles E of Minster off B29048

Train: Minster 2 miles

Bus: Stagecoach 42 from Ramsgate

ACQ.1912

MAP Page 339 (4J)
OS Map 179, 150: TR340642

ST JAMES' CHURCH, COOLING
KENT – ME3 8DG

© CCT

Charles Dickens used the churchyard of St James' as his inspiration for the opening chapter of *Great Expectations*. Surrounded by marshes, the site can look desolate, but inside the church is light and spacious. Its vestry walls are lined with thousands of cockle shells, the emblem of St James.

Owned and managed by The Churches Conservation Trust.

OPENING TIMES
Open daily   10am-4pm

VISIT US
Train: Higham 3¼ miles

Bus: Arriva 133 & 193 and Nu Venture 417 to Cliffe then 1½ mile walk

20 mins from Rochester Castle, 40 mins from Eltham Palace and Gardens, 45 mins from The Home of Charles Darwin

MAP Page 339 (4G)
OS Map 178, 163: TQ756759

ST JOHN'S COMMANDERY
KENT

The flint-walled 13th-century chapel and hall of a 'Commandery' of Knights Hospitallers, later converted into a farmhouse. It has a remarkable medieval crown-post roof and 16th-century ceilings with moulded beams.

OPENING TIMES
Any reasonable daylight hours for exterior viewing. Internal viewing by appointment only; please call 01304 211067

ST JOHN'S COMMANDERY

VISIT US
Direction: 2 miles NE of Densole, off A260

Train: Kearsney 4 miles

Bus: Stagecoach in East Kent 16/A ⇌ Folkestone Central – Canterbury, to within 1 mile

ACQ.1978

MAP Page 339 (5J)
OS Map 179/189, 138: TR232440

ST LEONARD'S TOWER
KENT

An early and well-preserved example of a small free-standing Norman tower keep, surviving almost to its original height. It was probably built c. 1080 by Gundulf, Bishop of Rochester, and takes its name from a chapel of St Leonard which once stood nearby.

Managed by West Malling Parish Council.

OPENING TIMES
Any reasonable daylight hours for exterior viewing

VISIT US
Direction: Nr West Malling, on unclassified road W of A228

Train: West Malling 1 mile

Bus: Nu 70, 123, 149, 151; Arriva 72, 77 & 147

ACQ.1937

Disabled access (grounds only).

MAP Page 339 (4G)
OS Map 178/188, 148: TQ676571

ST MARY'S CHURCH, HIGHAM
KENT – ME3 7LS

© CCT Neil Rushton

This remote church stands in the middle of orchards, on the edge of the Thames marshes. It has a great charm and eccentricity, with striped walls of ragstone and flint, and a near-symmetrical arrangement of two naves and two chancels.

Owned and managed by The Churches Conservation Trust.

OPENING TIMES

Open daily   9am-6pm

VISIT US

Train: Higham 1 mile

Bus: Nu Venture bus service 417 to Lower Higham then 1 mile walk

15 mins from Upnor Castle, 40 mins from Eltham Palace and Gardens, 40 mins from The Home of Charles Darwin

MAP Page 339 (4G)
OS Map 178, 163: TQ716742

To discover more about **The Churches Conservation Trust,** visit **www.visitchurches. org.uk**

THE CHURCHES
CONSERVATION TRUST

ST MARY'S CHURCH, SANDWICH
KENT – CT13 9EU

© CCT

Immense, barn-like St Mary's occupies what may be the oldest church site in Sandwich. During its rich history, it has twice survived town sackings by the French in the 13th and 15th centuries; an earthquake in the 16th century; and the collapse of its tower in the 17th century.

Owned and managed by The Churches Conservation Trust.

OPENING TIMES

Open daily   10am-4pm

Occasionally closed for events

VISIT US

Train: Sandwich ½ mile

Bus: Stagecoach services 13, 13A, 14, 87 & 88

15 mins from Deal Castle, 25 mins from Dover Castle

MAP Page 339 (4J)
OS Map 179, 150: TR329584

ST PETER'S CHURCH, SANDWICH
KENT – CT13 9DA

© CCT

This spacious 800-year-old Cinque Port church is a local landmark. The handsome tower has a distinctive onion dome built by Flemish refugees, and the atmospheric crypt was once a charnel house where bones from the graveyard were stored.

Owned and managed by The Churches Conservation Trust.

OPENING TIMES

Open daily but occasionally closed at short notice for events; please telephone 01304 621554 in advance of your visit

VISIT US

Train: Sandwich ¼ mile

Bus: Stagecoach services 13, 13A, 14, 87 & 88

5 mins from Richborough Roman Fort and Amphitheatre, 25 mins from Dover Castle

MAP Page 339 (4J)
OS Map 179, 150: TR331580

SUTTON VALENCE CASTLE
KENT

The ruins of a small 12th-century Norman keep, with panoramic views over the Weald.

OPENING TIMES
Any reasonable daylight hours

VISIT US
Direction: 5 miles SE of Maidstone, in Sutton Valence village, on A274

Train: Headcorn 4 miles, Hollingbourne 5 miles

Bus: Arriva 12 Maidstone – Tenterden (passes ⇌ Headcorn)

 ACQ.1976

MAP Page 339 (5G)
OS Map 188, 137: TQ815491

TEMPLE MANOR
KENT

Part of a manor house of the Knights Templar, built in about 1240, with a fine first floor hall displaying traces of wall paintings.

Managed by Medway Council.
www.visitmedway.org

OPENING TIMES
5 Apr-2 Nov, Sat-Sun	11am-4pm
3 Nov-29 Mar	Closed
6 May, 27 May, 26 Aug	Closed

For group visits please call 01634 332901

VISIT US
Direction: Located in Strood (Rochester), off A228

Train: Strood ¾ mile

Bus: Arriva and Nu Venture operate services in Strood. Alight in Knight Road, Strood and then short walk

ACQ.1950
Disabled access (grounds only).

MAP Page 339 (4G)
OS Map 178, 148/163: TQ733685

UPNOR CASTLE
KENT – ME2 4XG

Set in tranquil grounds adjoining a riverside village, this rare example of an Elizabethan artillery fort was begun in 1559 and strengthened in 1599-1601 to protect warships moored at Chatham dockyard (p.94). Despite a brave attempt, it entirely failed to do so in 1667, when the Dutch sailed past it to burn or capture the English fleet at anchor.

Managed by Medway Council.
www.visitmedway.org

NON-MEMBERS
Adult	£6.00
Concession	£3.80
Child	£3.80
Family	£15.80

Members also get discounted entry to Chatham Historic Dockyard (p.94)

OPENING TIMES
1 Apr-30 Sep, daily	10am-6pm
1 Oct-2 Nov, daily	10am-4pm
3 Nov-29 Mar	Closed

Last admission 45 mins before closing

May close early on Fri and Sat for weddings. Please call in advance to check

VISIT US
Direction: At Upnor, on unclassified road off A228

Train: Strood 2 miles

Bus: Arriva service 197 from Chatham

Tel: 01634 332902 or when castle is closed 01634 332901

UPNOR CASTLE

ACQ.1961
Audio guide (small charge).
Disabled access (grounds only).
Parking (at a slight distance from castle – park before village).

MAP Page 339 (4G)
OS Map 178, 163: TQ759706

WALMER CASTLE AND GARDENS
SEE FEATURE – PAGE 74

WESTERN HEIGHTS, DOVER
KENT

A huge fortification constructed during the Napoleonic Wars and completed in the 1860s, designed to protect Dover from French invasion.

OPENING TIMES
External viewing any reasonable daylight hours

Free to visit the outside and moat. Drop Redoubt Fortress open 3rd Sun Apr-Sep for pre-booked guided tours, plus events 12-13 Jul/4-5 Oct (charges apply)

Group visits at other times by arrangement visit www.doverwesternheights.org

VISIT US
Direction: Above Dover town on W side of harbour

Train: Dover Priory ¾ mile

Bus: Stagecoach East 93 from Dover town centre

Tel: 01304 211067

ACQ.1968

MAP Page 339 (5J)
OS Map 179, 138: TR312408

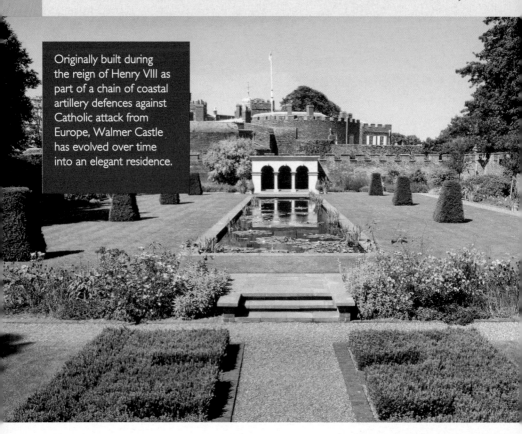

Originally built during the reign of Henry VIII as part of a chain of coastal artillery defences against Catholic attack from Europe, Walmer Castle has evolved over time into an elegant residence.

VISIT US

Address: Walmer Castle, Kingsdown Road, Deal, Kent

Direction: On coast S of Walmer, on A258; Junction 13 of M20 or from M2 to Deal

Train: Walmer 1 mile

Bus: Stagecoach East Kent service 82/82A

Tel: 01304 364288

Local Tourist Information
Deal: 01304 369576 and
Dover: 01304 205108

NON-MEMBERS

Adult	£7.90
Concession	£7.10
Child	£4.70
Family	£20.50

OPENING TIMES

1 Apr-30 Sep, daily	10am-6pm
1 Oct-2 Nov, daily	10am-5pm
3 Nov-29 Mar	Closed

Closed 11-12 Jul and re-opening at 2pm 13 Jul when Lord Warden in residence

Walmer will be closed during the winter for major refurbishment and conservation work. Check website for more information.

Audio tours (also in Dutch, French and German).

Disabled access (three ground floor display rooms, tearooms, shop courtyard and garden only; parking available near approach to castle).

MAP Page 339 (5J)
OS Map 179, 138: TR378501

⌂ HOLIDAY COTTAGES AT **WALMER CASTLE**

Walmer Castle has two holiday cottages, the Greenhouse Apartment (see above) and the Garden Cottage, both offering great views over the traditional kitchen garden to the castle beyond, and only a few minutes walk from a secluded expanse of shingle beach and the sea.

Walmer Castle is the official residence of the Lord Warden of the Cinque Ports. Once an important military command, supervising the five ('Cinque') south-eastern ports which provided ships for medieval England's defence, the Lord Wardenship was later granted as an honorary distinction. It is easy to imagine why the Duke of Wellington, who held the post for 23 years, enjoyed his time here so much.

Wellington's spirit lives on at Walmer Castle, where the armchair in which he died in 1852 can still be seen. His campaign bed also remains on display as a testament to his spartan tastes, along with a pair of original 'Wellington boots' and many personal effects in the fascinating on-site Wellington museum.

Successive Lords Warden have left their mark on Walmer Castle. Thus Lady Hester Stanhope created new landscaping as a surprise for her uncle, Lord Warden William Pitt: while Lord Warden W.H. Smith – member of the famous stationer's family – saved many of the historic and valuable furnishings now on display. Recent Lords Warden have been provided with

private apartments above the gatehouse, and both Sir Robert Menzies (former Australian Prime Minister) and Her Majesty Queen Elizabeth the Queen Mother made regular visits to the castle, as does the current title holder, Admiral the Lord Boyce. Some of the rooms used by the Queen Mother are open to visitors, as is her magnificent garden, given to Her Majesty on her 95th birthday.

The beautiful gardens also include the Broad Walk, with formal borders framed by the famous Cloud Yew Hedge; a commemorative lawn; woodland walk; croquet lawn and a working kitchen garden. The gardens include areas carefully managed to encourage wild flowers and insects. These wild garden areas are also a great place to spot birds.

Home-made lunches and teas are available at the Lord Warden's Tearoom and there is a well-stocked gift shop. An audio tour is available and plants are on sale.

OXFORDSHIRE

ABINGDON COUNTY HALL MUSEUM
OXFORDSHIRE – OX14 3HG

Designed by colleagues of Sir Christopher Wren, this delightful 17th-century 'English Baroque' building housed a courtroom for assizes, raised on arches over a market space. It now houses the Abingdon Museum, and has fine rooftop views.

Managed by Abingdon Town Council, maintained by English Heritage.

www.abingdonmuseum.org.uk

OPENING TIMES
1 Apr-23 Dec, Tue-Sun & Bank Hols	10am-4pm
24 Dec-2 Jan	Closed
3 Jan-29 Mar, Tue-Sun	10am-4pm

Roof open Sat-Sun, Easter to Oct & daily in summer, weather permitting (charges apply)

VISIT US
Direction: In Abingdon, 7 miles south of Oxford; in Market Place

Train: Radley 2½ miles

Bus: Oxford Bus Co X2, X3, 4, X13, 35; Stagecoach X15, 31, 34, Thames Travel 32, 32B, 32C, 114, 116; Oxfordshire CC 43; Heyfordian 40, 41, 42, 44

Tel: 01235 523703

ACQ.1952

MAP Page 338 (3C)
OS Map 164, 170: SU498971

DEDDINGTON CASTLE
OXFORDSHIRE

These extensive earthworks are the remains of an 11th-century motte and bailey castle, generally thought to be associated with Odo, Bishop of Bayeux and half-brother of William the Conqueror.

Managed by Deddington Parish Council.

OPENING TIMES
Any reasonable daylight hours

VISIT US
Direction: S of B4031 on E side of Deddington; 17 miles N of Oxford

Train: King's Sutton 5 miles

Bus: Heyfordian 81 (Thu, Fri, Sat only) – passes site; Stagecoach in Oxfordshire S4 & Oxfordshire CC 90 to within ½ mile

ACQ.1951

MAP Page 338 (2C)
OS Map 151, 191: SP472316

MINSTER LOVELL HALL AND DOVECOTE
OXFORDSHIRE – OX29 0RR

The extensive and picturesque ruins of a 15th-century riverside manor house, including a fine hall, south-west tower and complete nearby dovecote.

MINSTER LOVELL HALL AND DOVECOTE

The home of Richard III's henchman Lord Lovell.

OPENING TIMES
Any reasonable daylight hours. Dovecote – exterior only

VISIT US
Direction: Adjacent to Minster Lovell church; 3 miles W of Witney, off A40

Train: Charlbury 7 miles

Bus: Stagecoach in Oxford S2, 233; Swanbrook 853; also Villager Community Bus then short walk

ACQ.1935 Minster Lovell Hall

ACQ.1957 Dovecote

MAP Page 338 (2B)
OS Map 164, 180: SP325113

NORTH HINKSEY CONDUIT HOUSE
OXFORDSHIRE

Roofed conduit for Oxford's first water mains, constructed during the early 17th century.

A free podcast is available on our website www.english-heritage.org.uk/northhinksey

OPENING TIMES
Exterior viewing only
1 Apr-30 Sep, Thu-Sun & Bank Hols	10am-4pm

VISIT US
Direction: In North Hinksey off A34; 1½ miles W of Oxford. Located off track leading from Harcourt Hill; use the footpath from Ferry Hinksey Lane (near railway station)

Train: Oxford 1½ mile

Bus: Heyfordian service 44; also Stagecoach Brookes bus service U1 passes within ¾ mile

ACQ.1973

MAP Page 338 (3C)
OS Map 164, 180: SP495050

NORTH LEIGH ROMAN VILLA OXFORDSHIRE

The remains of a large, well-built Roman courtyard villa. The most important feature is a nearly complete mosaic tile floor, patterned in reds and browns.

OPENING TIMES

Grounds – any reasonable daylight hours. There is a viewing window for the mosaic tile floor

VISIT US

Direction: 2 miles N of North Leigh; 10 miles W of Oxford, off A4095

Train: Hanborough 3½ miles

Bus: Stagecoach in Oxford 11 & 242 to within 1½ miles

 ACQ.1952

Pedestrian access only from main road – 550 metres (600 yards).

Parking (lay-by, not in access lane).

MAP Page 338 (2B)
OS Map 164, 180: SP397154

ROLLRIGHT STONES OXFORDSHIRE

Traditionally a monarch and his courtiers petrified by a witch, the Rollright Stones consist of three groups: the King's Men stone circle; the Whispering Knights burial chamber; and the single King Stone. These funerary and ceremonial monuments span nearly 2000 years of Neolithic and Bronze Age development.

ROLLRIGHT STONES

Managed and owned by the Rollright Trust. Refreshments, toilet, guidebook and postcards available at Wyatts Farm Shop: approx. 1 mile east towards Great Rollright.

ENTRY

Admission charges applies to EH members and non-members   £1.00

Children   50p

OPENING TIMES

Entry between sunrise and sunset all year by permission of the Rollright Trust

VISIT US

Direction: Off unclassified road between A44 and A3400, 3 miles NW of Chipping Norton, near villages of Little Rollright and Long Compton

Train: Moreton-in-Marsh 6½ miles

Bus: Stagecoach 50 (Chipping Norton – Stratford Upon Avon) passes within ½ mile

Contact: sitemanager@rollright stones.co.uk

ACQ.1883

Parking (in lay-by).

MAP Page 338 (2B)
OS Map 151, OL45/191: SP297309

UFFINGTON CASTLE, WHITE HORSE AND DRAGON HILL OXFORDSHIRE

These atmospheric sites lie along the Ridgeway. Uffington 'Castle' is a large Iron Age hillfort, Dragon Hill a natural mound associated in legend with St George. The famous and enigmatic White Horse is the oldest chalk-cut hill figure in Britain, and is believed to be more than 3000 years old.

Managed by the National Trust on behalf of English Heritage.

UFFINGTON CASTLE, WHITE HORSE AND DRAGON HILL

OPENING TIMES

Any reasonable daylight hours

VISIT US

Direction: S of B4507, 7 miles W of Wantage. Ridgeway National Trail runs directly past the site

Bus: Thames Travel service 67 operates to Kingston Lisle approx. 1 mile from the site; Thames Travel service X47 (Sat only) pass closer to the sites

ACQ.1936

Parking (pay and display). Free to EH members.

MAP Page 338 (3B)
OS Map 174, 170: SU301866

WAYLAND'S SMITHY OXFORDSHIRE

A fine and atmospheric Neolithic chambered long barrow 2km (1¼ miles) along the Ridgeway from the Uffington White Horse: it was once believed to be the habitation of the Saxon smith-god Wayland.

Managed by the National Trust on behalf of English Heritage.

OPENING TIMES

Any reasonable daylight hours

VISIT US

Direction: On the Ridgeway (closed to vehicles); ¾ mile NE of B4000, Ashbury – Lambourn Road

Bus: Go Ride service 90 then a short walk along the Ridgeway path. Thames Travel service X47 (Sat only) provide additional facilities

ACQ.1922

Parking at White Horse (pay and display).

MAP Page 338 (3B)
OS Map 174, 170: SU281854

SURREY

FARNHAM CASTLE KEEP
SURREY – GU9 0JA

The impressive motte and shell keep of a castle founded in 1138 by Bishop Henry of Blois. A residence of the wealthy bishops of Winchester, the accommodation in the keep was updated in the 1520s. The keep was abandoned after Civil War service, but much-altered parts of the medieval bishops' residence remain in use in private hands. A viewing platform and stairway reveal the buried remains of an earlier tower. Tours of the Bishop's Palace are available on Wednesday afternoons for an additional fee.

Managed by Farnham Castle.

OPENING TIMES

1 Apr-23 Dec, Mon-Fri	9am-5pm
(or dusk, whichever is earlier)	
Sat-Sun & Bank Hols	10am-4pm
24 Dec-31 Jan	Closed
1 Feb-29 Mar, Mon-Fri	9am-5pm
Sat-Sun & Bank Hols	10am-4pm

Last admission 30 mins before closing

VISIT US

Direction: ½ mile N of Farnham

Train: Farnham ¾ mile

Bus: Stagecoach services 4, 5, 16, 17, 18, 19, 46 and 65 stop in the town centre which is a ¾ mile walk uphill

Tel: 01252 721194

ACQ.1933

MAP Page 338 (5D)
OS Map 186, 145: SU837473

WAVERLEY ABBEY
SURREY

Ruins of the church and monastic buildings of the first Cistercian abbey in England, founded in 1128. A free downloadable audio tour is available from the English Heritage website.

🎬 *Elizabeth*.

OPENING TIMES

Any reasonable daylight hours

VISIT US

Direction: 2 miles SE of Farnham, off B3001; off Junction 10 of M25

Train: Farnham 2 miles

Bus: Stagecoach in Hants & Surrey 46 Guildford – Aldershot (passing ≩ Farnham)

ACQ.1961

Parking (limited).

MAP Page 338 (5D)
OS Map 186, 145: SU868453

ENGLISH HERITAGE PROPERTY GUIDEBOOKS

Want to know more about a property near you?

Visit www.english-heritageshop.org.uk

SUSSEX (EAST)

1066 BATTLE OF HASTINGS, ABBEY AND BATTLEFIELD
SEE FEATURE – PAGE 80

CAMBER CASTLE
EAST SUSSEX

The ruins of an unusually unaltered artillery fort, built by Henry VIII to guard the port of Rye. There are limited opening times, but regular guided walks around Rye Harbour Nature Reserve include the castle.

Contact the Reserve Manager for further details.

Managed by Rye Harbour Nature Reserve.

www.wildrye.info/reserve/cambercastle

NON-MEMBERS

Adult	£3.00
Concession	£1.50
Child	Free
when accompanied by an adult	

OPENING TIMES

Jul-Sep open on the first Sat of the month at 2pm for guided tour. Regular guided walks around the Rye Harbour Nature Reserve include the castle

Please check website or visit wildrye.info/dates

VISIT US

Direction: 1 mile walk across fields, off the A259; 1 mile S of Rye, off Harbour Road. No vehicle access. Follow the public footpath from Brede Lock

Train: Rye 1¼ miles

Bus: From surrounding areas to Winchelsea or Rye, then 1½ mile walk; or Stagecoach 344 Hastings – Northiam then ¾ mile walk

Tel: Nature reserve office number 01797 227784 (Mon-Fri, 9am-5pm only, please call customer services outside office hours)

ACQ.1967

MAP Page 339 (6H)
OS Map 189, 125: TQ922185

PEVENSEY CASTLE EAST SUSSEX – BN24 5LE

ST PETER'S CHURCH, PRESTON PARK
EAST SUSSEX – BN1 6SD

With a history stretching back over 16 centuries, Pevensey Castle chronicles more graphically than any other fortress the story of Britain's south coast defences.

Beginning in the late 3rd century as one of the last and strongest of the Roman 'Saxon Shore' forts – two-thirds of whose towered walls still stand – Pevensey was the landing place of William the Conqueror's army in 1066.

During the century after the Conquest a full-scale Norman castle, with a great square keep and a powerful gatehouse, was built within one corner of the fort. In the 1250s the towered bailey wall was constructed, and soon put to the test during the great siege of 1264. Later still the castle was strengthened to face the threat of the Spanish Armada in 1588. This was not Pevensey's last military service: during the Second World War, pillboxes and machine-gun posts were cunningly camouflaged among its ancient walls.

An exhibition with artefacts found on site and an audio tour tell the story of the castle.

OPENING TIMES

1 Apr-30 Sep, daily	10am-6pm
1 Oct-2 Nov, daily	10am-5pm
3 Nov-29 Mar, Sat-Sun	10am-4pm
24-26 Dec, 31 Dec-1 Jan	Closed

VISIT US
Direction: In Pevensey off A259

Train: Pevensey & Westham or Pevensey Bay, both ½ mile

Bus: Stagecoach 55 passes the site; Cuckmere Community Bus service 46 (Sat) terminates adjacent to the castle; frequent Stagecoach service 99 also runs within ½ mile – alight at Pevensey, Church Lane

Tel: 01323 762604

NON-MEMBERS

Adult	£5.20
Concession	£4.70
Child	£3.10
Family	£13.50

ACQ.1925

Dogs on leads (restricted areas only).

Parking (charge payable). Car park managed by Pevensey Town Trust.

Toilets (nearby).

MAP Page 339 (6G)
OS Map 199, 123/124: TQ645048

This simple, 800-year-old church stands in the beautiful landscaped park of Preston Manor. The church nearly lost its greatest treasures – its magnificent 14th-century wall paintings – in a fire in 1906; but today the interior glows with a gorgeous mix of pattern and colour.

Owned and managed by The Churches Conservation Trust.

OPENING TIMES

Open daily	11am-3pm
Sometimes longer in the summer	

VISIT US
Train: Preston Park less than ½ mile

Bus: Brighton & Hove services 5, 5A & 91

20 mins from Bramber Castle

MAP Page 339 (6F)
OS Map 198, 122: TQ304064

For information on events taking place at Battle Abbey, visit **www.english-heritage.org.uk/events**

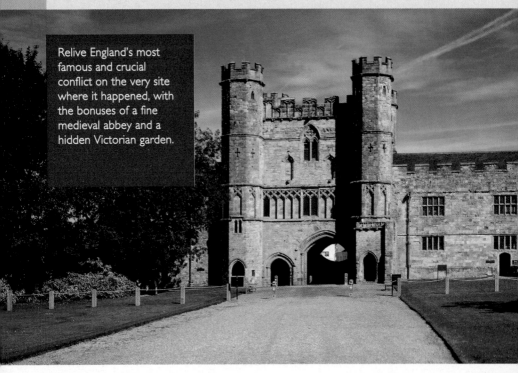

Relive England's most famous and crucial conflict on the very site where it happened, with the bonuses of a fine medieval abbey and a hidden Victorian garden.

VISIT US

Address: Battle Abbey, High Street, Battle, East Sussex

Direction: In Battle, at south end of High St. Take the A2100 off the A21

Train: Battle ½ mile

Bus: Renown Coaches 95, 355; Stagecoach 304, 305 & 384; Battle Community Transport B67, B73, B75, B79

Tel: 01424 775705/776787 (shop)

Local Tourist Information
Battle and Bexhill Tourist information: 01424 776789/776790

NON-MEMBERS

Adult	£8.00
Concession	£7.20
Child	£4.80
Family	£20.80

OPENING TIMES

1 Apr-30 Sep, daily	10am-6pm
1 Oct-2 Nov, daily	10am-5pm
3 Nov-15 Feb, Sat-Sun	10am-4pm
16-20 Feb, daily	10am-4pm
21 Feb-29 Mar, Sat-Sun	10am-4pm
24-26 Dec, 31 Dec-1 Jan	Closed

ACQ.1976

Audio tours (suitable for families, the visually impaired and for those in wheelchairs or with learning difficulties. Also available in Dutch, French, German, Japanese and Spanish; braille guides in English only). Audio tours are complimentary but will not be issued on special events days.

Disabled access (grounds and visitor centre).

Dogs on leads (restricted areas only).

Parking – Charge payable for members and non-members. Members parking concessionary rate available during open hours only.

MAP Page 339 (6G)
OS Map 199, 124: TQ749157

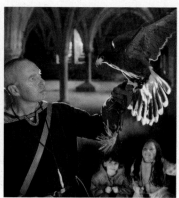

Perhaps the most famous date in English history – 1066 is the year the Normans defeated the English at the Battle of Hastings. William the Conqueror founded 'Battle' Abbey as penance for the bloodshed and as a memorial to the dead. Here, on the site of its high altar, you can stand on the spot where King Harold of England is said to have fallen.

An imaginative exhibition, *1066: The Battle for England*, brings the background and impact of this renowned conflict vividly to life. Up-to-date technology and interactive displays draw a striking picture, from both English and Norman viewpoints, of the years which led up to the conflict. They also illustrate how this pivotal battle shaped English history. Listening points, graphic presentations, exhibits and touch-screen displays explore how life was for the opposing sides. Central to the exhibition is a short film, narrated by Dr David Starkey, which dramatically recounts the events preceding the bloody struggle, culminating on 14 October 1066 when 'the fields were covered in corpses, and all around the only colour to meet the gaze was blood-red'. [*The Chronicle of Battle Abbey*].

The audio tour vividly describes and re-creates the sounds of the battle on the very site where it took place. From their ridge-top 'shield wall' the English watched the Normans advancing towards them. Early in the battle, part of the Norman army panicked and retreated, but William rallied his soldiers and successfully counter-attacked. Several 'pretended retreats' followed, in which the English were lured into breaking ranks in pursuit, only to be cut down. After some ten hours of fighting, the Normans launched an assault which finally broke the fatally weakened English shield wall.

At this stage King Harold was killed, perhaps struck in the eye by an arrow as depicted in the famous Bayeux Tapestry. By nightfall the Norman victory was complete. The audio tour uses 'interviews' with soldiers, monks and key figures of the time to retell the story of this fateful event: there also is a version especially created for children.

Battle Abbey enjoyed great wealth and special privileges as the symbol of Norman triumph. Though little of its original Norman structure survives, you can still see many later monastic buildings, including the dormitory range with its fine vaulted novices' chamber. Best preserved and most impressive of all is the Great Gatehouse, rebuilt in about 1338 and among the finest surviving monastic entrances in Britain.

CONTINUED ▶

Walled Garden

🏠 HOLIDAY COTTAGE AT BATTLE ABBEY

South Lodge is the former gatehouse, which sleeps four and comes with its own fully enclosed garden. There is so much to see and experience here but nothing beats soaking up the atmosphere as the evening sun lights up the Great Gatehouse – one of the finest in England.

Take a rest from warfare in the tranquillity of the hidden Walled Garden, in a quiet corner of the monastic precinct. Monks may once have grown herbs here, but when Battle Abbey was a Victorian country house estate it became a private garden for the Duchess of Cleveland. Inspired by historic plans, the atmosphere of her orchard garden has now been evoked with historic varieties of fruit trees native to the area – including 16 types of apple, nine kinds of pear, and cherry, quince and

medlar – as well as East Sussex wild flowers and grasses. There are even bees in Victorian-style beehives, which the property manager has been specially trained to care for. Relax and enjoy the views and wildlife.

Visit the Abbey Museum, which explores the history of the abbey and includes artefacts found during excavations. Children will also enjoy the Discovery Centre, open every weekend and throughout the school holidays. Look out too, for our programme of family friendly events.

Take a break in the stylish café, serving light lunches and all-day refreshments. It has both indoor and outdoor seating, and wonderful views of the historic gatehouse.

From Battle you can take the '1066 Walk' to Pevensey Castle (one of Britain's oldest strongholds, see p.79) where William first landed before moving to Hastings.

BOXGROVE PRIORY WEST SUSSEX

BRAMBER CASTLE
WEST SUSSEX

In a beautiful setting at the foot of the South Downs, the small Benedictine priory of Boxgrove was founded in about 1117 – originally for just three monks – by Robert de la Haye, as a 'cell' or dependency of Lessay Abbey in Normandy. Like most such 'alien priories', it was 'nationalised' at the outset of the Hundred Years War in 1339, becoming independent of its French mother-house.

The principal survivor of the monastic buildings is the two-storey lodging house for guests and travellers, roofless but standing to full height at the gable ends. One arcaded wall of the chapter house also remains, attached to the north transept of the priory church. This lovely building (not in the guardianship of English Heritage) became Boxgrove's parish church at the Dissolution of the Monasteries.

Though much of its west end was demolished in the 18th century, the church's splendid 12th-century chancel, central tower and unusual transepts still survive complete, along with the Early Tudor de la Warr chantry chapel with its fine Renaissance carvings. There is a model of the monastic buildings in the church.

Nearby, in Boxgrove gravel pit, archaeological excavation (funded by English Heritage) has produced much the oldest human remains yet discovered in England: a shinbone and two teeth dating from around 500,000 years ago.

OPENING TIMES
Priory open for viewing at any reasonable daylight hours

VISIT US
Direction: N of Boxgrove; 4 miles E of Chichester, on minor road off A27

Train: Chichester 4 miles

Bus: Stagecoach bus 55/55a (Sun only); Compass bus 99/99A

ACQ.1977 🐕 P

MAP Page 338 (6D)
OS Map 197, 121: SU908076

The remains of a Norman motte-and-bailey castle on the banks of the River Adur, founded by William de Braose c. 1073. The earthworks are dominated by a towering wall of the keep-gatehouse.

OPENING TIMES
Any reasonable daylight hours

VISIT US
Direction: On W side of Bramber village, off A283

Train: Shoreham-by-Sea 4½ miles

Bus: Brighton & Hove 2A, 20; Compass Bus 100 & 106

ACQ.1975 🐕 P
Parking (limited).

MAP Page 338 (6E)
OS Map 198, 122: TQ185107

Don't forget to check opening times online before you visit.

www.english-heritage.
org.uk/daysout/
properties

APPULDURCOMBE HOUSE
ISLE OF WIGHT – PO38 3EW

NEW FOR 2014

New interpretative panels.

APPULDURCOMBE HOUSE

The shell of Appuldurcombe, once the grandest house on the Isle of Wight and still an important example of English Baroque architecture, standing in 'Capability' Brown-designed grounds. The 1701 east wing has been re-roofed.
You can also visit the Freemantle Gate (part of the 1770s neo-Classical addition to the estate) on the nearby public footpath, and the adjacent Falconry Centre (not under the care of English Heritage – charges apply).

APPULDURCOMBE HOUSE

OPENING TIMES

1 Apr-30 Sep, daily
except Sat   10am-6pm

1 Oct-29 Mar, Sat & Sun   10am-4pm

VISIT US

Direction: Wroxall ½ mile, off B3327

Train: Shanklin 3½ miles then bus 3

Bus: Southern Vectis 3

Ferry: Ryde 11 miles (Wightlink 0870 582 7744; Hovercraft 01983 811000); West Cowes 12 miles, East Cowes 12 miles (both Red Funnel 0844 844 9988)

Tel: 01983 852484

ACQ.1952

MAP Page 338 (7C)
OS Map 196, OL29: SZ543800

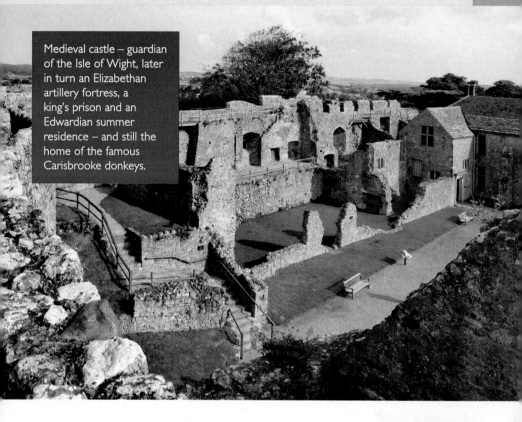

Medieval castle – guardian of the Isle of Wight, later in turn an Elizabethan artillery fortress, a king's prison and an Edwardian summer residence – and still the home of the famous Carisbrooke donkeys.

VISIT US

Address: Carisbrooke Castle, Castle Hill, Newport, Isle of Wight

Direction: 1¼ miles SW of Newport. Follow signs to Carisbrooke village, then castle

Bus: Southern Vectis 6, 7, 12, 38 pass nearby to within ¼ mile

Ferry: West Cowes 5 miles, East Cowes 6 miles (Red Funnel – 0844 844 9988); Fishbourne 6 miles, Ryde 8 miles, Yarmouth 9 miles (Wightlink 0870 5827744)

Tel: 01983 522107

Local Tourist Information 01983 813813

NON-MEMBERS

Adult	£8.00
Concession	£7.20
Child	£4.80
Family	£20.80

OPENING TIMES

1 Apr-30 Sep, daily	10am-6pm
1 Oct-2 Nov, daily	10am-5pm
3 Nov-15 Feb, Sat-Sun	10am-4pm
16-20 Feb, daily	10am-4pm
21 Feb-29 Mar, Sat-Sun	10am-4pm
24-26 Dec, 31 Dec-1 Jan	Closed

Last admission 1 hour before closing

Disabled access (grounds and lower levels only).

Tearoom (open Apr-Oct). Closed in winter.

MAP Page 338 (7C)
OS Map 196, OL29: SZ486878

🏠 HOLIDAY COTTAGE AT **CARISBROOKE CASTLE**

The secluded location of the holiday cottage within the castle walls and the romance of its unique history make this the ideal hideaway for a peaceful break. Enjoy the grounds of the castle in private once the gates close to the public.

A fascinatingly varied site to visit, Carisbrooke Castle has been the key to the Isle of Wight's security for more than nine centuries. This great hilltop-crowning fortress has a keep to climb for panoramic views, a colourful history, and of course the famous Carisbrooke donkeys.

There has been a fortress here since Saxon times, but the present castle was begun in c.1100, when the Isle of Wight was granted to the de Redvers family. They raised the great stone shell-keep on its towering mound, and after 1262 the formidable Countess Isabella de Redvers extensively rebuilt the whole stronghold. Following the addition of its double-towered 14th-century

gatehouse, Carisbrooke Castle experienced its only siege in 1377, beating off a French raiding force. After the Spanish Armada passed alarmingly close in 1588, the castle was updated as an artillery fortification by surrounding it with 'bastioned' outer earthworks, still impressively visible.

Most famous among the castle's extensive cast of past residents was Charles I, imprisoned here in 1647-48 after his defeat in the Civil War. At first comfortably accommodated in the Constable's Lodging, he later became a closely guarded captive: an attempt to escape was foiled only when he became wedged in the window bars.

Much later, Princess Beatrice, Queen Victoria's youngest daughter and Governor of the

Isle of Wight between 1896-1944, made Carisbrooke Castle her summer home. Princess Beatrice also commissioned the altar painting in the tranquil castle chapel in memory of a son killed in action in 1914. The Edwardian-style Princess Beatrice garden, designed by TV and radio gardening presenter Chris Beardshaw, was inspired by the Princess, and includes a fountain and plantings in the rich colours of the royal arms. We are grateful to the late Mrs Dorothy Frazer, whose generous bequest and devotion to the island has made the creation of this garden possible.

The castle's most beloved modern residents are undoubtedly the renowned Carisbrooke donkeys. These happy, hard-working animals still operate the tread wheel in the Elizabethan wheelhouse, which raises water 49 metres (161 feet) from the castle well. They give daily demonstrations, and their story is told in a film hosted by Jupiter the cartoon donkey, voiced by locally-raised comedian Phill Jupitus.

The on-site Carisbrooke Museum (managed by the Carisbrooke Museum Trust) provides more historical information about the castle, as well as Charles I memorabilia.

An extensive presentation – including film, hands-on weapons and family interactives and a virtual tour – highlights Carisbrooke Castle's long and often tumultuous history.

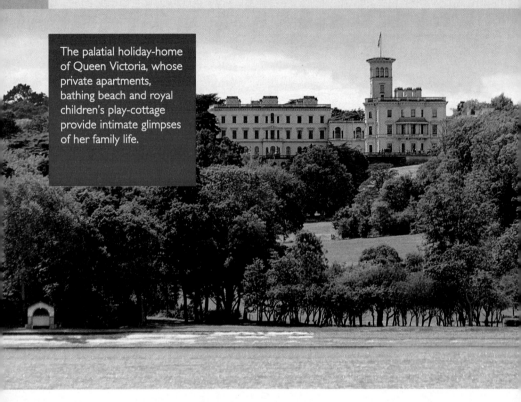

The palatial holiday-home of Queen Victoria, whose private apartments, bathing beach and royal children's play-cottage provide intimate glimpses of her family life.

VISIT US

Address: York Avenue, East Cowes, Isle of Wight

Direction: 1 mile SE of East Cowes. For sat nav use postcode PO32 6JT

Train: Ryde Esplanade 7 miles

Bus: Southern Vectis services 4 & 5

Ferry: East Cowes 1½ miles (Red Funnel. Tel: 0844 844 9988); Fishbourne 4 miles; Ryde 7 miles (Wightlink. Tel: 0870 5827744)

Hovertravel: 08434 878887

Tel: 01983 200022

Local Tourist Information
Cowes and Newport: 01983 813818

NON-MEMBERS

House and Grounds

Adult	£13.90
Concession	£12.50
Child	£8.30
Family	£36.10

Winter opening: House ground floor only and Grounds
(excluding Swiss Cottage Quarter)

Adult	£10.30
Concession	£9.30
Child	£6.20
Family	£26.80

OPENING TIMES

House and Grounds

1 Apr-30 Sep, daily (house closes 5pm)	10am-6pm
1 Oct-2 Nov, daily	10am-5pm

House guided tours and grounds

3 Nov-15 Feb, Sat-Sun	10am-4pm
16-20 Feb, daily	10am-4pm
21-28 Feb, Sat-Sun	10am-4pm

Pre-booked guided tours of selected ground floor rooms in house and grounds only

Last tour starts 2.30pm

Property fully open

1-29 Mar, Sat-Sun	10am-4pm
24-26 Dec, 31 Dec-1 Jan	Closed

Victorian Christmas Event
6-7 Dec, Sat-Sun

Festive guided tours Dec weekends
Ground floor of house open for pre-booked guided visits

ACQ.1986

Baby carriers are available at the house entrance as pushchairs are not permitted within the house, but are welcome in the garden.

Disabled access – access for wheelchairs to the first floor is by an existing lift. Manual wheelchairs are available to borrow on a first come, first served basis. Mobility scooters are not permitted inside the house, but they can be used in the gardens.

MAP Page 338 (7C)
OS Map 196, OL29: SZ516948

Available for corporate and private hire

After her marriage to Prince Albert in 1840, Queen Victoria felt the need for a family residence in the country. To use her own words, 'a place of one's own – quiet and retired'. With the opening of the Queen's private bathing beach, and in 2014 the re-presentation of her children's 'Swiss Cottage' area, you can now share even more of the Victorian royal family's holiday life here.

Queen Victoria knew and liked the Isle of Wight after visiting as a child, and she and the future Prince Consort were determined to buy a property there. 'It is impossible to imagine a prettier spot,' wrote the Queen after a visit to Osborne. In 1845 the royal couple purchased the property with an estate of 342 acres. Before the deeds had even changed hands, master builder Thomas Cubitt had been approached – firstly to build a pavilion to house private apartments and then to demolish the old house and add further wings for the royal household. Eventually an exquisite pair of Italianate towers dominated the landscape, and looked out over passing ships on the nearby Solent.

The interiors of Osborne House abound with opulence in both architectural design and decoration. Marble sculptures line the Grand Corridor of the house, and recall the royal couple's love of the arts. Portraits and frescos adorn the walls, serving as a reminder of the family's links to the crowned heads of Europe, and of the unrivalled supremacy of the British

CONTINUED ▶

NEW FOR 2014

In 2014, a new 'family-focused' re-presentation of the entire Swiss Cottage quarter will give visitors – especially young ones – a vivid insight into the lives at Osborne of Queen Victoria's many children.

The Swiss Cottage, where the royal children learnt 'hands-on' housekeeping duties including cooking, will feature a ground floor exhibition looking at why it was built, the personalities of the children, and what play activities they enjoyed. Dressed rooms will tell the story of one day in the life of the cottage, 11 July 1861, when the children were preparing afternoon tea for their parents. This was one of the last occasions before the death of Prince Albert when most of the royal family were together.

There will also be a trail around the grounds, revealing more clues to the personalities of the nine royal children, including characters such as the Queen's Chihuahua dog and other animals they were given.

The once-private Royal Museum, displaying an amazing range of treasures from all over the Victorian world, will highlight artefacts which tell stories about the wider history of the royal family and the Victorian empire. Museum Explorer packs for children will help them turn detective, tracking down particular objects in the collection.

Children will also be able to experience playing like the royal children, in a specially designed play area with its own fort and miniature cottage – modern counterparts of those built for Victoria and Albert's family.

On Saturday 6 and Sunday 7 December, Osborne celebrates the festive season with its popular annual Victorian Christmas event. The ground floor of the house, dressed festively for the season, is open for guided tours on December weekends. Find out how the Victorian Royal Family celebrated Christmas with these fascinating tours led by our expert guides.

Empire. Queen Victoria's role as Empress of India is celebrated in the Durbar Room. Constructed from 1890-91, the room served as an elaborate banqueting hall and every surface, from floor to ceiling, is ornately embellished. The walls are decorated with symbols from India, including Ganesh – the elephant god of good fortune. The completion of the room coincided with the introduction of electricity, so the Indian-influenced lamp stands were designed to take full advantage of this emerging technology. Prince Albert worked with Cubitt on the Italianate designs for the terraced formal gardens which complement the house. Visitors can now enjoy the Walled Garden with cut flowers and fruit displays, restored by English Heritage.

Prince Albert was responsible for the layout of the Terrace overlooking the Solent and for the introduction of many fine trees onto the estate. An original palm on the terrace was a gift to the royal couple from King Ferdinand of Portugal, and one of the first ever to be planted in this country. The current tree – its direct descendent – was planted in 2004 by Queen Elizabeth II. The Terraces are planted to recreate their Victorian appearance.

Family visitors shouldn't miss the Swiss Cottage area, domain of the nine royal children, which is comprehensively re-presented for 2014. The charming Cottage was constructed and furnished to help the

⌂ HOLIDAY COTTAGE AT
OSBORNE

The early 1900s holiday cottage
brims with period character and
once served as a cricket pavilion.
Enjoy tranquil views and explore
the grounds in private after the
gates close to the public.

royal children learn domestic skills. The
surrounding grounds include a museum,
displaying treasures collected by the children
or given to Queen Victoria, as well as a child-
sized fort, and vegetable gardens where the
children grew their own produce. A beautiful
wild flower meadow is nearby, and rare red
squirrels can sometimes be seen. Queen
Victoria loved to stroll through the gardens,
and the primroses in the woods were her
particular favourites. Most of the gardens are
accessible on tarmac and compacted gravel
paths. There is a courtesy minibus, with
wheelchair access, to the Swiss Cottage.

One of the many joys of royal family holidays
at Osborne was sea bathing – for which, of
course, 'we have quite a charming beach
to ourselves', where no passing boats were
permitted to land. The Queen's once strictly
private beach is now open to visitors. Its
attractions include the original royal bathing
machine, now fully restored: designed to
protect the Queen's modesty, it includes a
plumbed-in toilet as well as a changing room
and curtained verandah. Here too is the
Queen's refurbished reading and sketching
'Alcove', bedecked with vibrant blue and
pink Minton tiles and equipped with a seat
supported by cast iron dolphins.

Modern visitors can also recreate traditional
'beach holidays' by relaxing in deckchairs and
enjoying the Solent views, or enjoy traditional
seaside refreshments from the beach café. In
summer there are also beach games, Punch
and Judy shows, and other events. The beach
is a 1.2km (¾ mile) walk from the house and
minibus transfers are available in the summer.

The exhibition in the Petty Officers Quarters
is the best place to start any visit. It covers
various aspects of the sumptuously furnished
house and magnificent grounds, as well as
the lives and personalities of the Victorian
royal family and their servants. A play area for
children and picnic tables are near the visitors'
car park.

Visitors can bring a picnic to enjoy in the
glorious grounds, or enjoy a light lunch in
the stylish café, located near the shop in the
visitor entrance building. You can also enjoy a
delicious served lunch or afternoon tea in the
elegant Terrace Restaurant, which is nearer the
house and offers wonderful views across the
Terrace Gardens towards the Solent. Please
note, non-members will need to purchase an
admission ticket to the house to gain access
to the restaurant.

ST CATHERINE'S ORATORY
ISLE OF WIGHT

The tall, medieval, octagonal tower, allegedly a lighthouse, was built here in 1328 as penance for stealing church property from a wrecked ship. Affectionately known as the Pepperpot, it stands on one of the highest parts of the Isle of Wight. It is part of the Tennyson Heritage Coast, a series of linked cliff-top monuments. A later lighthouse can be seen nearby.

Managed by the National Trust on behalf of English Heritage.

OPENING TIMES
Any reasonable daylight hours

VISIT US
Direction: E of Blackgang roundabout, off A3055. Approx. ¼ mile ascent across fields

Train: Shanklin 9 miles

Bus: Southern Vectis service 6 or Island Coaster (Summer) to Blackgang Chine and then ½ mile walk

Ferry: West Cowes 14 miles, East Cowes 14 miles (both Red Funnel – Tel: 0870 444 8898); Yarmouth 15 miles (Wightlink – Tel: 0844 844 9988)

 ACQ.1952

MAP Page 338 (7C)
OS Map 196, OL29: SZ494773

OSBORNE
SEE FEATURE – PAGE 88

YARMOUTH CASTLE ISLE OF WIGHT – PO41 0PB

Built to protect strategic Yarmouth harbour and (in conjunction with Hurst Castle on the mainland) to defend the western end of the Solent against invasion fleets, this last and most sophisticated addition to Henry VIII's chain of coastal forts was completed after his death in 1547. Unlike Henry's earlier circular forts – such as Deal, Portland and Pendennis Castles – Yarmouth Castle is a square blockhouse, with a battery to the front and the first new-style 'arrowhead' bastion built in England protecting its most exposed angle. In the 1560s the castle's central square was filled in to provide a solid gun platform.

Displays inside the castle include atmospheric recreations of how the rooms were used in the 16th century, and an exhibition about the many wrecks which occurred in 'Yarmouth Roads', the treacherous stretch of sea which the castle overlooks. Also a magnificent picnic site, with views over the Solent.

NON-MEMBERS

Adult	£4.00
Concession	£3.60
Child	£2.40

OPENING TIMES

1 Apr-30 Sep, Wed-Sun & Bank Hols	10am-4pm
1-31 Oct, Wed-Sun	10am-4pm
1 Nov-29 Mar	Closed

VISIT US

Direction: In Yarmouth town centre, adjacent to car ferry terminal. Located just off Quay Street, up the short walkway and through the main gates into the Castle

Train: Lymington Pier ⊠ adjoins the ferry berth for the Wightlink service to Yarmouth

Bus: Southern Vectis 7 & Needles Tour & Island Coaster (summer only)

Ferry: Yarmouth, adjacent (Wightlink – Tel: 0870 582 7744)

Tel: 01983 760678

ACQ.1913

Disabled access (ground floor only).

Parking (coaches and cars 200 metres (220 yards). Charges payable).

MAP Page 338 (7B)
OS Map 196, OL29: SZ354898

DISCOUNTED ATTRACTIONS: **SOUTH EAST**

Use your membership to get exclusive discounts at these independent attractions in the South East. Please remember to show your card as proof of membership.

Discount applies to:

KEY	⊞ MEMBERS	OVP OVP HOLDERS	⚤? NO. OF MEMBER'S CHILDREN

Terms and conditions may apply, so make sure you check the individual pages on our website or call the individual property for more details.

⊞

ANNE OF CLEVES HOUSE
East Sussex BN7 1JA
Impressive 15th-century timber framed Wealden Hall House & Garden with Tudor plants and planting scheme. Given to Anne as part of her divorce settlement from Henry VIII.
www.sussexpast.co.uk/anneofcleves
Tel. 01273 474610

⊞

ARUNDEL CASTLE
West Sussex BN18 9AB
Ancient Castle and Stately Home of The Duke of Norfolk with outstanding gardens, including the new Collector Earl's Garden based on early 17th-century classical designs.
www.arundelcastle.org
Tel. 01903 882173

⊞ OVP ⚤ 6

BLETCHLEY PARK
Buckinghamshire MK3 6EB
Bletchley Park was the Home of the Codebreakers during the Second World War. Their achievements helped shorten the war by an estimated two years, saving countless lives.
www.bletchleypark.org.uk
Tel. 01908 640404

⊞

DOVER MUSEUM AND BRONZE AGE BOAT GALLERY – Kent CT16 1PB
This modern museum tells the story of Dover's history and is home to the Dover Bronze Age Boat. Managed by Dover District Council.
www.dovermuseum.co.uk
Tel. 01304 201066

⊞

FISHBOURNE ROMAN PALACE
West Sussex PO19 3QR
Remains of a 1st-century palatial building, with the largest collection of early Roman mosaic floors in Britain and recreated Roman garden.
www.sussexpast.co.uk/fishbourne
Tel. 01243 785859

⊞ ⚤ 6

FORT AMHERST
Kent ME4 4UB
Fort Amherst is a Napoleonic fortress. Visit the 2500ft tunnel system, gun batteries and Second World War Civil Defence Centre. Café and children's play area on site.
www.fortamherst.com
Tel. 01634 847747

DISCOUNTED ATTRACTIONS:

Use your membership to get exclusive discounts at these independent attractions in the South East. Please remember to show your card as proof of membership.

50% DISCOUNT ON ENTRY

GOODWOOD HOUSE
West Sussex PO18 0PX
The family seat of the Dukes of Richmond, set in the heart of the Sussex Downs, houses astonishing treasures, including celebrated paintings by George Stubbs and Canaletto.
www.goodwood.com
Tel. 01243 755040

15% DISCOUNT ON ENTRY

THE HISTORIC DOCKYARD, CHATHAM
Kent ME4 4TZ
This award-winning dockyard has a remarkable range of galleries, buildings and warships to explore and programme of events, activities and exhibitions.
www.thedockyard.co.uk
Tel. 01634 823800

50% DISCOUNT ON ENTRY

LEWES CASTLE & BARBICAN HOUSE MUSEUM
East Sussex BN7 1YE
This imposing Norman castle offers magnificent views across the town of Lewes and surrounding Downland.
www.sussexpast.co.uk/lewescastle
Tel. 01273 486290

2 for 1 ENTRY

LULLINGSTONE CASTLE AND THE WORLD GARDEN Kent DA4 0JA
Lullingstone Castle is one of England's oldest family estates. Visit the World Garden, containing nearly 8000 different plant species.
www.lullingstonecastle.co.uk
Tel. 01322 862114

50% DISCOUNT ON ENTRY

MARLIPINS MUSEUM
West Sussex BN43 5DA
Once a medieval customs house, Marlipins now holds artefacts and archaeological material from the Shoreham area and its maritime past.

www.sussexpast.co.uk/marlipins
Tel. 01273 462994

50% DISCOUNT ON ENTRY

MICHELHAM PRIORY
East Sussex BN27 3QS
Explore the beautiful and tranquil gardens and historic house. Visit the watermill, working forge, Elizabethan Great Barn, playground and café.
www.sussexpast.co.uk/michelham
Tel. 01323 844224

SOUTH EAST CONTINUED

Discount applies to:

| KEY | ⊞ MEMBERS | OVP OVP HOLDERS | 🏃? NO. OF MEMBER'S CHILDREN |

Terms and conditions may apply, so make sure you check the individual pages on our website or call the individual property for more details.

30% DISCOUNT ON ENTRY

⊞ OVP 🏃6

NEWPORT ROMAN VILLA
Isle of Wight PO30 1HA

Discover this Romano-British farmhouse with its fine bath suite. Hands-on activities, weaving, herb garden and museum display.

www.iwight.com/museums
Tel. 01983 529720

FREE ADMISSION TO HOUSE, IF GROUNDS TICKET PURCHASED

⊞ 🏃6

PENSHURST PLACE & GARDENS
Kent TN11 8DG

Stunning family-owned stately home with a place in history – unique medieval Baron's Hall and historic gardens. Adventure playground for children.

www.penshurstplace.com
Tel. 01892 870307

50% DISCOUNT ON ENTRY

⊞ 🏃3

THE PRIEST HOUSE
West Sussex RH19 4PP

This 15th-century Wealden Hall House stands in a traditional cottage garden on the edge of the Ashdown Forest.

www.sussexpast.co.uk/priesthouse
Tel. 01342 810479

20% OFF ADULT TICKET

⊞ 🏃2

THE ROYAL PAVILION
Brighton BN1 1EE

Discover the magnificent seaside residence of King George IV. The Indian architecture contrasts with interiors inspired by China. Regency gardens, tearoom and gift shop.
www.brighton-hove-pavilion.org.uk
Tel. 03000 290900

CONCESSIONARY RATE APPLIES

⊞

RYCOTE CHAPEL
Oxfordshire OX9 2PE

The 15th-century chapel has original furniture, including exquisitely carved and painted woodwork. Managed by the Rycote Buildings Charitable Foundation.
www.visitsouthoxfordshire.co.uk
Tel. 01844 210210

GIVE THE GIFT OF MEMBERSHIP

Give friends and family the opportunity to enjoy these fantastic discounts too!

- Free entry to over 400 historic properties
- Kids go free (up to six per adult in a family group)
- Free or discounted entry to hundreds of events
- Free handbook worth £10.95
- Exclusive Members' Magazine

See page 355 for full details.

SOUTH WEST

Stonehenge

Gloucestershire

59 55 52
57 Cheltenham 47
48 Gloucester
51 50
58 Stroud
54 Cirencester
56 60 61 49
53

Swindon

South Gloucestershire
Bristol
North Somerset
Bath & North East Somerset

Wiltshire

Chippenham
Bristol 4
1 Marlborough
2 Bath
Weston-super-mare 3 73 Devizes 75
64 74 76
Wells 69 77
67 66 78
62 70 Warminster
65 63 Glastonbury 79
Somerset 68 80
Taunton Salisbury
Yeovil 45 37 40
Dorset
46 42 Dorchester Poole 36
39 41 38 Bournemouth
Lyme Regis 35 Swanage
44 43 Weymouth

71, 72, 81, 82, 83
84, 85, 86, 87
see Stonehenge
and Avebury
page 129

Keep up to date with
events, news and offers
www.english-heritage.
org.uk/newsletter

Ilfracombe

Barnstaple
Bideford

Devon

Tiverton

Bude
14
19 31 Okehampton
12 29 Exeter 24
Launceston 26 27 Exmouth
30 Teignmouth
Cornwall 11 10 34 23 Torquay
Padstow 8 33 28
16 21 Totnes 27
Newquay 15 Plymouth Dartmouth 25
St Austell 17 32
Truro
St Ives 7 18
5 Falmouth 13
6 Penzance 9
20

Isles of Scilly

Hugh Town

88-95: see Isles of Scilly page 139

Details of local public transport
information in England are available
from Traveline **www.traveline.org.uk**
or call 0871 200 2233.

Remember to check opening times before you visit any of our properties
www.english-heritage.org.uk/daysout

HIGHLIGHTS FOR 2014/15 IN THE **SOUTH WEST**

p.104

p.107

p.134

Pendennis Castle: Tudor fortress, with a First World War exhibition opening 2014.

Tintagel Castle: spectacular Medieval and Dark Ages remains, traditionally the birthplace of King Arthur.

Stonehenge: Experience the long-awaited transformation of the setting of this world-famous monument.

PROPERTIES

BRISTOL & BATH

CHURCH OF ST THOMAS THE MARTYR, BRISTOL
BRISTOL – BS1 6JG

© David Martyn

Located in Bristol city centre, this handsome Georgian building replaced a medieval church deemed unsafe for use. The light-filled Classical interior is elegantly presented and there is a fine ring of eight bells, all cast by local founders.

Owned and managed by The Churches Conservation Trust.

OPENING TIMES
Mon–Fri   9.30am–5pm

Other days by appointment, please call 0117 929 1766 before your visit

VISIT US
Train: Bristol Temple Meads ¼ mile

Bus: Close to bus routes to city centre and bus station, operated mainly by First, Wessex and ABus. Bus and coach terminus 1 mile

2 mins walk from Temple Church

MAP Page 337 (3H)
OS Map 172, 154/155: ST591727

SIR BEVIL GRENVILLE'S MONUMENT
BATH & NE SOMERSET

Erected to commemorate the heroism of a Royalist commander and his Cornish pikemen at the Battle of Lansdown, 1643.

SIR BEVIL GRENVILLE'S MONUMENT

OPENING TIMES
Any reasonable daylight hours

VISIT US
Direction: Located 4 miles NW of Bath on the N edge of Lansdown Hill, near the road to Wick

Train: Bath Spa 4½ miles

Bus: Wessex service 620 Bath Spa – Tetbury

ACQ.1953 Parking (in lay-by).

MAP Page 337 (3H)
OS Map 172, 155: ST722703

STANTON DREW CIRCLES AND COVE
BATH & NE SOMERSET

The third largest complex of prehistoric standing stones in England, although the three circles and three-stone 'cove' of Stanton Drew are surprisingly little-known. Recent surveys have revealed that they were only part of a much more elaborate ritual site.

OPENING TIMES
Cove: Any reasonable daylight hours.
Two main stone circles: access at the discretion of the landowner, who may levy a charge

VISIT US
Direction: Cove: in the garden of the Druid's Arms public house. Circles: E of Stanton Drew village

Train: Bristol Temple Meads 7 miles

Bus: Abus service 67; Somerbus 640 (Fri only) & 754 (Mon only); Bugler Coaches service 683 (Tue only); BANES 752 (Wed only); Citistar 134 (Tue only); CT/Bugler Coaches 672 all serve the village of Stanton Drew

ACQ.1883

Cove: parking. Stones: limited parking at entrance to Stones field. Cattle on site.

MAP Page 337 (3H)
OS Map 172/182, 154/155
Cove: ST597631
Circles: ST601633

STONEY LITTLETON LONG BARROW
BATH & NE SOMERSET

One of the finest accessible examples of a Neolithic chambered tomb, with its multiple burial chambers open to view.

OPENING TIMES
Any reasonable daylight hours

VISIT US
Direction: 1 mile S of Wellow off A367. Narrow lane west of village leads to small parking area (1 mile), then ¼ mile walk

Train: Bath Spa 6 miles

Bus: Somerbus service 757 (Wed only) to Wellow then 1 mile walk from village. Otherwise take First 173, 178 or 184 to Peasedown St John and walk 2½ miles

ACQ.1884

Parking (limited). Sheep grazing.

Note: visitors are advised to bring a torch.

MAP Page 337 (3H)
OS Map 172, 142: ST735572

TEMPLE CHURCH
BRISTOL

Originally built by the Knights Templar, the 'leaning tower' and walls of this large, late medieval church survived bombing during the Second World War. The graveyard is now a public garden.

OPENING TIMES
Exterior only: Any reasonable daylight hours

VISIT US
Direction: Located in Temple St, off Victoria St

Train: Bristol Temple Meads ¼ mile

Bus: From surrounding areas

ACQ.1958

MAP Page 337 (3H)
OS Map 172, 154/155: ST593727

CORNWALL

BALLOWALL BARROW
CORNWALL

In a spectacular cliff-edge position, this unique Bronze Age cairn has a long and complex history as a burial site. Seen as excavated in 1878 by Cornish antiquarian William Borlase.

Managed by the National Trust.

OPENING TIMES
Any reasonable daylight hours

VISIT US
Direction: 1 mile W of St Just, near Carn Gloose

Train: Penzance 8 miles

Bus: First 10, 10A, 300 (summer only); West Penwith Community Bus 509

ACQ.1954 P
Parking limited.

MAP Page 336 (7A)
OS Map 203, 102: SW355312

CARN EUNY ANCIENT VILLAGE CORNWALL

Among the best preserved ancient villages in the South West, occupied from the Iron Age until late Roman times. It includes the foundations of stone houses and an intriguing 'fogou' underground passage.

Managed by the Cornwall Heritage Trust.

OPENING TIMES
Any reasonable daylight hours

VISIT US
Direction: 1½ miles W of Sancreed along narrow but signed lanes

Train: Penzance 6 miles

Bus: West Penwith Community bus service 509 to Grumbla

ACQ.1957 P

Parking 600 metres (660 yards) away in Brane.

MAP Page 336 (7A)
OS Map 203, 102: SW402288

CHYSAUSTER ANCIENT VILLAGE
CORNWALL – TR20 8XA

This Romano-British settlement was originally occupied 2000 years ago. The village consisted of stone-walled homesteads known as 'courtyard houses', found only on the Land's End peninsula and the Isles of Scilly. The houses line a 'village street', and each had an open central courtyard surrounded by a number of thatched rooms. There are also the remains of an enigmatic 'fogou' underground passage.

NON-MEMBERS
Adult	£3.70
Concession	£3.30
Child	£2.20

OPENING TIMES
1 Apr-30 Jun, daily	10am-5pm
1 Jul-31 Aug, daily	10am-6pm
1-30 Sep, daily	10am-5pm
1 Oct-2 Nov, daily	10am-4pm
3 Nov-29 Mar	Closed
Last admission 1 hour before closing	

VISIT US
Direction: Located 2½ miles NW of Gulval, off B3311

Train: Penzance 3½ miles

Bus: On First service 16 journeys via Zennor alight New Mill, then 1½ miles walk. Alternatively First 16 to Castle Gate and then about 1¾ miles walk

Tel: 07831 757934

Local Tourist Information
Penzance: 01736 335530

ACQ.1931

MAP Page 336 (7B)
OS Map 203, 102: SW472350

DUPATH WELL CORNWALL

This charming well-house of c. 1500 stands over an ancient spring believed to cure whooping cough. Built by the Augustinian canons of nearby St Germans priory, it houses the remains of an immersion pool for cure-seekers.

Managed by the Cornwall Heritage Trust.

OPENING TIMES
Any reasonable daylight hours

VISIT US
Direction: 1 mile E of Callington off A388

Train: Gunnislake 4½ miles

Bus: DAC 283 and Western Greyhound 573 pass the site. Main services to Callington are First 76 or Western Greyhound 576 then ½ mile

ACQ.1937 P Parking off the farmyard.

MAP Page 336 (6D)
OS Map 201, 108: SX375692

HALLIGGYE FOGOU
CORNWALL

Roofed and walled in stone, this complex of passages is the largest and best-preserved of several mysterious underground tunnels associated with Cornish Iron Age settlements. The purpose of such 'fogous' – a Cornish-language word meaning 'cave' – is unknown. Refuges, storage chambers or ritual shrines have all been suggested.

Free entry to the fogou. Entry to the rest of the Trelowarren Estate is charged.

Managed by the Trelowarren Estate.

OPENING TIMES
Reasonable daylight hours May-Sep, but completely blocked Oct-Apr inclusive

HALLIGGYE FOGOU

VISIT US

Direction: 5 miles SE of Helston off B3293. Follow signs for Trelowarren Estate. Park in the lay-by on the lane through the Trelowarren Estate. Walk up the hill and the entrance to the fogou is signposted through a gate

Train: Penryn 6 miles

Bus: First 36 to Garras and then c. 1 mile walk

Parking (free to members).

Steps down into the fogou can be slippery: take care when descending.

Visitors are strongly advised to bring a torch.

MAP Page 336 (7B)
OS Map 203, 103: SW713239

HURLERS STONE CIRCLES
CORNWALL

Three fine late Neolithic or early Bronze Age stone circles arranged in a line, a grouping unique in England. Probably the best examples of ceremonial circles in Cornwall, they are traditionally reputed to be the remains of men petrified for playing 'hurling' on a Sunday.

Managed by the Cornwall Heritage Trust.

OPENING TIMES

Any reasonable daylight hours

VISIT US

Direction: Located ½ mile NW of Minions, off B3254

Train: Liskeard 7 miles

Bus: Western Greyhound service 573 to Darite and walk (1 mile). Also DAC occasional services 236 & demand responsive service 261 to Upton Cross (1¼ miles walk)

Parking ¼ mile walk.

MAP Page 336 (6D)
OS Map 201, 109: SX258714

KING DONIERT'S STONE
CORNWALL

Two richly carved pieces of a 9th-century 'Celtic' cross, with an inscription commemorating Dumgarth, British King of Dumnonia, who drowned in c. AD 875.

Managed by the Cornwall Heritage Trust.

OPENING TIMES

Any reasonable daylight hours

VISIT US

Direction: 1 mile NW of St Cleer, off B3254

Train: Liskeard 7 miles

Bus: Western Greyhound service 573

ACQ.1933   P

Parking (in lay-by).

MAP Page 336 (6D)
OS Map 201, 109: SX236688

LAUNCESTON CASTLE
CORNWALL – PL15 7DR

Set on a large natural mound, Launceston Castle dominates the surrounding landscape. Begun soon after the Norman Conquest, its focus is an unusual keep consisting of a 13th-century round tower built by Richard, Earl of Cornwall, inside an earlier circular shell-keep. The tower top is now reached via an internal staircase.

The castle long remained a prison and George Fox, founder of the Quakers, suffered harsh confinement here in 1656. An exhibition traces 1000 years of history, with finds from site excavations.

LAUNCESTON CASTLE

NON-MEMBERS

Adult	£3.70
Concession	£3.30
Child	£2.20

OPENING TIMES

1 Apr-30 Sep, daily	10am-6pm
1 Oct-2 Nov, daily	10am-5pm
3 Nov-29 Mar	Closed

Last admission 30 mins before closing

VISIT US

Direction: In Launceston

Bus: First 76; Jackets X85 (Sat only); Western Greyhound 510, 576; Group Travel 208, 220, 223, 225 & DAC 236

Tel: 01566 772365

Local Tourist Information
Launceston: 01566 772321

ACQ.1952   OVP

Disabled access (outer bailey, exhibition and shop).

MAP Page 336 (5D)
OS Map 201, 112: SX331846

PENDENNIS CASTLE
SEE FEATURE – PAGE 104

PENHALLAM MANOR
CORNWALL

The low and grass-covered but complete ground-plan of a moated 13th-century manor house, in a delightful woodland setting.

OPENING TIMES

Any reasonable daylight hours

VISIT US

Direction: Signposted from Week St Mary, off a minor road. From A39 heading north turn right at Treskinnick Cross. (10 minute walk from the car park along a forest track)

Bus: Western Greyhound service 595 stops at Treskinnick Cross (2 miles); Group Travel service 208 (Mon, Wed, Thu, Fri only) and 220 (Tue only) to the nearby village of Week St Mary (approx. 1 mile walk)

ACQ.1981   P   Parking (5 spaces).

MAP Page 336 (5D)
OS Map 190, 111: SX224974

RESTORMEL CASTLE
CORNWALL – PL22 0EE

The great 13th-century circular shell-keep of Restormel still encloses the principal rooms of the castle in remarkably good condition. It stands on an earlier Norman mound surrounded by a deep dry ditch, atop a high spur beside the River Fowey. Twice visited by the Black Prince, son of Edward III, it finally saw action during the Civil War in 1644. It commands fantastic views and is a favourite picnic spot.

NON-MEMBERS
Adult	£3.70
Concession	£3.30
Child	£2.20

OPENING TIMES
1 Apr-30 Jun, daily	10am-5pm
1 Jul-31 Aug, daily	10am-6pm
1-30 Sep, daily	10am-5pm
1 Oct-2 Nov, daily	10am-4pm
3 Nov-29 Mar	Closed
Last admission 30 mins before closing	

VISIT US
Direction: Located 1½ miles N of Lostwithiel, off A390

Train: Lostwithiel 1½ miles

Bus: Travel Cornwall 423 or 482 (Wed only); Roselyn 296 (Tue only); Gorran & District Community Bus G4 to Lostwithiel then 1½ mile walk

Tel: 01208 872687

Local Tourist Information
Lostwithiel: 01208 872207

ACQ.1925 OVP

Access via a stock grazing area, appropriate footwear is advisable. There are steps on the entrance path. Disabled visitors may wish to call the site in advance to arrange alternative access.

MAP Page 336 (6C)
OS Map 200, 107: SX104614

ST BREOCK DOWNS
MONOLITH CORNWALL

Originally 5 metres (16 feet) high and weighing some 16¾ tonnes, this is Cornwall's largest and heaviest prehistoric standing stone. It stands on the summit of St Breock Downs, offering wonderful views.

Managed by the Cornwall Heritage Trust.

OPENING TIMES
Any reasonable daylight hours

VISIT US
Direction: Located on St Breock Downs; 3½ miles SW of Wadebridge off unclassified road to Rosenannon

Train: Roche 5½ miles

Bus: Western Greyhound services 594 to St Jidgey, then walk along the Saints Way (2½ mile)

ACQ.1965 P

MAP Page 336 (6C)
OS Map 200, 106: SW968683

ST CATHERINE'S CASTLE
CORNWALL

One of a pair of small artillery forts built by Henry VIII in the 1530s to defend Fowey Harbour, consisting of two storeys with gun ports at ground level.

OPENING TIMES
Any reasonable daylight hours

VISIT US
Direction: 1½ miles SW of Fowey, along a woodland footpath off A3082

Train: Par 4 miles

Bus: Western Greyhound 524, 525 & 526 to within ¾ mile walk

ACQ.1909 P

Parking (Ready Money Cove Car Park, Fowey, ¾ mile walk). Charge (not EH).

Steep drops within castle; keep children under close control.

MAP Page 336 (6C)
OS Map 200/204, 107: SX119509

ST MAWES CASTLE
SEE FEATURE – PAGE 106

TINTAGEL CASTLE
SEE FEATURE – PAGE 107

TREGIFFIAN BURIAL
CHAMBER CORNWALL

The remains of a Neolithic chambered tomb with an entrance passage, walled and roofed with stone slabs, leading into the central chamber. The main feature is a decorated slab in the entrance. The original is in Truro museum.

Managed by the Cornwall Heritage Trust.

OPENING TIMES
Any reasonable daylight hours

VISIT US
Direction: Located 2 miles SE of St Buryan, on B3315

Train: Penzance 5½ miles

Bus: First 1, 1A, 300 (Summer)

ACQ.1971 P Parking (in lay-by).

MAP Page 336 (7B)
OS Map 203, 102: SW431244

TRETHEVY QUOIT
CORNWALL

This well-preserved and impressive Neolithic 'dolmen' burial chamber stands 2.7 metres (8.9 feet) high. There are five standing stones, surmounted by a huge capstone.

Managed by the Cornwall Heritage Trust.

OPENING TIMES
Any reasonable daylight hours

VISIT US
Direction: 1 mile NE of St Cleer, near Darite; off B3254

Train: Liskeard 3½ miles

Bus: Western Greyhound 573

ACQ.1931 P

Sheep may be grazing in field.

MAP Page 336 (6D)
OS Map 201, 109: SX259688

PENDENNIS CASTLE Cornwall – TR11 4LP

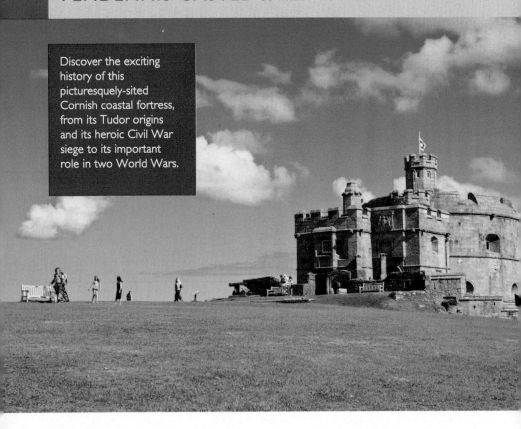

Discover the exciting history of this picturesquely-sited Cornish coastal fortress, from its Tudor origins and its heroic Civil War siege to its important role in two World Wars.

VISIT US

Address: Pendennis Castle, Castle Close, Falmouth, Cornwall

Direction: On Pendennis Headland, 1 mile SE of Falmouth

Train: Falmouth Docks ½ mile

Bus: Fal River Buses service 329 – circular route connecting Falmouth town, the beaches and the Park & Ride with Pendennis Castle

Tel: 01326 316594

Local Tourist Information: 0905 325 4534

NON-MEMBERS

Adult	£7.00
Concession	£6.30
Child	£4.20
Family	£18.20

Additional charges for members and non-members may apply on event days

OPENING TIMES

1 Apr-30 Sep, daily	10am-6pm*
1 Oct-2 Nov, daily	10am-5pm*

*The castle may be closed from 4pm on Saturdays if an event is booked. Please check with the property in advance

3 Nov-15 Feb, Sat-Sun	10am-4pm
16-20 Feb, daily	10am-4pm
21 Feb-29 Mar, Sat-Sun	10am-4pm
24-26 Dec, 31 Dec-1 Jan	Closed

Last admission 1 hour before closing

The Castle Keep may close for 1 hour if an event is booked

Free guided tours of the Half Moon Battery and Castle, check availability on arrival

Wheelchair access to the grounds, but steep slopes or drops in places. There is also full wheelchair access to the shop, tearoom, Discovery Centre and the Barracks, which contains a virtual tour of the whole site.

Tearoom closes ½ hour before the castle.

MAP Page 336 (7C)
OS Map 204, 103/105: SW824318

Pendennis Castle is home to a collection of wartime cartoons by George Butterworth. The acclaimed cartoons, which appeared daily throughout the Second World War, lampooned both Hitler and Mussolini, enraging the Nazi leader so much that the cartoonist was put on his 'hit-list'. During your visit to Pendennis, set aside some time to view the cartoons, generously given to English Heritage by George Butterworth's widow.

⌂ HOLIDAY COTTAGES
AT **PENDENNIS**

Enjoy the castle grounds in private after it
closes to the public when you stay in the
Custodian's House or **Callie's Cottage**.

Constructed between 1540 and 1545, Pendennis and its sister castle at St Mawes form the Cornish end of the chain of coastal castles built by Henry VIII to counter a threat from France and Spain. Pendennis was frequently adapted to face new enemies over 400 years, right through until the Second World War.

In 1598, during Elizabeth I's reign, a new type of defensive rampart was added around the original fort. The castle was strengthened again prior to the Civil War and played host to the future Charles II in 1646, before he escaped to the Isles of Scilly. It then withstood five months of siege, before becoming the penultimate Royalist garrison on the British mainland to surrender.

Pendennis continued to play a vital role in Cornwall's defences throughout the late 19th and early 20th centuries, and saw significant action during the Second World War. Evidence of its fascinating history is on show throughout the site, and the Guardhouse has been returned to its First World War appearance. On the free guided tour you can visit the Half Moon Battery, including the underground magazine which is not normally open to the public, as well as the original 16th-century gun tower with its recreated Tudor gun deck.

The refurbished 1901 Royal Artillery Barracks houses an interactive exhibition, tracing the history of the castle, its people, and its links with Falmouth and the trade routes of the British Empire. There is a hands-on scale model of the castle and children can step into the shoes of a soldier on kit parade. A virtual tour in the Barracks brings the Keep to life for visitors not able to fully explore the site.

After a busy day exploring, sample the delicious selection of refreshments and snacks in the tearoom, situated within the Royal Artillery Barracks.

The pre-bookable education suite, with rooms for creative workshops, can accommodate up to 35 children. The fully-equipped hospitality wing serves as both a conference centre and a stunning wedding venue, with the Fal Estuary as the backdrop.

NEW FOR 2014

From late summer, a new exhibition will highlight the important role of Pendennis and the fortress of Falmouth during the First World War. Focussing on Falmouth as a coastal artillery station, a training area, and a naval base for the new science of anti-submarine warfare, it will home in on people who worked or trained here, and what individual parts they played in the war at home and abroad.

☒ Available for corporate and private hire
▣ Licensed for civil wedding ceremonies

VISIT US

Direction: In St Mawes on A3078

Train: Penmere (Falmouth), 4 miles via Prince of Wales Pier and ferry

Bus: Western Greyhound service 550, ½ mile, but better to catch ferry from Falmouth

Ferry: St Mawes ferry from Falmouth

Tel: 01326 270526

Local Tourist Information St Mawes: 01326 270440

NON-MEMBERS

Adult	£4.60
Concession	£4.10
Child	£2.80

OPENING TIMES

1 Apr-30 Sep, daily	10am-6pm*
1 Oct-2 Nov, daily	10am-5pm*
3 Nov-15 Feb, Sat-Sun	10am-4pm
16-20 Feb, daily	10am-4pm
21 Feb-29 Mar, Sat-Sun	10am-4pm
24-26 Dec, 31 Dec-1 Jan	Closed

Last admission 30 mins before closing

*The castle may be closed on a Saturday if an event is booked please check with the property in advance.

ACQ. 1961

MAP Page 336 (7C)
OS Map 204, 105: SW841328

St Mawes Castle is among the best-preserved of Henry VIII's coastal artillery fortresses, and the most elaborately decorated of them all. One of the chain of forts built between 1539 and 1545 to counter an invasion threat from Catholic France and Spain, it guarded the important anchorage of Carrick Roads, sharing the task with Pendennis Castle on the other side of the Fal estuary.

A charming clover-leaf shape surrounded by outer defences, St Mawes was designed to mount heavy 'ship-sinking' guns. But particular care was also taken with its embellishment, and it is still bedecked with carved Latin inscriptions in praise of Henry VIII and his son Edward VI. It owes its fine preservation to the fact that, unlike Pendennis Castle, it was little developed after its completion. Easily falling to landward attack by Civil War Parliamentarian forces in 1646, it remained neglected until partial re-arming during the 19th and early 20th centuries. Other coastal forts built by Henry VIII include Portland, Deal and Walmer Castles.

⌂ HOLIDAY COTTAGE AT **ST MAWES CASTLE**

The Fort House sleeps four and is ideal for families with young children, not least because the garden is fenced and wonderfully sheltered.

⊤ Available for corporate and private hire

⚑ Licensed for civil wedding ceremonies

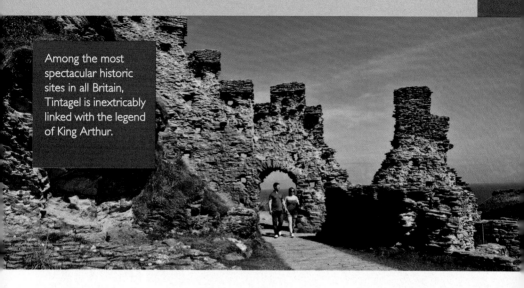

Among the most spectacular historic sites in all Britain, Tintagel is inextricably linked with the legend of King Arthur.

VISIT US

Address: Tintagel Castle
Castle Road, Tintagel, Cornwall

Direction: On Tintagel Head, 600 metres (660 yards) along uneven track from Tintagel; no vehicles except Land Rover service (extra charge)

Bus: Western Greyhound 595 (with connections available at Wadebridge, Camelford, Bude and Boscastle)

Tel: 01840 770328

Local Tourist Information: Tintagel: 01840 779084

NON-MEMBERS

Adult	£6.10
Concession	£5.50
Child	£3.70
Family	£15.90

OPENING TIMES

1 Apr-30 Sep, daily	10am-6pm
1 Oct-2 Nov, daily	10am-5pm
3 Nov-15 Feb, Sat-Sun	10am-4pm
16-20 Feb, daily	10am-4pm
21 Feb-29 Mar, Sat-Sun	10am-4pm
24-26 Dec, 31 Dec-1 Jan	Closed

Last admission 30 mins before closing

Beach Café closes 30 mins before the castle

Planned conservation works and improvements from autumn 2014 may lead to some disruption on site – please check website for more information

ACQ.1931 P 🅿 🍴 ⬆ ♿ 🛍 🐕 🚾 ⚠ OVP

Disabled access is limited. A Land Rover service to the castle (Apr-Oct) is available at a separate charge. Please call the site for more details.

Parking (600 metres (660 yards) in the village) – not managed by EH.

MAP Page 336 (5C)
OS Map 200, 111: SX049891

A dramatic rocky headland now connected to the mainland only by a slender neck of rock, 'Din Tagell' – 'the fortress with the narrow entrance' – was clearly an important power-centre of local Cornish rulers between the 5th and 7th centuries, the post-Roman 'Dark Age' period when a historical Arthur may have flourished. Excavations here have uncovered fragments of luxury pottery and glass imported from lands round the Mediterranean, confirming the prosperity and high status of its inhabitants.

The link with King Arthur himself – perhaps stemming from traditions of Tintagel's Dark Age importance – is not however recorded until the 12th century, when the 'romantic novelist' Geoffrey of Monmouth wrote his largely fictional *History of the Kings of Britain*. According to Geoffrey, Duke Gorlois of Cornwall shut his wife Igerna (or Ygraine) away in Tintagel to protect her from the lusts of Uther Pendragon, King of Britain. But Merlin magically transformed Uther into the likeness of Ygraine's husband: in this disguise, Uther slept with her here, and fathered Arthur. By the 12th century, moreover, Tintagel was also linked with the separate legend of the tragic lovers, Tristan and Yseult (Isolde), whose husband (and Tristan's uncle) King Mark traditionally held court here.

It was almost certainly the Arthur connection which

CONTINUED ▶

prompted the rich and ambitious Richard, Earl of Cornwall, younger brother of King Henry III, to build his castle here during the 1230s. Remote Tintagel had no strategic importance: but Richard may have wished to claim a link with a hero by then renowned throughout western Europe.

The atmospheric ruins of Richard's castle stand partly on the 'mainland', where two outer courtyards remain: and partly on the 'island' headland, the site of his great hall. Today a deep rocky chasm separates the two, the result of frequent landslips: but originally the two halves of the castle were linked by a fortified stone bridge. Visitors can approach the mainland castle via a relatively gentle slope, and then descend steep steps before crossing a modern bridge and ascending to the 'island': or they can ascend directly to either part of the castle from the ticket office. The climb is richly rewarded: for the windswept island displays not only Earl Richard's hall ruins but also the remains of many Dark Age houses and an atmospheric medieval chapel – as well as amazing views along the dramatic rocky coast.

Was Tintagel really connected with King Arthur? This burning question is reviewed in the introductory audio-visual, *Searching for Arthur*. Sir Thomas Malory's famous *Morte Darthur* reinforced the link in the later 15th century, when the statement that Arthur was born as well as conceived here also first appears. But perhaps the most influential association of Arthur with Tintagel was proclaimed in Alfred, Lord Tennyson's *Idylls of the King*, published in 1859-85 and enthusiastically illustrated by the Pre-Raphaelites. Great excitement was also provoked in 1998 by the discovery of a slate with a scratched 6th-century inscription including the name 'Artognou'.

While considering these things, or enjoying a well-earned rest from exploring the ruins, visitors can enjoy excellent locally-sourced food and drink in the Beach Café, in a spectacular position overlooking Tintagel Haven and the legendary Merlin's Cave.

Access to the castle and (via many steep steps) the island is difficult for disabled visitors. A Land Rover service from the village (extra charge) can take visitors to the exhibition and shop.

DEVON

BAYARD'S COVE FORT:
SEE DARTMOUTH, BAYARD'S COVE FORT

BERRY POMEROY CASTLE
DEVON – TQ9 6LJ

Tucked away in a steep wooded valley, Berry Pomeroy Castle is the perfect romantic ruin. Within the 15th-century defences of the Pomeroy family castle, still displaying a wall painting of the Three Kings in its gatehouse chamber, looms the dramatic ruined shell of its successor, the great mansion of the Seymours. Begun in the 1560s and ambitiously enlarged from c.1600, their mansion was intended to become the most spectacular house in Devon, a match for Longleat and Audley End.

Never completed, and abandoned by 1700, it became the focus of blood-curdling ghost stories, recounted in the audio tour.

NON-MEMBERS

Adult	£5.00
Concession	£4.50
Child	£3.00

OPENING TIMES

1 Apr-30 Sep, daily	10am-6pm
1 Oct-2 Nov, daily	10am-5pm
3 Nov-29 Mar, Sat-Sun	10am-4pm
24-26 Dec & 1 Jan	Closed

BERRY POMEROY CASTLE

VISIT US

Direction: 2½ miles E of Totnes off A385

Train: Totnes 3½ miles

Bus: Country Bus 149

Tel: 01803 866618

Local Tourist Information
Totnes: 01803 863168

ACQ.1977 ⌂ ▢ 🧍 🧍 ✕ P 🏠 ⬜ ♿ OVP

Disabled access (grounds and ground floor only).

Parking (no coach access) at end of long drive (approx. ¾ mile).

MAP Page 337 (6F)
OS Map 202, OL20/110: SX839623

BLACKBURY CAMP
DEVON

An Iron Age hillfort with impressive ramparts and defended single entrance, now surrounded by woodland with delightful picnic area.

NEW FOR 2014

New interpretation panels and podcast.

OPENING TIMES

Any reasonable daylight hours

VISIT US

Direction: Off B3174/A3052

Train: Honiton 6½ miles

Bus: Stagecoach Devon 52A; First X53 alight at Three Horseshoes on A3052 between Sidford & Seaton and then public footpath (steep climb c. 1 mile)

ACQ.1930 ✕ P

MAP Page 337 (5G)
OS Map 192/193, 115: SY187924

DARTMOUTH, BAYARD'S COVE FORT DEVON

Small Tudor artillery fort guarding Dartmouth's inner harbour, picturesquely sited on the quayside.

NEW FOR 2014

New interpretation panels.

OPENING TIMES

Any reasonable daylight hours

VISIT US

Direction: Located in Dartmouth, on the riverside

Train: Paignton 8 miles via ferry

Bus: First service 90, 93; Stagecoach Gold; alternatively Stagecoach bus 22, 24 or 120 to Kingswear Banjo then cross the River Dart Lower or passenger ferry

ACQ.1954 ✕ ♿

Disabled access via town quay.

MAP Page 337 (6F)
OS Map 202, OL20: SX879509

DARTMOUTH CASTLE
SEE FEATURE – PAGE 111

GRIMSPOUND DEVON

The best known of many Dartmoor prehistoric settlements, Grimspound dates from the late Bronze Age. The remains of 24 stone houses survive within a massive boundary wall.

Managed by the Dartmoor National Park Authority.

OPENING TIMES

Any reasonable daylight hours

GRIMSPOUND

VISIT US

Direction: 6 miles SW of Moretonhampstead, off B3212

Bus: Summer only, First Transmoor Link service 82 Exeter St David's – Plymouth. Alight at Challacombe Cross then walk 1¼ mile. Year-round service 98 operated by Beacon Bus between Tavistock and Bellever (Postbridge) with a 5 mile walk to Grimspound

ACQ.1977 🐕 P

MAP Page 336 (5E)
OS Map 191, OL28: SX701809

HOUND TOR DESERTED MEDIEVAL VILLAGE DEVON

The remains of four 13th-century longhouses with their barns and garden plots. This isolated Dartmoor hamlet was probably abandoned in the early 15th century. A free downloadable audio tour is available from the English Heritage website.

Managed by the Dartmoor National Park Authority.

OPENING TIMES

Any reasonable daylight hours

VISIT US

Direction: 1½ miles S of Manaton, ½ mile from the Ashburton road

Bus: Country Bus Summer Saturday 'Haytor Hoppa' service 271 to Swallerton Gate. Country Bus 193 (Wed & Fri only) or 672 to Widecombe In The Moor (3 miles) (Wed only) or the Carmel Coaches service 671 (Wed only) to Manaton (2¼ mile)

ACQ.1972 🎧 🐕 P

Parking at Swallerton Gate (1½ mile walk across moor to monument).

MAP Page 336 (5E)
OS Map 191, OL28: SX746788

KIRKHAM HOUSE, PAIGNTON DEVON

This late medieval stone house, afterwards split into three cottages, was restored in the 1960s. Furnished with modern furniture, illustrating traditional craftsmanship and the original use of the rooms.

Managed in association with the Paignton Heritage Society.

OPENING TIMES

18 & 21 Apr, 5 & 26 May, 25 Aug & every Sun in Jul-Aug   2pm-5pm

Heritage Open Days   11am-4pm

VISIT US

Direction: Located in Kirkham St, off Cecil Rd, Paignton

Train: Paignton ½ mile

Bus: From surrounding areas

ACQ.1948 🎫

MAP Page 337 (6F)
OS Map 202, OL20/110: SX885610

LYDFORD CASTLE, TOWN BANKS AND SAXON TOWN DEVON

Beautifully sited on the fringe of Dartmoor, Lydford boasts three defensive features. Near the centre is a small-scale Norman keep on a mound, built as a prison. It later became notorious for harsh punishments – 'the most annoyous, contagious and detestable place within this realm'. To the south is an earlier Norman earthwork castle; to the north, Saxon town defences. A free downloadable audio tour is available from the English Heritage website.

OPENING TIMES

Any reasonable daylight hours

LYDFORD CASTLE, TOWN BANKS AND SAXON TOWN

VISIT US

Direction: In Lydford off A386; 8½ miles S of Okehampton

Bus: Beacon Bus 118 and Dartmoor Rover First bus service 187 (summer & Sun only)

ACQ.1934	Castle	ACQ.1965	North of Town Banks
ACQ.1968	South of Town Banks		
ACQ.1972	Norman Fort		

🎧 🐕 P

MAP Page 336 (5E)
OS Map 191/201, OL28: SX509848

MERRIVALE PREHISTORIC SETTLEMENT DEVON

The remains of a Bronze Age settlement, along with several sacred sites, including three stone rows, a stone circle, standing stones and burial cairns, probably constructed over a long period between c. 2500 BC and 1000 BC.

Managed by the Dartmoor National Park Authority.

OPENING TIMES

Any reasonable daylight hours

VISIT US

Direction: South of B3357 W of Princetown

Train: Gunnislake 10 miles

Bus: Beacon Bus service 98 Yelverton – Tavistock (with connections from Plymouth)

ACQ.1973 🐕 P

Parking at Four Winds car park.

MAP Page 336 (6E)
OS Map 191, OL28: SX554748

VISIT US

Direction: 1 mile SE of Dartmouth off B3205, narrow approach road. No coach access

Train: Paignton 8 miles via ferry

Bus: First service 90, 93; Stagecoach Gold; alternatively Stagecoach bus 22, 24 or 120 to Kingswear Banjo then cross the River Dart Lower or passenger ferry

Tel: 01803 833588

Local Tourist Information
Dartmouth: 01803 834224

NON-MEMBERS

Adult	£5.50
Concession	£5.00
Child	£3.30
Family	£14.30

OPENING TIMES

1 Apr-30 Sep, daily	10am-6pm
1 Oct-2 Nov, daily	10am-5pm
3 Nov-29 Mar, Sat-Sun	10am-4pm
24-26 Dec, 31 Dec-1 Jan	Closed
Last admission 30 mins before closing	

ACQ. 1909

Parking (not owned by EH, charged).

Tearooms and toilets (not managed by EH).

MAP Page 337 (6F)
OS Map 202, OL20: SX887503

One of the most picturesquely-sited forts in England. For over six hundred years Dartmouth Castle has guarded the narrow entrance to the Dart Estuary and the busy port of Dartmouth.

This fascinating complex of defences was begun in 1388 by John Hawley, privateering mayor of Dartmouth and the prototype of the flamboyant 'Shipman' in Chaucer's *Canterbury Tales*. About a century later the townsmen added the imposing and well-preserved 'gun tower', probably the very first fortification in Britain purpose-built to mount 'ship-sinking' heavy cannon. Climb to the top for breathtaking views across the estuary, and see how this could be blocked in wartime by a heavy chain.

Unusually incorporating the fine church of St Petrox, the castle saw action during the Civil War and continued in service right up until the Second World War. Successive up-dating included the Victorian 'Old Battery' with its remounted heavy guns, guardrooms and maze of passages to explore. Here, a dramatic film-sequence recreates a Victorian gun-firing, and throughout the fortress displays retell the castle's six centuries of history.

Take the scenic boat trip to the castle from the bustling town quay.

Visit **www.english-heritage. org.uk/dartmouth** for details of special events.

OKEHAMPTON CASTLE
DEVON – EX20 1JA

The remains of the largest castle in Devon, set on a wooded spur above the River Okement. Begun soon after the Norman Conquest as a motte and bailey castle with a stone keep, it was converted into a sumptuous residence in the 14th century by Hugh Courtenay, Earl of Devon, much of whose work survives. After the last Courtenay owner fell foul of Henry VIII in 1538, it declined into an allegedly haunted ruin. Riverside picnic area and woodland walks within the grounds and nearby.

NON-MEMBERS

Adult	£4.00
Concession	£3.60
Child	£2.40

OPENING TIMES

1 Apr-30 Jun, daily	10am-5pm
1 Jul-31 Aug, daily	10am-6pm
1 Sep-2 Nov, daily	10am-5pm
3 Nov-29 Mar	Closed

Last admission 30 mins before closing

VISIT US

Direction: Located ½ mile SW of Okehampton town centre (signposted). Turn into Castle Road by Post Office

Train: Dartmoor Railway, Okehampton (summer Sundays only) ½ mile

Bus: Stagecoach service X9, Beacon Bus service 118, Western Greyhound service 510 & 599; Dartline service 178 & Jackett's Coaches service

---

OKEHAMPTON CASTLE

318. Also Dartmoor Rover First service 187 (summer, Sun only)

Tel: 01837 52844

Local Tourist Information
Okehampton: 01837 53020

ACQ.1967 [icons] OVP

Audio Tour (also available for the visually impaired).

Woodland Walk Guide available from kiosk.

MAP Page 336 (5E)
OS Map 191, OL28/113: SX583942

ROYAL CITADEL, PLYMOUTH DEVON

A dramatic 17th-century fortress built to defend the coastline from the Dutch, and keep watch on a recently rebellious town. Still in use by the military today.

ENTRY

Non-member	£5.00
EH members and children	£4.00

OPENING TIMES

By guided tour only,
6 May-30 Sep, Tue & Thu   2.30pm

Phone Armada Tours on 07933 429604 to book or meet outside the main entrance, or to book additional or group tours at other times of the year

The Citadel is an operational military establishment and tours may be curtailed without notice. Limited photography permitted and no large bags

VISIT US

Direction: At E end of Plymouth Hoe

Train: Plymouth 1 mile

Bus: Plymouth Citybus 25

Local Tourist Information
Plymouth: 01752 304849

ACQ.1966 [icons]

Parking on Plymouth Hoe. Allow 90 minutes for the tour. No large bags. Bags may be searched. No toilets on site.

MAP Page 336 (6E)
OS Map 201, OL20/108: SX480538

ST MARTIN'S CHURCH, EXETER
DEVON – EX1 1EZ

This 1000-year-old church in the shadow of the cathedral is one of the oldest buildings in Exeter. Its tiny parish – smaller than a football pitch – included workers and traders from the surrounding streets. The distinctive red and white exterior complements the light and simple interior.

Owned and managed by The Churches Conservation Trust.

OPENING TIMES

Mon-Fri	9.30am-4.30pm
Sat	10am-5pm

VISIT US

Train: Exeter Central 5 mins walk, Exeter St David's 15 mins walk or a 5 mins bus ride

Bus: Exeter bus and coach station approx. 7 mins walk. Stagecoach 173 & 360

30 mins from Hound Tor deserted medieval village

MAP Page 337 (5F)
OS Map 192, 114: SX922926

TOTNES CASTLE
DEVON – TQ9 5NU

A classic Norman motte and bailey castle, founded soon after the Conquest to overawe the Saxon town. A later stone

TOTNES CASTLE

shell-keep crowns its steep mound, giving sweeping views across the town rooftops to the River Dart.

NON-MEMBERS

Adult	£3.70
Concession	£3.30
Child	£2.20

OPENING TIMES

1 Apr-30 Sep, daily	10am-6pm
1 Oct-2 Nov, daily	10am-5pm
3 Nov-29 Mar, Sat-Sun	10am-4pm
24-26 Dec, 31 Dec-1 Jan	Closed

Last admission 30 mins before closing

VISIT US

Direction: In centre of Totnes, at Castle Street, off Station Road opposite railway station. From town centre, turn north off High Street

Train: Totnes ¼ mile

Bus: From surrounding areas

Tel: 01803 864406

Local Tourist Information
Totnes: 01803 863168

ACQ.1947

Parking (charged, 64 metres (210 feet); cars only, narrow approach roads).

Keep accessible only via steep steps.

MAP Page 336 (6E)
OS Map 202, OL20/110: SX800605

UPPER PLYM VALLEY
DEVON

Some 300 Bronze Age and medieval sites, covering 15½ square kilometres (6 square miles) of Dartmoor landscape.

OPENING TIMES

Any reasonable daylight hours

VISIT US

Direction: 4 miles E of Yelverton

ACQ.1978

Parking with ½ mile walk to monuments.

MAP Page 336 (6E)
OS Map 202, OL20/OL28: SX580660

DORSET

ABBOTSBURY ABBEY REMAINS DORSET

Part of a monastic building, perhaps the abbot's lodging, of the Benedictine Abbey of Abbotsbury. St Catherine's Chapel is within half a mile.

OPENING TIMES

Any reasonable daylight hours

VISIT US

Direction: Located in Abbotsbury, off B3157, near the churchyard

Train: Upwey 7½ miles

Bus: First X53; Damory 61 (Wed only), 253

ACQ.1948

Parking charged (not EH).

MAP Page 337 (5H)
OS Map 194, OL15: SY578852

ABBOTSBURY, ST CATHERINE'S CHAPEL DORSET

Set high on a hilltop overlooking Abbotsbury Abbey, this sturdily buttressed and barrel-vaulted 14th-century chapel was built by the monks as a place of pilgrimage and retreat.

ABBOTSBURY, ST CATHERINE'S CHAPEL

OPENING TIMES

Any reasonable daylight hours

VISIT US

Direction: ½ mile S of Abbotsbury; by steep path from village, off B3157

Train: Upwey 7 miles

Bus: First X53; Damory 61 (Wed only), 253

ACQ.1922

Parking charged (not EH).

MAP Page 337 (5H)
OS Map 194, OL15: SY573848

CHRISTCHURCH CASTLE AND NORMAN HOUSE DORSET

The remains of Christchurch Castle include parts of the mound-top keep and, more unusually, the 12th-century riverside chamber block or 'Constable's House'. This very early example of domestic architecture includes a rare Norman chimney. There is an important 12th-century priory church nearby.

OPENING TIMES

Any reasonable daylight hours

VISIT US

Direction: Located in Christchurch, near the Priory

Train: Christchurch ¾ mile

Bus: More services X1 & X2; Yellow Bus 111

ACQ.1946

On street parking.

MAP Page 337 (5K)
OS Map 195, OL22: SZ160927

FIDDLEFORD MANOR
DORSET

The principal parts of a small stone manor house, probably begun c. 1370 for William Latimer, Sheriff of Somerset and Dorset. The hall and solar chamber display outstandingly fine timber roofs.

Please note: The adjoining building is a private residence and is not open to visitors.

OPENING TIMES

1 Apr-2 Nov, daily	10am-6pm
3 Nov-29 Mar, daily	10am-4pm
24-26 Dec & 1 Jan	Closed

VISIT US
Direction: 1 mile E of Sturminster Newton off A357

Bus: Damory 310 & 368; More service X8

ACQ.1961 ⬛⬛⬛⬛

Disabled access (ground floor only – with 1 step).

Parking (no coach access).

MAP Page 337 (4H)
OS Map 194, 129: ST801136

JORDAN HILL ROMAN TEMPLE DORSET

The foundations of a 4th-century AD Romano-Celtic temple.

OPENING TIMES
Any reasonable daylight hours

VISIT US
Direction: Located 2 miles NE of Weymouth, off A353

Train: Upwey or Weymouth, 2 miles

Bus: First 4/4A, 31, X53

ACQ.1933 ⬛⬛

On-street parking.

MAP Page 337 (5H)
OS Map 194, OL15: SY699821

KINGSTON RUSSELL STONE CIRCLE DORSET

A late Neolithic or early Bronze Age circle of 18 fallen stones, on a hilltop overlooking Abbotsbury and the sea.

OPENING TIMES
Any reasonable daylight hours

VISIT US
Direction: Turn left off Bishop's Road, approximately 1½ miles NE of Abbotsbury

Train: Weymouth (10½ miles) or Dorchester South/West (8 miles)

Bus: First X53; Damory 61 (Wed only), 253 then 2 mile walk

ACQ.1887 ⬛

Limited parking on road verge at access to farm. Access to Stone Circle on foot only via public footpaths, approx. ½ mile. No off-road vehicle access.

MAP Page 337 (5H)
OS Map 194, OL15: SY578878

KNOWLTON CHURCH AND EARTHWORKS DORSET

The siting of this ruined medieval church at the centre of a Neolithic ritual henge earthwork symbolises the transition from pagan to Christian worship.

OPENING TIMES
Any reasonable daylight hours

VISIT US
Direction: SW of Cranborne on B3078

Bus: Damory service 300 serves Knowlton. Damory service 319 serves the nearby villages of Wimborne St Giles and Gussage All Saints

ACQ.1959 ⬛⬛

Parking limited.

MAP Page 337 (4J)
OS Map 195, 118: SU024103

MAIDEN CASTLE DORSET

Among the largest and most complex Iron Age hillforts in Europe, Maiden Castle's huge multiple ramparts enclose an area equivalent to 50 football pitches, protecting several hundred residents. Past excavations have helped reveal the site's 4000-year history – from a Neolithic causewayed enclosure to a small Roman

temple built on the site in the 4th century AD – and produced evidence of an extensive late Iron Age cemetery. Information panels guide you around the hillfort, illustrating its long history, and a free downloadable audio tour is available on the website.

OPENING TIMES
Any reasonable daylight hours

VISIT US
Direction: 2 miles S of Dorchester, off A354, N of bypass

Train: Dorchester South/West (2 miles)

Bus: Damory service 1 to Maiden Castle Lane and then walk ½ mile. Alternatively First service 10 or Damory service 183 to Winterbourne Monkton (¾ mile walk) or First service 31 or Damory service 61 (Wed only) and alight between Martinstown and Poundbury and use footpath 1 mile

ACQ.1908 ⬛⬛⬛

Sheep grazing on site.

MAP Page 337 (5H)
OS Map 194, OL15: SY669884

THE NINE STONES DORSET

Now in a wooded glade, this small prehistoric circle of nine standing stones was constructed around 4000 years ago. Winterbourne Poor Lot Barrows (p.117) are nearby.

OPENING TIMES
Any reasonable daylight hours

VISIT US
Direction: 1½ miles SW of Winterbourne Abbas, on A35

Train: Weymouth 4½ miles

Bus: First 31 Weymouth – ⬛ Axminster (passing ⬛ Dorchester South)

ACQ.1895 ⬛⬛

Park in Little Chef car park in Winterbourne Abbas and use permissive path parallel to A35.

MAP Page 337 (5H)
OS Map 194, OL15/117: SY611904

VISIT US

Direction: Overlooking Portland Harbour in Castletown, Isle of Portland

Train: Weymouth 4½ miles

Bus: First summer service 501 serves the castle direct. At other times South West Coaches service 206 & First service 1 pass close by

Ferry: From Weymouth Harbour, Good Fri-end Oct (weather permitting). Call the castle for details

Tel: 01305 820539

Local Tourist Information
Portland: 01305 861233

NON-MEMBERS

Adult	£4.90
Concession	£4.40
Child	£2.90
Family	£12.70

OPENING TIMES

1 Apr-30 Sep, daily	10am-6pm
1 Oct-2 Nov, daily	10am-5pm
3 Nov-29 Mar	Closed

Last admission 30 mins before closing

Parts of the castle may be closed if an event is booked

Disabled access – Captain's House, ground floor of castle and Governor's Garden. Disabled toilet.

Captain's House Tearoom closes ½ hour before the castle.

Overlooking and defending Portland harbour, this coastal artillery fortress was built by Henry VIII to counter threats from France and Spain. It strikingly retains its squat, rounded seaward form, designed to deflect incoming cannon shot. Visit the Tudor kitchen, armoury and gun decks.

Much fought over during the Civil War, Portland Castle was taken and retaken several times by both Parliamentarians and Royalists. It later protected shipping against pirates, and vainly tried to control the local smuggling industry, before 'standing-to' again when Napoleonic invasion loomed.

Following a spell as a private home, during the First World War it became a station for seaplanes flying anti-submarine patrols, and during the Second World War it was an important anti-submarine base and signal post. In 1944 British and American forces carried out top-secret preliminary training for the D-Day landings in the bays nearby.

Presentations and interactive exhibits around the site, along with an audio tour, bring the fort's long and varied story to life.

The Governor's Garden, designed by Christopher Bradley-Hole as part of the Contemporary Heritage Garden series, is a perfectly sheltered spot to enjoy the dramatic sea and harbour views.

The Captain's House Tearoom offers visitors a range of homemade sandwiches, cakes and snacks with locally-sourced ingredients, as well as hot and cold drinks.

MAP Page 337 (6H)
OS Map 194, OL15: SY685744

⬦ Available for corporate and private hire

⬦ Licensed for civil wedding ceremonies

ST CATHERINE'S CHAPEL, ABBOTSBURY: SEE
ABBOTSBURY,
ST CATHERINE'S CHAPEL –
PAGE 113

SHERBORNE OLD CASTLE
DORSET – DT9 3SA

Built by Bishop Roger of Salisbury in the 12th century as a strongly-defended palace, Sherborne Old Castle became a powerful Royalist base during the Civil War. Described as 'malicious and mischievous' by Cromwell, it fell in 1645 after a fierce eleven-day siege. Sherborne 'New' Castle is nearby (see p.143).

NON-MEMBERS

Adult	£3.70
Concession	£3.30
Child	£2.20

OPENING TIMES

1 Apr-30 Jun, daily	10am-5pm
1 Jul-31 Aug, daily	10am-6pm
1 Sep-2 Nov, daily	10am-5pm
3 Nov-29 Mar	Closed
Last admission 30 mins before closing	

VISIT US

Direction: Located ½ mile E of Sherborne, off B3145

Train: Sherborne ¾ mile

Bus: First 57, 58 & 58A and Damory services 74, 216 & 368 or South West Coaches 34 & 42 to Sherborne town centre then ½ mile walk
Tel: 01935 812730

SHERBORNE OLD CASTLE

Local Tourist Information
Sherborne: 01935 815341

ACQ.1956 ⚐ ♿ ⛺ ♿ P 🏕 📷 ♿
⚠ OVP

Refreshments available.

Secure cycle parking available.
National network route 26.

MAP Page 337 (4H)
OS Map 183, 129: ST648168

ST GEORGE'S CHURCH, PORTLAND
DORSET – DT5 2JP

© CCT

This vast solitary church rises from a rocky peninsula. Inspired by St Paul's Cathedral, it is one of Dorset's most magnificent 18th-century buildings. The interior is fabulously preserved, and the headstones in the sprawling churchyard are a treasure trove of tales of murder, piracy and adventure.

Owned and managed by The Churches Conservation Trust.

OPENING TIMES

Apr-Oct	10am-5pm
Oct-Mar	10am-3pm

VISIT US

Train: Weymouth 4½ miles

Bus: First bus services 1 & 10

5 mins from Portland Castle

MAP Page 337 (6H)
OS Map 194, OL15: SY686720

WHITCOMBE CHURCH, WHITCOMBE
DORSET – DT2 8NY

© CCT

The setting of this medieval church evokes the rustic atmosphere of old Dorset life. Its great treasures are the stunning medieval wall paintings inside. However, the church still holds on to its final secret – its name – the dedication is lost in time.

Owned and managed by The Churches Conservation Trust.

OPENING TIMES

Open daily during daylight hours

VISIT US

Train: Dorchester West (2 miles)

Bus: Damory services 101 and 103

10 mins from Maiden Castle

MAP Page 337 (5H)
OS Map 194, OL15: SY716884

For information on events in the South West, visit
www.english-heritage.org.uk/events

WINTERBOURNE POOR LOT BARROWS
DORSET

A 'cemetery' of 44 Bronze Age burial mounds of varying types and sizes, by the A35 main road.

OPENING TIMES
Any reasonable daylight hours

VISIT US
Direction: 2 miles W of Winterbourne Abbas, S of junction of A35 with a minor road to Compton Valence. Access via Wellbottom Lodge – 180 metres (200 yards) E along A35 from junction

Train: Dorchester West or South, both 7 miles

Bus: First 31 Weymouth – Axminster (passes ⭤ Dorchester South)

No adjacent parking. Warning: cross road with care.

Sheep grazing.

MAP Page 337 (5H)
OS Map 194, OL15/117: SY590907

Why not visit **Stonehenge**, with its spectacular new visitor centre?
See page 134 for details.

GLOUCESTERSHIRE

BELAS KNAP LONG BARROW
GLOUCESTERSHIRE

A particularly fine example of a Neolithic long barrow of c. 3800 BC, featuring a false entrance and side chambers. Excavated in 1863 and 1865, when the remains of 31 people were found in the chambers. The barrow has since been restored.

Managed by Gloucestershire County Council.

OPENING TIMES
Any reasonable daylight hours

VISIT US
Direction: Near Charlton Abbots; ½ mile on Cotswold Way

Train: Cheltenham 9 miles

Bus: Castleways service 606 & N.N.Cresswell's 656 to within 1¾ miles or Castleways 559 to Winchcombe village then walk

ACQ.1928 🕾 **P**

Parking with ½ mile walk to monument.

MAP Page 337 (1J)
OS Map 163, OL45: SP021254

CIRENCESTER AMPHITHEATRE
GLOUCESTERSHIRE

The earthwork remains of one of the largest Roman amphitheatres in Britain, built in the early 2nd century. It served the Roman city of Corinium (now Cirencester), then second in size and importance to London, and had a capacity of around 8000 spectators. Later fortified against Saxon invaders.

Managed by Cirencester Town Council.

OPENING TIMES
Any reasonable daylight hours

CIRENCESTER AMPHITHEATRE

VISIT US
Direction: Located W of Cirencester, next to the bypass. Access from the town, or along Chesterton Lane from the W end of the bypass, on to Cotswold Ave

Train: Kemble 4 miles

Bus: From surrounding areas

ACQ.1973 🕾

MAP Page 337 (2J)
OS Map 163, OL45/169: SP020014

GLOUCESTER, BLACKFRIARS
GLOUCESTERSHIRE

One of the most complete surviving friaries of Dominican 'black friars' in England, later converted into a Tudor house and cloth factory. Notable features include the church and the fine scissor-braced dormitory roof, as well as the earliest surviving purpose-built library in England, in the south range.

Managed by Gloucester City Council.

OPENING TIMES
1 Apr-27 Oct, Sun-Mon	10am-4pm
28 Oct-28 Mar	Closed

VISIT US
Direction: In Blackfriars Lane, off Ladybellegate St, off Southgate St, Gloucester

Train: Gloucester ½ mile

Bus: Short walk from Gloucester Bus Station

Tel: 01452 503050

ACQ.1955 🕾 **P** ♿

Parking (adjacent. Charge applies, not managed by EH).

Guided tours available on Sundays in July and August at 2.30pm (charged) or tours can be booked on request.

MAP Page 337 (2J)
OS Map 162, 179: SO829184

GLOUCESTER, GREYFRIARS
GLOUCESTERSHIRE

Substantial remains of a medieval friary church of Franciscan 'grey friars', rebuilt in the Tudor period.

OPENING TIMES
Any reasonable daylight hours

VISIT US
Direction: On Greyfriars Walk

Train: Gloucester ½ mile

Bus: Gloucester Bus Station ½ mile

ACQ.1969 🐕 ♿

MAP Page 337 (2J)
OS Map 162, 179: SO832184

GREAT WITCOMBE ROMAN VILLA GLOUCESTERSHIRE

The remains of a large and luxurious Roman villa built c. AD 250, with a bathhouse complex and possibly the shrine of a water spirit. Mosaics are preserved in a small building to the north east of the site.

OPENING TIMES
Exterior: Any reasonable daylight hours

There is no access to the building which houses the mosaics

VISIT US
Direction: Located 5 miles SE of Gloucester off A46; ½ mile S of reservoir in Witcombe Park; 400 metres (440 yards) from Cotswold Way National Trail

Train: Gloucester 6 miles

Bus: Stagecoach service 46 to Green Street then 1 mile walk, or Stagecoach 10 to Brockworth and 2 mile walk. Also infrequent Swanbrook service 852 serves Witcombe

ACQ.1919 🐕 P

Parking (no access for coaches. No parking permitted in the lane to or beyond the car park).

MAP Page 337 (2J)
OS Map 163, 179: SO899142

HAILES ABBEY
GLOUCESTERSHIRE
GL54 5PB

The Cistercian abbey of Hailes was founded in 1246 by Richard Earl of Cornwall, King Henry III's brother, in thanksgiving for deliverance from shipwreck, and dissolved on Christmas Eve 1539. Though never housing large numbers of monks, it had extensive and elaborate buildings, financed by pilgrims visiting its renowned relic, 'the Holy Blood of Hailes' – allegedly a phial of Christ's own blood.

Interpretation panels guide you around the abbey buildings, and an audio tour brings the site to life. Sculptures, stonework and other site finds are displayed in the museum. The adjacent parish church displays notable medieval wall-paintings. Hot drinks and snacks available in the shop.

Owned by the National Trust, managed and maintained by English Heritage.

NON-MEMBERS
Adult	£4.50
Concession	£4.10
Child	£2.70

National Trust members free, but charged for audio tour (£1) and special events

OPENING TIMES
1 Apr-30 Jun, daily	10am-5pm
1 Jul-31 Aug, daily	10am-6pm
1 Sep-2 Nov, daily	10am-5pm
3 Nov-29 Mar	Closed

Last admission 30 mins before closing

HAILES ABBEY

VISIT US
Direction: 2 miles NE of Winchcombe off B4632. On the Cotswold Way National Trail

Train: Cheltenham 10 miles

Bus: Castleways service 606 from Cheltenham and occasional journeys on service 559 to within 1 mile

Tel: 01242 602398

ACQ.1948 🎧 🐕 🚶 ♿ 🏛 P 📷 ♿ OVP

Disabled access (ramp to museum, disabled toilet).

Refreshments available.

MAP Page 337 (1J)
OS Map 150/163, OL45: SP050300

KINGSWOOD ABBEY GATEHOUSE
GLOUCESTERSHIRE

This 16th-century gatehouse, one of the latest monastic buildings in England, displays a richly sculpted mullioned window. It is the sole survivor of this Cistercian abbey.

OPENING TIMES
Exterior: any reasonable daylight hours

Interior: key available from 3 Wotton Road, Kingswood 10am-3.30pm weekdays only

VISIT US
Direction: In Kingswood, off B4060; 1 mile SW of Wotton-under-Edge

Train: Yate 8 miles

Bus: First 311; Wessex 84 & 626; Mikes Travel 201

ACQ.1950 🐕 P

Public toilets near to monument.

On-street parking.

MAP Page 337 (2H)
OS Map 162/172, 167: ST747920

NYMPSFIELD LONG BARROW
GLOUCESTERSHIRE

A large Neolithic burial mound with spectacular vistas over the Severn Valley. Its internal burial chambers are uncovered for viewing.

Managed by Gloucestershire County Council.

OPENING TIMES
Any reasonable daylight hours

VISIT US
Direction: Located 1 mile NW of Nympsfield on B4066

Train: Stroud 5 miles

Bus: Cotswold Green 35 (weekdays) passes the site. Cotswold Green service 264 (Tue & Fri) also serves the village of Nympsfield (¾ mile from the site)

MAP Page 337 (2H)
OS Map 162, 167/168: SO794013

ODDA'S CHAPEL
GLOUCESTERSHIRE

One of the most complete surviving Saxon churches in England, this chapel was built in 1056 by Earl Odda, and rediscovered in 1865 subsumed into a farmhouse. Nearby is the equally famous Saxon parish church.

OPENING TIMES
1 Apr-2 Nov, daily	10am-6pm
3 Nov-29 Mar, daily	10am-4pm
24-26 Dec & 1 Jan	Closed

VISIT US
Direction: Located in Deerhurst off B4213, at Abbots Court; SW of parish church

Train: Cheltenham 8 miles

Bus: Astons service 351 serves Apperley. From there it is a 1½ mile walk

ODDA'S CHAPEL

Parking (not EH, charges apply).

MAP Page 337 (1J)
OS Map 150, 179: SO869298

OFFA'S DYKE
GLOUCESTERSHIRE

A three-mile section of the great earthwork boundary dyke built along the Anglo-Welsh border by Offa, King of Mercia, probably during the 780s. This especially impressive wooded stretch includes the Devil's Pulpit, with fine views of Tintern Abbey.

OPENING TIMES
Any reasonable daylight hours

VISIT US
Direction: Located 3 miles NE of Chepstow, off B4228. Via Forest Enterprise Tidenham car park, 1 mile walk (waymarked) down to The Devil's Pulpit on Offa's Dyke (access is suitable only for those wearing proper walking shoes and is not suitable for the very young, old or infirm)

Train: Chepstow 7 miles

Bus: Forest Community Transport 707 (Tue, Thu & Fri only) passes the site. Alternatively Town & Country Bus/New Adventure Travel (Sun only) service 69 to Tintern then 1 mile walk or James Bevan 755 to Wibdon and then 1 mile walk

MAP Page 337 (2H)
OS Map 162, OL14/167
SO546011-ST549975

ENGLISH HERITAGE PROPERTY GUIDEBOOKS
Want to know more about a property near you?

Visit www.english-heritage shop.org.uk

OVER BRIDGE
GLOUCESTERSHIRE

A single-arch stone bridge spanning the River Severn, built in 1825-30 by the great engineer Thomas Telford.

OPENING TIMES
Any reasonable daylight hours

VISIT US
Direction: 1 mile NW of Gloucester, at junction of A40 (Ross) and A417 (Ledbury)

Train: Gloucester 2 miles

Bus: Stagecoach 23, 24, 24A, 30, 31, 32, 33, 71, 97, 98, 132; Astons 351

MAP Page 337 (1H)
OS Map 162, 179: SO816196

ST BRIAVELS CASTLE
GLOUCESTERSHIRE

The fine twin-towered gatehouse of this castle, built by Edward I in 1292, once defended a crossbow-bolt factory which used local Forest of Dean iron. Once a prison, it is now a youth hostel in wonderful walking country.

OPENING TIMES
Exterior: Any reasonable daylight hours

Bailey 1 Apr-30 Sep, daily	1pm-4pm

VISIT US
Direction: In St Briavels; 7 miles NE of Chepstow off B4228

Train: Chepstow 8 miles

Bus: Forest Community Transport service 701 or 707 (Tue, Thu, Fri only) and Geoff Willetts Coaches Monday service 787

Tel: 01594 530272

MAP Page 337 (2H)
OS Map 162, OL14: SO559046

ST MARY'S CHURCH, KEMPLEY GLOUCESTERSHIRE

A delightful Norman church, displaying one of the most outstandingly complete and well-preserved sets of medieval wall-paintings in England, dating from the 12th-15th centuries.

Managed by the Friends of Kempley Church.

A free virtual tour is available on our website **www.english-heritage.org.uk/stmaryskempley**

OPENING TIMES

1 Apr-31 Oct, daily	10am-6pm
1 Nov-28 Feb	Closed
1-29 Mar, daily	10am-6pm

VISIT US

Direction: 1 mile N of Kempley off B4024; 6 miles NE of Ross-on-Wye

Train: Ledbury 8 miles

Bus: Young's service 677 (Tue & Fri only)

Tel: 0117 975 0714/0709 for all group bookings and winter appointments

ACQ.1979 ✈ P ♿ Parking (in lay-by).

MAP Page 337 (1H)
OS Map 149, 189: SO670313

Don't forget to check opening times online before you visit.

www.english-heritage.org.uk/daysout/properties

ST NICHOLAS' CHURCH, GLOUCESTER
GLOUCESTERSHIRE
GL1 2PG

© CCT

This church beside Gloucester's (now vanished) west gate is known for its leaning, truncated white stone spire (damaged during the Siege of Gloucester in 1643). Formerly one of Gloucester's most prosperous parish churches, it was built for merchant traders, many of whom have memorials within.

Owned and managed by The Churches Conservation Trust.

OPENING TIMES

Tue-Sat	10am-5pm
Keyholder nearby	

VISIT US

Train: Gloucester ½ mile

Bus: Many bus services in Gloucester pass nearby. Most are operated by Stagecoach

5 mins walk from Greyfriars and Blackfriars; 10 mins walk from Over Bridge

MAP Page 337 (1H)
OS Map 162, 179: SO829188

ULEY LONG BARROW (HETTY PEGLER'S TUMP)
GLOUCESTERSHIRE

A partly reconstructed and recently restored Neolithic chambered mound, 37 metres (120 ft) long, atmospherically

ULEY LONG BARROW
(HETTY PEGLER'S TUMP)

sited overlooking the Severn Valley. 'Hetty Pegler' was its 17th-century landowner. The internal chambers are accessible – a torch is recommended.

Managed by Gloucestershire County Council.

OPENING TIMES
Any reasonable daylight hours

VISIT US

Direction: Located 3½ miles NE of Dursley, on B4066. Take care crossing road

Train: Stroud 6 miles

Bus: Stagecoach in the Cotswolds service 20 Stroud – Uley (passes close to ⊒ Stroud); Cotswold Green service 35 from Dursley. All to within 1 mile

ACQ.1883 ✈ P ⚠
Parking (in lay-by).
Warning: cross road with care.

MAP Page 337 (2H)
OS Map 162, 167/168: SO790000

WINDMILL TUMP LONG BARROW, RODMARTON
GLOUCESTERSHIRE

A Neolithic chambered tomb with an enigmatic 'false entrance'. Managed by Gloucestershire County Council.

OPENING TIMES
Any reasonable daylight hours

VISIT US

Direction: 1 mile SW of Rodmarton

Train: Kemble 5 miles

Bus: Cotswold Green service 881 Cirencester – Kemble ⊒ Tetbury

ACQ.1979 P
Dogs on leads.
Parking in lay-by.

Map Page 337 (2J)
OS Map 163, 168: ST933973

SOMERSET

ALL SAINTS' CHURCH, LANGPORT
SOMERSET – TA10 9QF

All Saints' stands on a hill, overlooking the remains of a Benedictine abbey. Its bold pinnacled tower, bedecked with gargoyles known locally as 'Hunky Punks', is a local landmark. However, the church's special treasure is the largest collection of medieval stained glass in Somerset.

Owned and managed by The Churches Conservation Trust.

OPENING TIMES
Keyholder nearby

Open every other Wed	7pm-9pm

VISIT US
Train: Bridgwater 9½ miles

Bus: First service 54, Hatch Green Coaches service 16

3 mins from Muchelney Abbey

MAP Page 337 (4G)
OS Map 193, 129: ST423267

BUTTER CROSS, DUNSTER:
SEE DUNSTER, BUTTER CROSS – PAGE 122

CLEEVE ABBEY SOMERSET – TA23 0PS

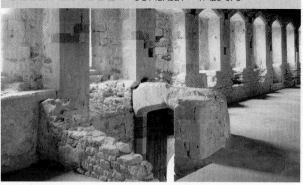

The atmospheric Cistercian abbey of Cleeve boasts the most impressively complete and unaltered set of monastic cloister buildings in England. Standing roofed and two storeys high, they include the gatehouse; the 15th-century refectory with its glorious angel roof; an unusual 'painted chamber'; and the floor of an earlier refectory, decked from end to end with 13th-century heraldic tiles, the protection of which was the subject of a high profile English Heritage research project. The great dormitory is one of the finest examples in the country. Beneath it are the newly-vaulted warming room, and the sacristy with more early 13th-century tilework and decoration.

An exhibition and touch-screen virtual tour tell the story of abbey life, and a story bag, *Brother Cedric and the Missing Sheep,* is a fun way for families to explore the abbey together.

🎟 Available for corporate and private hire

💍 Licensed for civil wedding ceremonies

NON-MEMBERS
Adult	£4.50
Concession	£4.10
Child	£2.70

OPENING TIMES
1 Apr-30 Jun, daily	10am-5pm
1 Jul-31 Aug, daily	10am-6pm
1 Sep-2 Nov, daily	10am-5pm
3 Nov-29 Mar	Closed
Last admission 30 mins before closing	

The abbey may be closed if an event is booked. Please check with the site in advance

From Sep-Nov 2014, access to the medieval tiles may be restricted due to planned conservation maintenance work

VISIT US
Direction: Located in Washford, ¼ mile S of A39

Train: Washford ½ mile (West Somerset Steam Railway)

Bus: First 28 & Webber 18

Tel: 01984 640377

Local Tourist Information
Watchet: 01984 632101

Disabled access (grounds and ground floor only, plus toilet).

Dogs on leads (in grounds only).

Refreshments available.

MAP Page 337 (4F)
OS Map 181, OL9: ST047407

CHURCH OF ST MARY THE VIRGIN, STOCKLINCH OTTERSEY
SOMERSET – TA19 9JN

© CCT

This hillside landmark, made of golden Ham stone, is an atmospheric gem. St Mary's is linked to its sister church, St Mary Magdalene, by an old legend of two sisters who both fell in love with a vicar, each building a church for him.

Owned and managed by The Churches Conservation Trust.

OPENING TIMES
Open daily during daylight hours

VISIT US
Train: Crewkerne 6½ miles
Bus: No bus nearby
20 mins from Muchelney Abbey

MAP Page 337 (4G)
OS Map 193, 128: ST388172

DUNSTER, BUTTER CROSS
SOMERSET

The transplanted stump of a medieval stone cross, once a meeting-place for butter-sellers.

Managed by the National Trust.

OPENING TIMES
Any reasonable daylight hours

VISIT US
Direction: Beside minor road to Alcombe, 350 metres (400 yards) NW of Dunster parish church
Train: Dunster (West Somerset Railway) 1 mile
Bus: Beacon Bus service 398. Also Riddlers service 107 (Wed only) & Quantock service 564 (Mon & Fri only). First service 28 and Webber

Bus services 18 & 106 serve Dunster Steep with a ½ mile walk

ACQ.1951 P

Parking in village (charged, not EH).

MAP Page 337 (4F)
OS Map 181, OL9: ST823604

DUNSTER, GALLOX BRIDGE
SOMERSET

This ancient stone bridge – originally 'gallows bridge'– once carried packhorses bringing fleeces to Dunster market.

Managed by the National Trust.

OPENING TIMES
Any reasonable daylight hours

VISIT US
Direction: Located off A396 at the S end of Dunster village
Train: Dunster ¾ mile (West Somerset Railway)
Bus: Beacon Bus service 398. Also Riddlers service 107 (Wed only) & Quantock service 564 (Mon & Fri only). First service 28 and WebberBus services 18 & 106 serve Dunster Steep. From there it is about a ½ mile walk

ACQ.1951 P

Parking in village (charged, not EH).

MAP Page 337 (4F)
OS Map 181, OL9: SS989432

DUNSTER, YARN MARKET
SOMERSET

This fine 17th-century timber-framed octagonal market hall is a monument to Dunster's once-flourishing cloth trade.

Managed by the National Trust.

OPENING TIMES
Any reasonable daylight hours

VISIT US
Direction: In Dunster High St
Train: Dunster (West Somerset Railway) ½ mile
Bus: Beacon Bus service 398. Also Riddlers service 107 (Wed

DUNSTER, YARN MARKET

only) & Quantock service 564 (Mon & Fri only). First service 28 and WebberBus services 18 & 106 serve Dunster Steep. From there it is about a ½ mile walk

ACQ.1951

MAP Page 337 (4F)
OS Map 181, OL9: SS992438

FARLEIGH HUNGERFORD CASTLE
SEE FEATURE OPPOSITE

GALLOX BRIDGE, DUNSTER:
SEE DUNSTER, GALLOX BRIDGE – SEE LEFT

GLASTONBURY TRIBUNAL
SOMERSET – BA6 9DP

A fine, late 15th-century stone town house, with an early Tudor façade and panelled interiors. Now contains a Tourist Information Centre with the Glastonbury Lake Village Museum on first floor (charged).

Managed by Glastonbury Tribunal Ltd.

NON-MEMBERS
Museum:

Adult	£2.50
Concession	£2.00
Child	£1.00

OPENING TIMES

1 Apr-29 Mar, Mon-Sat (last entry 3.30pm)	10am-4pm
25-26 Dec & 1 Jan	Closed

Opening hours may be varied during winter season

VISIT US
Direction: In Glastonbury High St
Bus: Bakers-Dolphin service 668 passes site. First 29, 375 & 377; Webber Bus 37 & 38 and Frome Minibuses 669 pass within ½ mile
Tel: 01458 832954

ACQ.1932 M P

Disabled access (ground floor – 2 steps).
Parking (charged, not EH).

MAP Page 337 (4H)
OS Map 182/183, 141: ST499389

FARLEIGH HUNGERFORD CASTLE
SOMERSET – BA2 7RS

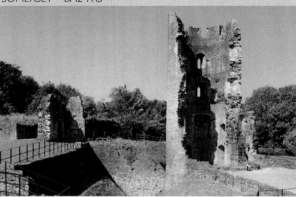

Farleigh Hungerford was begun in the 1370s by Sir Thomas Hungerford, Speaker of the Commons, and extended in the 15th century by his son Walter, Lord Hungerford, distinguished soldier and statesman. The remains of their fortified mansion include two tall corner towers and a complete castle chapel, crowded with family monuments and bedecked with wall-paintings. In the chapel's crypt the coffins of many Hungerfords are still visible, several with attached 'death masks'.

The colourful Hungerford family included two members executed during the Wars of the Roses and another – who imprisoned his wife here for four years – beheaded by Henry VIII. A Tudor Lady Hungerford burnt her murdered husband's body in the kitchen furnace.

The story of Farleigh is told in an audio tour and extensive displays in the Priests House. There is a virtual tour for disabled visitors, family and educational facilities, and a schools base with historic costumes.

NON-MEMBERS

Adult	£4.20
Concession	£3.80
Child	£2.50

OPENING TIMES

1 Apr-30 Sep, daily	10am-6pm
1 Oct-2 Nov, daily	10am-5pm
3 Nov-29 Mar, Sat-Sun	10am-4pm
24-26 Dec, 31 Dec-1 Jan	Closed

Last admission 30 mins before closing

VISIT US

Direction: In Farleigh Hungerford, 9 miles SE of Bath; 3½ miles W of Trowbridge on A366

Train: Avoncliffe 2 miles; Trowbridge 3½ miles

Bus: Libra 94; Frome Minibuses X96 from Trowbridge (pass close Trowbridge ⬆] to Wingfield then 1½ miles walk

Tel: 01225 754026

Local Tourist Information
Trowbridge: 01225 710535

ACQ. 1915 🎧 📷 📚 🎭 🅴 f 🤚 ❋ ☐
🧍 🧍 🍴 P 🎪 📷 🚻 ♿ ⚠ OVP

Disabled access (Chapel and Priest's House, ground floor only. Disabled toilet).

Refreshments available.

MAP Page 337 (3H)
OS Map 173, 143/156: ST801576

MEARE FISH HOUSE
SOMERSET

The only surviving building of comparable purpose in England, this housed Glastonbury Abbey's official in charge of the (then) adjacent lake fishery. Its design, miniaturising the components of larger medieval houses, is also unique.

OPENING TIMES

Any reasonable daylight hours. Key available from Manor Farm house

VISIT US

Direction: In Meare village, on B3151

Bus: Bakers-Dolphin service 668 Cheddar – Street

ACQ. 1911 🍴 P
Parking in lay-by.

MAP Page 337 (4G)
OS Map 182, 141: ST458417

MUCHELNEY ABBEY
SOMERSET – TA10 0DQ

This atmospheric and once-remote 'great island' amid the Somerset Levels has many rewards for visitors. Beside the clearly laid out foundations of the wealthy medieval Benedictine abbey (and its Anglo-Saxon predecessor) stands a complete early Tudor house in miniature. Originally the abbots' lodgings, this charming building includes a magnificent great chamber with ornate fireplace, carved settle and stained glass; two rooms with time-faded walls painted to

MUCHELNEY ABBEY

resemble cloth hangings; and a pair of kitchens with fine timber roof. Parts of the richly decorated cloister walk and refectory are incorporated, and nearby is the thatched two-storey monks' lavatory, unique in Britain.

Exhibitions illustrate monastic life with a fascinating collection of site finds, including decorated tiles and stonework. Much improved facilities for disabled visitors include a touch-screen tour. A 'story bag' is a fun way for families to explore the abbey together.

The adjacent parish church (with 17th-century painted ceiling) and medieval Priest's House are not managed by English Heritage.

NON-MEMBERS

Adult	£4.50
Concession	£4.10
Child	£2.70

OPENING TIMES

1 Apr-30 Jun, daily	10am-5pm
1 Jul-31 Aug, daily	10am-6pm
1 Sep-2 Nov, daily	10am-5pm
3 Nov-29 Mar	Closed

VISIT US

Direction: In Muchelney, 2 miles S of Langport via Huish Episcopi

Bus: Somerset County Transport 850 (Thu only); otherwise use First service 54 and walk 1 mile from Langport

Cycle: Sustrans: National Route 339

Tel: 01458 250664

Local Tourist Information
Langport: 01458 253527

Dogs on leads (in grounds only).

Disabled access (grounds and most of ground floor, adapted toilet).

MUCHELNEY ABBEY

Light refreshments available.

MAP Page 337 (4G)
OS Map 193, 129: ST429249

NUNNEY CASTLE
SOMERSET

The striking and picturesque moated castle of Nunney was built in the 1370s by Sir John de la Mere, a local knight who was beginning to enjoy royal favour. Extensively modernised in the late 16th century, the castle was held for the King during the Civil War, but quickly fell to Parliamentarian cannon in 1645: not until Christmas Day 1910, however, did the gun-damaged portion of the wall finally collapse.

OPENING TIMES
Any reasonable daylight hours

VISIT US

Direction: Located in Nunney, 3½ miles SW of Frome, off A361 (no coach access)

Train: Frome 3½ miles

Bus: First 161 Frome – Wells

Disabled access (exterior only).

MAP Page 337 (3H)
OS Map 183, 142: ST737457

ST MARTIN OF TOURS, ELWORTHY
SOMERSET – TA4 3PY

© Robert Cutts

Tucked into the hillside above the road, this church has a distinctive battlemented tower with an unusual outside stairway. Inside, there is charming stained glass, and medieval and Jacobean woodwork, including a carved screen across the chancel arch.

Owned and managed by The Churches Conservation Trust.

OPENING TIMES
Open daily during daylight hours

VISIT US

Train: Taunton 10¾ miles or closer station at Stogumber then 2 mile walk on West Somerset Railway

Bus: No bus nearby

10 mins from Cleeve Abbey

MAP Page 337 (4F)
OS Map 181, OL09: ST082352

YARN MARKET, DUNSTER: SEE DUNSTER, YARN MARKET – PAGE 122

WILTSHIRE

BRADFORD-ON-AVON
TITHE BARN WILTSHIRE

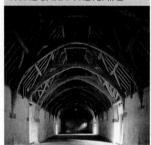

A spectacular 14th-century monastic stone barn, 51 metres (168 ft) long, with a sophisticated timber-cruck roof.

Managed by Bradford-on-Avon Preservation Trust.

OPENING TIMES

1 Apr–29 Mar, daily	10.30am–4pm
24–26 Dec & 1 Jan	Closed

Barn may be closed whilst hosting local events – check website for details.

VISIT US

Direction: Located ½ mile S of town centre off B3109

Train: Bradford-on-Avon ½ mile

Bus: Faresaver Zig Zag service; First 264 & 265; Frome Minibuses service 14 & X96

Parking (adjacent, not managed by EH – charge applies).

MAP Page 337 (3H)
OS Map 173, 156: ST823604

BRATTON CAMP AND
WHITE HORSE WILTSHIRE

BRATTON CAMP AND WHITE HORSE

Below an Iron Age hillfort, enclosing a much earlier long barrow, lies the Westbury White Horse. Cut into the hillside in 1778, this replaced a slightly older horse, commemorating King Alfred's legendary victory over the Danes nearby.

OPENING TIMES

Any reasonable daylight hours

VISIT US

Direction: 2 miles E of Westbury off B3098, 1 mile SW of Bratton

Train: Westbury 3 miles

Bus: Faresaver 87/87A Trowbridge-Devizes (passes ≩ Westbury)

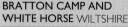

Sheep grazing on site.

MAP Page 337 (3J)
OS Map 184, 143: ST900516

CHISBURY CHAPEL
WILTSHIRE

A pretty, thatched and flint-walled 13th-century chapel, later used as a barn.

OPENING TIMES

Any reasonable daylight hours

VISIT US

Direction: Off unclassified road, ¼ mile E of Chisbury, off A4; 6 miles E of Marlborough

Train: Bedwyn 1 mile

Bus: Wiltshire Bus services 22 to Chisbury turn then ½ mile walk. Alternatively Wiltshire Bus services 20 & 22 to Great Bedwyn then ¾ mile walk

ACQ.1982 Parking (in lay-by).

MAP Page 337 (3K)
OS Map 174, 157: SU280660

HATFIELD EARTHWORK
(MARDEN HENGE)
WILTSHIRE

Part of the earthworks of a Neolithic henge and

HATFIELD EARTHWORK

monumental mound, by a loop in the River Avon.

OPENING TIMES

Any reasonable daylight hours

VISIT US

Direction: 5½ miles SE of Devizes, off A342; NE of village of Marden. Look for small section of fence in hedgerow to access site.

Train: Pewsey 5 miles

Bus: Tourist Coaches 210 (Thu, Sat only) & 244 (Mon-Fri & Sun only)

ACQ.1972

MAP Page 337 (3J)
OS Map 173, 130: SU092583

LUDGERSHALL CASTLE
AND CROSS
WILTSHIRE

The ruins and earthworks of a royal castle dating mainly from the 12th and 13th centuries, frequently used as a hunting lodge. The remains of the medieval cross stand in the centre of the village.

OPENING TIMES

Any reasonable daylight hours

VISIT US

Direction: Located on the N side of Ludgershall, off A342

Train: Andover 7 miles

Bus: Salisbury Red 'Active 8' service, Stagecoach 8 & 80

ACQ.1915 Castle ACQ.1952 Cross

Disabled access (part of site only and village cross).

Parking (limited).

MAP Page 337 (3K)
OS Map 184/185, 131: SU264512

NETHERAVON DOVECOTE
WILTSHIRE

A charming 18th-century brick dovecote, still with most of its 700 or more nesting boxes.

OPENING TIMES
Exterior viewing only from nearby roadside, as there is no access across the field in which dovecote is situated

VISIT US
Direction: In Netheravon, 4½ miles N of Amesbury on A345

Train: Pewsey 9 miles, Grateley 11 miles

Bus: Stagecoach Swindon 5; Salisbury Reds service X5 Salisbury – Swindon (pass close Pewsey, Salisbury & Swindon 🚆)

ACQ.1939 🏹

MAP Page 337 (3J)
OS Map 184, 130: SU147484

OLD CHURCH ST MARY'S, WILTON
WILTSHIRE – SP2 0HQ 🏛

© Fergus McNeill

This 'old' church was partially demolished, leaving the surviving building standing surrounded by the romantic ruins of its arcades and tower arch. Apart from the charming 18th-century ceiling, there are some fascinating memorials to the people of Wilton inside.

Owned and managed by The Churches Conservation Trust.

OLD CHURCH ST MARY'S, WILTON

OPENING TIMES
Please call us on 0117 929 1766 to arrange access

VISIT US
Train: Salisbury 2½ miles

Bus: Salisbury Reds rural routes 2, 25, 26 & 27; Wilton Park & Ride service 502

10 mins from Old Sarum, 20 mins from Stonehenge

MAP Page 337 (4J)
OS Map 184, 130: SU097313

OLD SARUM
SEE FEATURE – PAGE 128

OLD WARDOUR CASTLE
SEE FEATURE OPPOSITE

THE SANCTUARY
SEE PAGE 131

SILBURY HILL
SEE PAGE 131

ST ANDREW'S CHURCH, ROLLESTONE
WILTSHIRE – SP3 4HG 🏛

© Cameron Newham

ST ANDREW'S CHURCH, ROLLESTONE

This tiny, charming church, overlooking the River Till, was built of flint and stone chequerwork and has two large perpendicular windows. The church was owned by the religious crusading order of the Knights Hospitaller for 350 years, and still contains its original font.

Owned and managed by The Churches Conservation Trust.

OPENING TIMES
Open daily during daylight hours

VISIT US
Train: Salisbury 9 miles

Bus: Salisbury Reds services 2 & 4

5 mins from Stonehenge

MAP Page 337 (4J)
OS Map 184, 130: SU073431

STONEHENGE
SEE FEATURE – PAGE 134

WEST KENNET AVENUE
SEE PAGE 132

WEST KENNET LONG BARROW
SEE PAGE 132

WINDMILL HILL
SEE PAGE 132

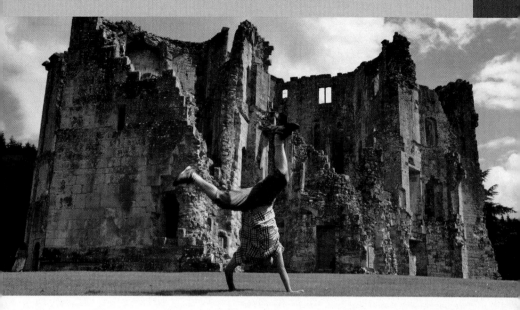

VISIT US

Direction: Located off A30 3½ miles SW of Tisbury. Also accessible from A350 (narrow rural roads), coaches approach with care

Train: Tisbury 3½ miles

Bus: Salisbury Reds service 26 Salisbury – Shaftesbury (passes Tisbury ⟩)

Tel: 01747 870487

Local Tourist Information
Shaftesbury: 01747 853514

NON-MEMBERS

Adult	£4.20
Concession	£3.80
Child	£2.50

OPENING TIMES

1 Apr-30 Sep, daily	10am-6pm
1 Oct-2 Nov, daily	10am-4pm
3 Nov-29 Mar, Sat-Sun	10am-4pm
24-26 Dec, 31 Dec-1 Jan	Closed

Last admission 30 mins before closing

ACQ.1936 🎧 ♿ 🐕 ▮ f ✋ ▢ ▮
🚶 🚹 P 🚐 ♿ ⚠ OVP
Disabled access (grounds and ground floor only), disabled toilet.

Refreshments available.

MAP Page 337 (4J)
OS Map 184, 118: ST939263

Beautifully sited beside a lake, Old Wardour Castle was built in the late 14th century by John Lord Lovel as a lightly fortified but showy and luxurious residence. A hexagonal tower house ranged round a central courtyard, its form is very unusual in England.

Substantially updated by the staunchly Roman Catholic Arundell family after c. 1570, the castle saw much fighting during the Civil War. In 1643 the 60-year-old Lady Arundell was forced to surrender it to Parliament. But the new garrison was almost immediately besieged in turn by Royalist forces led by her son. After an eventful three months of bombardment and undermining, they finally capitulated in March 1644.

The abandoned castle became a romantic ruin, and was incorporated in the 18th century into the landscaped grounds of Lord Arundell's New Wardour House (not managed by English Heritage, no public access). The castle's setting in a Registered Landscape enhances the significance of this hidden jewel.

Visit the website for details of special events.

🔲 Licensed for civil wedding ceremonies

VISIT US

Direction: 2 miles N of Salisbury, off A345

Train: Salisbury 2 miles

Bus: Salisbury Reds service X5 (Stagecoach 5 on Sundays), 8; Stagecoach Hampshire 8; Wiltshire Buses 501 Park and Ride service and Stonehenge Tour service. See www.thestonehengetour.info

Tel: 01722 335398

Local Tourist Information
Salisbury: 01722 334956

NON-MEMBERS

Adult	£4.00
Concession	£3.60
Child	£2.40

OPENING TIMES

1 Apr–30 Jun, daily	10am–5pm
1 Jul–31 Aug, daily	9am–6pm
1 Sep–31 Oct, daily	10am–5pm
1 Nov–29 Mar, daily	10am–4pm
24–26 Dec, 31 Dec–1 Jan	Closed

ACQ.1892

Disabled access (outer bailey and grounds only, disabled toilet).

Toilets located in the car park.

Refreshments available.

MAP Page 337 (4J)
OS Map 184, 130: SU138327

The great earthwork of Old Sarum stands near Salisbury on the edge of Wiltshire's chalk plains. Its mighty ramparts were raised in about 500 BC by Iron Age peoples, and later occupied by the Romans, the Saxons and, most importantly, the Normans.

William the Conqueror paid off his army here in 1070, and in 1086 summoned all the great landowners of England here to swear an oath of loyalty. A Norman castle was built on the inner mound, and joined soon afterwards by a royal palace. By the middle of the 12th century a new town occupied much of the great earthwork, complete with a noble new Norman cathedral, the mother church of a huge diocese.

But Norman Sarum was not destined to thrive. Soldiers and priests quarrelled and life on the almost waterless hilltop became intolerable. The solution was a move downhill to the new settlement now known as Salisbury, where a new cathedral was founded in 1220. Thereafter Old Sarum went into steep decline. Its cathedral was demolished and its castle was eventually abandoned. But the largely uninhabited site continued to 'elect' two MPs, becoming the most notorious of the 'Rotten Boroughs' swept away by the 1832 Reform Act.

Today, the remains of the prehistoric fortress and of the Norman palace, castle and cathedral evoke memories of thousands of years of history, which are interpreted by graphic panels throughout the site.

Visit the website for details of special events.

Combine your visit with a trip to Stonehenge, which is only 20 minutes away by car, or hop onto the Wilts & Dorset Stonehenge Tour bus service (www.thestonehengetour.info)

Stonehenge and Avebury and their associated sites were inscribed onto the UNESCO World Heritage List in 1986, one of the first of seven sites to be nominated by the UK that year. Stonehenge and Avebury stand alongside 981 other sites across the world – such as the Great Wall of China, the Taj Mahal of India and Machu Picchu in Peru – which have been selected for their 'outstanding universal value' to all the peoples of the world.

Stonehenge and Avebury were chosen for their extraordinary prehistoric monuments. They help us to understand Neolithic and Bronze Age ceremonial and mortuary practices, and demonstrate around 2000 years of continuous use and monument building between 3700 and 1600 BC.

Management Plans for both the Avebury and Stonehenge parts of the World Heritage site bring a whole range of organisations and individuals together. These work in partnership to manage the site and to protect and sustain its outstanding universal value.

Take some time to visit both parts of the World Heritage Site and you will be well rewarded. At Stonehenge itself, displays in the spectacular new visitor centre explore the amazing prehistoric landscape that surrounds this iconic monument. View the rich collections in the Wiltshire Museum at Devizes and the Salisbury and South Wiltshire Museum in Salisbury, and learn more about the people who built the hundreds of prehistoric monuments of the World Heritage Site. Stay longer in the beautiful county of Wiltshire to experience a very different but equally rich visit to the Avebury area, with its 'sacred landscape' of prehistoric monuments and the Alexander Keiller Museum, displaying and interpreting finds from the immediate area.

AVEBURY HENGE AND STONE CIRCLES
WILTSHIRE – SN8 1RF

Avebury henge and stone circles are one of the greatest marvels surviving from prehistoric Britain. The henge, built and altered over the centuries from about 2600 BC to 2400 BC, survives as a huge circular bank and ditch just over ¾ mile in circumference, enclosing an area of approximately 28 acres (11 hectares), including part of Avebury village. Long grassed over but once of gleaming chalk, this 'henge' ditch was originally nearly 30 feet (9 metres) deep, with a bank 13 feet (4 metres) high. Within it was a circle of originally about 100 great sarsen stones, making it the largest stone circle in Britain: 36 stones are now standing. This enclosed two more stone circles, each in turn enclosing a central stone setting.

The site's present appearance owes much to the marmalade heir Alexander Keiller, who

AVEBURY HENGE AND
STONE CIRCLES WILTSHIRE

excavated and re-erected 21 stones during the 1930s, and whose archaeological collections are displayed in the site museum. Many stones had been deliberately broken or buried in medieval and later times, one possibly crushing a man as it fell.

Avebury is part of a much wider complex of Neolithic and Bronze Age ceremonial and ritual sites. West Kennet Avenue joined it to the Sanctuary, and another stone avenue connected it with the Longstones enclosure and cove near Beckhampton. Older West Kennet Long Barrow and Windmill Hill are also nearby, as is later Silbury Hill, huge and mysterious. Many of these sites can be reached by pleasant walks from Avebury village. This extraordinary assemblage of monuments seemingly formed a huge 'sacred landscape', whose uses and purposes can still only be guessed at.

Avebury and its surroundings have, with Stonehenge, achieved international recognition as a World Heritage Site.

OPENING TIMES
Any reasonable daylight hours

VISIT US
See Alexander Keiller Museum

ACQ.1944 ▨ P ♿

Parking (see Alexander Keiller Museum).

MAP Page 337 (3J)
OS Map 173, 157: SU102700

AVEBURY, ALEXANDER KEILLER MUSEUM
WILTSHIRE – SN8 1RF

Set in traditional farm buildings on the edge of the picturesque village, the museum is a must for any visitor to the Avebury prehistoric landscape. The Stables Gallery houses one of the most important archaeological collections in Britain, including many notable finds from the World Heritage Site monuments. The Barn Gallery (itself a fine thatched, weatherboarded and timber-framed building) houses child-friendly interactive displays about the World Heritage Site and its people over the millennia, as well as Alexander Keiller's vintage car and a film about his colourful life. There are also a shop and a café, and directions and maps for walks to individual monuments within the World Heritage Site are available.

NON-MEMBERS

Adult	£4.40
Child	£2.20
Family (2+2)	£12.20
Family (1+3)	£7.90

Reduced price when arriving by cycle or public transport

OPENING TIMES

1 Apr–25 Oct, daily	10am–6pm
26 Oct–29 Mar, daily	10am–4pm (dusk if earlier)
24–26 Dec	Closed

VISIT US
Direction: In Avebury, 7 miles W of Marlborough

Train: Pewsey 10 miles; Swindon 11 miles

Bus: Stagecoach in Swindon service 49. Connect2 line 4

ACQ.1944 E ♿ ♿ ♿ ▨ ✕ P ♿

AVEBURY, ALEXANDER KEILLER MUSEUM

Parking (Visitor car park free to EH members. S of Avebury off A4361. Free disabled visitors' parking in village car park).

MAP Page 337 (3J)
OS Map 173, 157: SU099700

DURRINGTON WALLS
SEE WOODHENGE AND DURRINGTON WALLS – PAGE 133

THE SANCTUARY
NEAR AVEBURY, WILTSHIRE

The Sanctuary as it may have appeared in the final phase. Reconstruction by Judith Dobie.

Begun around 2500 BC, the Sanctuary was originally a complex concentric arrangement of six timber rings and two stone circles. These now-vanished components are today indicated by concrete slabs and posts. Various objects such as animal bones, pottery, flint tools and even human remains were deliberately

THE SANCTUARY

buried at the site, but its function remains a mystery. Like the similar monuments at Woodhenge and Durrington Walls, it was probably a free-standing ceremonial structure rather than a building. Later, the West Kennet Avenue was constructed to connect it with Avebury, reinforcing the status of this enigmatic but clearly very important site. Part of the Avebury section of the World Heritage Site.

OPENING TIMES
Any reasonable daylight hours

VISIT US
Direction: ½ mile S of West Kennett, beside S side of A4

Train: Pewsey 9 miles, Bedwyn 12 miles

Bus: Connect2 Wiltshire service 4 & 5 and Taxibus TL3. Tel 0845 652 5255; also limited service by Wiltshire Buses X76; also one journey on Tourist Coaches service 244 serves West Kennett village

ACQ.1944

Warning: Very limited parking in lay-by on S side of A4.

MAP Page 337 (3J)
OS Map 173, 157: SU118680

SILBURY HILL
NEAR AVEBURY, WILTSHIRE

SILBURY HILL

Unmistakably dominating the landscape around Avebury, mysterious Silbury Hill is the largest artificial prehistoric mound in Europe. At approximately 37 metres high and 500 metres round its base, it is comparable in height and volume with the roughly contemporary Egyptian pyramids. No doubt encouraged by tales of rich burials, antiquarians and archaeologists have dug three separate tunnels into the centre, but it contains no central grave. The mound was built in a series of stages over perhaps 100 years around 2400 BC, starting with a small gravel mound. The position of Silbury Hill near the source of the River Kennet was clearly important, but its purpose and significance remain unknown.

There is no access to the Hill itself. This is to prevent erosion of archaeological deposits and rare chalk grassland (the Hill is a Site of Special Scientific Interest). Part of the Avebury section of the World Heritage Site.

Find out more about the 2000-2008 conservation project at **www.english-heritage.org.uk/silbury**

OPENING TIMES
Viewing area during reasonable daylight hours. Strictly no access to the hill itself

VISIT US
Direction: 1 mile W of West Kennett on A4

USUAL FACILITIES MAY NOT BE AVAILABLE AROUND THE SUMMER SOLSTICE 20-22 JUNE. PLEASE CALL 01672 539250 BEFORE YOU VISIT.

SILBURY HILL

Train: Pewsey 9 miles, Swindon 13 miles

Bus: Stagecoach in Swindon service 49 passes within ¾ mile of the site. Also Connect2 Wiltshire services 4 & 5 and Taxibus TL3. Tel 0845 652 5255 for more details

ACQ.1883 🏹 **P** ♿

Disabled access (viewing area).

MAP Page 337 (3J)
OS Map 173, 157: SU100685

WEST KENNET AVENUE
NEAR AVEBURY, WILTSHIRE

An avenue, originally of around 100 pairs of prehistoric standing stones, raised to form a winding 1½ mile ritual link between the monuments of Avebury and the Sanctuary. The section nearest Avebury is the only part still visible. Many of the pairs, set around 20-30m from the next pair and around 15m apart, seem to follow a set form, with a large diamond-shaped stone matched with a slender straight-sided stone. Part of the Avebury section of the World Heritage Site.

OPENING TIMES

Any reasonable daylight hours

WEST KENNET AVENUE

VISIT US

Direction: Runs alongside B4003

Train: Pewsey 9 miles, Swindon 12 miles

Bus: Connect2 Wiltshire service 4 & 5 and Taxibus TL3. Tel 0845 652 5255. Also limited service by Wiltshire Buses X76; also one journey on Tourist Coaches service 244 serves West Kennett village

ACQ.1944 🏹 **P** ♿

Parking (in lay-by, or at Avebury).

Disabled access (on roadway).

MAP Page 337 (3J)
OS Map 173, 157: SU105695

WEST KENNET LONG BARROW
NEAR AVEBURY, WILTSHIRE

One of the largest, most impressive and most accessible Neolithic long barrows in Britain: crowning a ridge above the River Kennet, it is an oasis of wild flowers in summer. Its five atmospheric internal burial chambers, constructed of massive boulders, can still be explored.

Built around 3650 BC, it is among the oldest visible monuments in the Avebury landscape. The fragmented remains of around 50 people were deposited

WEST KENNET LONG BARROW

here, over a short period of time and according to a system; children predominate in some chambers, adults in others. Part of the Avebury section of the World Heritage Site.

OPENING TIMES

Any reasonable daylight hours

VISIT US

Direction: ¾ mile SW of West Kennett, along footpath off A4. 10-15 minutes uphill walk, on gravel and then grass track.

Train: Pewsey 9 miles, Swindon 13 miles

Bus: Connect2 Wiltshire service 4 & 5 and Taxibus TL3. Tel 0845 652 5255. Also limited service by Wiltshire Buses X76; also one journey on Tourist Coaches service 244 serves West Kennett village

ACQ.1883 🏹 **P**

Warning: Very limited parking in lay-by off S of A4.

MAP Page 337 (3J)
OS Map 173, 157: SU105677

WINDMILL HILL
NEAR AVEBURY, WILTSHIRE

The classic Neolithic causewayed enclosure, built around 3675 BC and thus pre-

WINDMILL HILL

dating the Avebury henge. Its three concentric but intermittent ditches cover an area of approximately nine hectares (22 acres). Large quantities of animal bones, cereal crops, stone tools, artefacts and pottery were found here, suggesting the communal gathering of people to feast, trade and carry out ritual ceremonies. This site can be reached by a 40-50 minute walk from Avebury village, along footpaths. Part of the Avebury section of the World Heritage Site.

OPENING TIMES
Any reasonable daylight hours

VISIT US
Direction: 1¼ miles NW of Avebury

Train: Swindon 11 miles

Bus: Stagecoach in Swindon service 49 passes within ¾ mile of the site. Alight between Winterbourne Monkton and Avebury and use footpath

ACQ.1944

Dogs on leads. Sheep grazing.

MAP Page 337 (3J)
OS Map 173, 157: SU087714

WOODHENGE AND DURRINGTON WALLS
WILTSHIRE

WOODHENGE AND DURRINGTON WALLS

Woodhenge is a late Neolithic monument, where concrete markers now indicate the location of six concentric oval rings of timber posts. The timber structure is surrounded by a circular bank and ditch and is aligned north-east towards the summer solstice sunrise. A small central flint cairn marks the location of a child burial.

Nearby is Durrington Walls, a massive circular earthwork henge 500 metres in diameter. It was also built in the late Neolithic period, in about 2500 BC. Excavations here have revealed two concentric timber monuments, similar to Woodhenge, and the remains of many small buildings, possibly the houses where the builders or users of Stonehenge lived.

Part of the Stonehenge section of the World Heritage Site.

OPENING TIMES
Any reasonable daylight hours

VISIT US
Direction: 1½ miles N of Amesbury, signposted off A345, just S of Durrington

Train: Salisbury 9 miles

Bus: Salisbury Reds services 8 & X5; Stagecoach Swindon 5 (Sun only)

ACQ. 1971 Durrington Walls
ACQ. 1932 Woodhenge

🍴 P ♿

Warning: Limited car parking.

MAP Page 337 (4J)
OS Map 184, 130: SU151434

AVEBURY MONUMENTS: OWNERSHIP, GUARDIANSHIP AND MANAGEMENT

Avebury Henge and Stone Circles; the Alexander Keiller Museum; West Kennet Avenue and Windmill Hill are in the freehold ownership of the National Trust: the Sanctuary is in Department of Culture, Media and Sport (DCMS) ownership: and Silbury Hill and West Kennet Long Barrow are in private ownership.

All the sites are in English Heritage guardianship, in the case of Alexander Keiller Museum on behalf of DCMS: the museum collection is on loan from DCMS.

All the sites are managed by the National Trust on behalf of English Heritage, and the two organisations share the cost of managing and maintaining the properties.

A World Heritage Site, Stonehenge and its surrounding prehistoric monuments remain powerful witnesses to the once great communities of the Neolithic and Bronze Ages, between 6000 and 3500 years ago.

VISIT US

Address: Stonehenge Exhibition and Visitor Centre, nr Shrewton, Wiltshire

Direction: Off the A360 at Airman's Corner (access is no longer available along the A344)

Train: Salisbury 9½ miles

Bus: Wilts & Dorset Stonehenge Tour service. See www.thestonehengetour.info

Tel: 0870 333 1181 (Customer Services)

Local Tourist Information
Amesbury Library: 01980 623491 and Salisbury: 01722 334956

NON-MEMBERS

Advanced Pre-booked Prices

Adult	£13.90
Concession	£12.50
Child	£8.30
Family	£36.10

Walk Up 'On the Day' Prices*

Adult	£14.90
Concession	£13.40
Child	£8.90
Family	£38.70

*Advanced booking required
Entrance to Stonehenge is now managed through timed tickets and advance booking online is strongly recommended. Bookings cannot be taken by phone and although a limited number of tickets will be available on site each day, to ensure your ticket book in advance at www.english-heritage.org.uk/stonehenge

NT members admitted free

Please note: All tourist and education groups must be pre-booked

OPENING TIMES

Last admission two hours before closing

1 Apr-31 May, daily	9.30am-7pm
1 Jun-31 Aug, daily	9am-8pm
1 Sep-15 Oct, daily	9.30am-7pm
16 Oct-15 Mar, daily	9.30am-5pm
16-29 Mar, daily	9.30am-7pm
24-25 Dec	Closed

Opening times from 20-22 June may be subject to change due to summer solstice. For details www.english-heritage.org.uk/stonehenge

When weather conditions are bad, access may be restricted and visitors may not be able to use the walkway around the stone circle

Stone Circle Access outside normal opening hours by advance booking only. Book during weekday office hours on telephone 0870 333 0605

New guidebook.

Audio tours (available in ten languages and hearing loop: subject to availability). Also available to download to your mobile device ahead of your visit, see website for details.

Catering, hot and cold refreshments available throughout the year.

Guidebooks (available to purchase in English, French, German, Italian, Japanese, Mandarin, Russian and Spanish).

No dogs allowed at the monument (except guide and hearing dogs).

Parking is free to members and Stonehenge ticket holders.

MAP Page 337 (4J)
OS Map 184, 130: SU122422

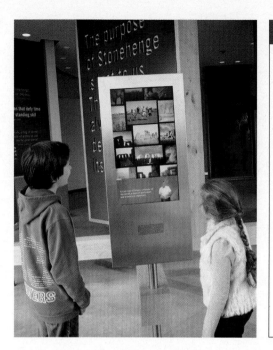

NEW FOR 2014

There will be a changing programme of temporary exhibitions at Stonehenge, entry to which is included in your ticket price. Until autumn 2014, the exhibition 'Set in Stone?' will display important objects, never seen together before, that tell the story of our changing understanding of Stonehenge. These include rare medieval manuscripts which are among the earliest known drawings of the monument; Roman coins and jewellery; and early surveying equipment.

For six months from autumn 2014, there will be an exhibition focusing on Salisbury Plain and Stonehenge at the outbreak of the First World War, visit our website for more details.

The prehistoric stone circle of Stonehenge is a unique and exceptional survival from the distant past.

Now long-awaited environmental improvements by English Heritage and its partners have restored the dignity of the famous stone circle, and an outstanding new visitor centre immensely enhances the experience of visiting this World Heritage Site.

The monument was begun about 3000 BC in the Neolithic period. The first major activity at the site was the construction of a circular ditch with inner and outer banks, about 120m in diameter. Inside was a ring of 56 large pits, which probably held wooden or stone posts. These pits are known as Aubrey Holes, after the 17th-century antiquary John Aubrey, who was the first to notice them as depressions in the grass. During this early stage, Stonehenge was used as a cremation cemetery, with an estimated 150 people being buried here.

Some 500 years later, about 2500 BC, the central stone settings were built. The larger stones, sarsens, some weighing 30 tons or more, were probably brought from the Marlborough Downs, over 27km (16 miles) to the north. The sarsens were set up in an outer circle, composed of 30 sarsen uprights, probably with a continuous circle of joining lintels. Within this were five sarsen trilithons (two upright stones capped by a horizontal lintel) arranged in a horseshoe shape. The trilithons were graded in height, with the tallest trilithon at the head of the horseshoe.

Among the sarsens, the smaller bluestones, transported over 240km (150 miles) from the Preseli Hills in Pembrokeshire, were set up in a double arc. At this stage, there may have been bluestone trilithons. Later, about 2300 BC, the bluestones were re-arranged to form an outer circle and an inner oval setting. At the centre was the Altar Stone, made of sandstone and on the periphery were the four Station Stones, with further standing stones at the entrance. The enormous Heel Stone, which stood near the north-east entrance to the circle, may have been one of the earliest stones to be erected at the site.

CONTINUED ▶

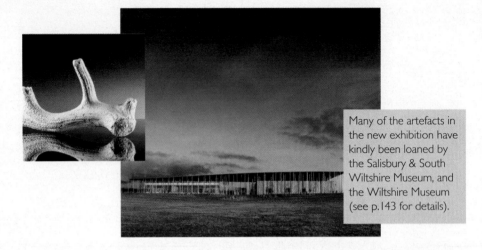

Many of the artefacts in the new exhibition have kindly been loaned by the Salisbury & South Wiltshire Museum, and the Wiltshire Museum (see p.143 for details).

The remains that can be seen today are the remarkable survival of the final phase of this ancient monument, after 4000 years of decay and destruction.

A huge and extraordinarily well co-ordinated communal effort was needed to build Stonehenge. The process of transporting the stones over long distances, carefully shaping and working them to create the joints and smooth surfaces, and the raising of the stones into position, took huge numbers of people. Only simple tools such as hammer stones were used to shape the stones and craft the mortice and tenon joints linking the uprights with the horizontal lintels – one of the unique features of Stonehenge. The monument is an astonishing testament to the sophisticated engineering skills of prehistoric people.

The orientation of the stone settings in relation to the rising and setting of the sun at the solstices is remarkable. Clearly the midsummer sunrise and midwinter sunset were important occasions in the annual cycle of the seasons for the people who built and used Stonehenge.

There has long been debate about the meaning and function of Stonehenge. Various theories have been put forward – from medieval legends that the stones had been raised by Merlin, to ideas that it was a Roman temple or a place of coronation for Danish kings. Perhaps the most famous and enduring idea, made popular by the 18th-century antiquary William Stukeley, was that it was built as a Druid temple. Today, archaeologists continue to come up with new theories about why people built Stonehenge.

Stonehenge was not built in isolation. When it was begun, this area was already the location of an early Neolithic monument complex. This included long barrows; the long rectangular enclosures of the Stonehenge (or Greater) and Lesser Cursus monuments, and the causewayed enclosure at Robin Hood's Ball. At the time that Stonehenge was being built, there was also the great henge at Durrington Walls (p.133), the site of a large Neolithic settlement and several timber monuments, including nearby Woodhenge. The Avenue, leading from Stonehenge to the River Avon and the recently discovered West Amesbury Henge, was also built at this time. After major construction activities at Stonehenge ended, hundreds of early Bronze Age round barrows were constructed in the surrounding area, particularly on ridges overlooking the monument.

By removing modern intrusions, the changes made by English Heritage do much to restore Stonehenge's relationship with these other prehistoric monuments, and with its surrounding landscape.

AN ENHANCED EXPERIENCE: YOUR VISIT TO STONEHENGE

It has taken English Heritage nearly 30 years of negotiations, setbacks and hard work to implement its vision – presenting and interpreting the world's most famous prehistoric monument in the way that the monument and our visitors deserve.

For decades the setting of Stonehenge has been marred by the close proximity of roads and buildings: and visitors have had to contend with inadequate cramped facilities and very limited interpretation.

Now this has been remedied. In 2014 visits to Stonehenge will be transformed.

THE STONES: RESTORED DIGNITY, ENHANCED APPROACH

Stonehenge itself will always be the core and focus of any visit. Re-united with its ancient processional approach, the Avenue, by the removal of the nearby road, and free from the clutter of buildings and car parks, the monument can now be reached by frequent shuttle vehicles from the new visitor centre. This is 2km (1¼ miles) away and invisible from Stonehenge.

Visitors will be transported to the stones on the visitor shuttle which takes about 10 minutes.

The visitor shuttle makes a stop halfway at Fargo Plantation, where you can choose to disembark. From there you can follow a path to an information point introducing the Stonehenge landscape and the other monuments that are still visible. From here you can walk the rest of the way to Stonehenge, taking in prehistoric monuments dating from about 3600 to 1500 BC, including the Stonehenge Cursus and Cursus Barrows.

Stonehenge is surrounded by 827 hectares of land cared for by the National Trust, with visible remains of many different types of prehistoric monuments. By exploring the Stonehenge landscape, you will appreciate the remarkable setting of these ancient sites. You can even approach Stonehenge using the route that prehistoric people may have used – up the ceremonial Avenue. Large areas of the landscape are owned by the National Trust and have 'permissive access', which means you are free to explore. The key sites are marked on the orientation leaflet, and interpretation panels at the monuments help to explain them.

Walking in the Stonehenge landscape is undemanding, but sturdy shoes and suitable clothing are recommended. (Walking is recommended only from July onwards, after the removal of the old visitor facilities has been completed).

THE VISITOR CENTRE EXHIBITIONS

You can find out about Stonehenge and its surrounding monuments at the new environmentally-sensitive visitor centre. Simple, elegant and reflecting the rolling landscape which surrounds it, the building has glass and sweet chestnut timber 'pods', covered by a canopy on slender columns, its edges perforated to cast dappled shade.

Within the visitor centre is an exhibition gallery which tells the story of Stonehenge. An immersive 360° introductory film gives visitors the experience of being inside the stone circle, both now and when it was first built. The winter and summer solstices, the passage of time and the changing seasons are all represented.

Large showcases display archaeological treasures excavated from Stonehenge and other monuments and sites in the surrounding landscape. These include the antler and stone tools used in its construction, pottery and flint tools from the settlement at Durrington Walls, and decorated pots and rich jewellery from surrounding burial mounds. These objects give glimpses of the lives of the people who lived in the area before, during and after Stonehenge was built. A huge widescreen film shows how the landscape around Stonehenge changed through prehistory, and a series of films show some of the different theories about the meaning of Stonehenge.

Also inside is a temporary gallery, which will host a series of changing exhibitions focusing on a variety of stories relating to Stonehenge (see New for 2014 on p.135).

An outdoor gallery features an example sarsen and bluestone, and a full-scale sarsen interactive. There will also be several reconstructed Neolithic houses, based on the discovery of houses dating from the time of Stonehenge at Durrington Walls. Due to be completed by Easter 2014, the houses will provide an opportunity to see the technology and lifestyles of the people who built Stonehenge.

IMPROVED FACILITIES

Even the most determined discoverers need food and relaxation, provided by immensely improved facilities housed in the visitor centre, with views over the landscape. The stylish new café has indoor seating for 110 and canopied outdoor seating for 60; the spacious shop has plenty of room for browsing books, gifts and souvenirs, many exclusive to Stonehenge. There is also a multi-functional education room for school and community group visitors.

The vastly enhanced experience of visiting Stonehenge is something you simply must try for yourself. With so much more to see and do, make sure you allow plenty of time for your visit.

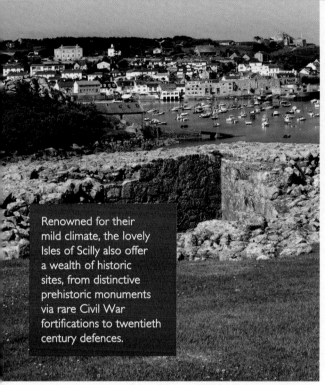

Renowned for their mild climate, the lovely Isles of Scilly also offer a wealth of historic sites, from distinctive prehistoric monuments via rare Civil War fortifications to twentieth century defences.

THE HERITAGE OF SCILLY

VISIT US

Bus: Details from St Mary's TIC on 01720 422536

Tel: 0117 975 0700 (Regional office)

OPENING TIMES

All EH properties on the Scillies are open at any reasonable daylight hours

The stunningly beautiful Isles of Scilly hold vast arrays of archaeological riches both above and below sea level. English Heritage recognises the importance of promoting this unique cultural landscape, and provides expert advice and significant funding to regeneration and conservation projects throughout the Isles.

This compact archipelago of about 100 islands lies around 28 miles to the south-west of Land's End. None of them is any bigger than three miles across and only five are inhabited. Despite their landmass of only 16 square kilometres (6.18 square miles), these islands contain a remarkable number of historic sites. These range from traditional farmhouses and dwellings to ritual burial monuments, cist grave cemeteries and Romano-Celtic shrines. Early settlements provide evidence of a distinctive Scillonian culture which thrived in the island group 2000 years ago. More recently, defensive monuments constructed during the Civil War and the Second World War stand as testament to the strategic importance of the islands. The Gulf Stream keeps the climate warm, enabling exotic plants and wildlife to thrive.

King Charles' Castle
Cromwell's Castle
Old Blockhouse
St Martin's
New Grimsby
Bryher
Tresco
Eastern Isles
Bants Carn Burial Chamber
Innisidgen Burial Chambers
Samson
St Mary's
Harry's Walls
Garrison Walls
Hugh Town
Porth Hellick Down
Annet
Gugh
St Agnes
Western Isles

BANT'S CARN BURIAL CHAMBER AND HALANGY DOWN ANCIENT VILLAGE
ST MARY'S, ISLES OF SCILLY

The remains a Romano-British village in a wonderfully scenic location. On the hill above stands a Bronze Age burial mound with entrance passage and inner chamber.

OPENING TIMES
Any reasonable daylight hours

VISIT US
Direction: 1 mile N of Hugh Town

ACQ.1950

MAP Page 336 (5B)
OS Map 203, 101: SV910123

CROMWELL'S CASTLE
TRESCO, ISLES OF SCILLY

Standing on a rocky promontory guarding the lovely anchorage between Bryher and Tresco, this round tower is one of the few surviving Cromwellian fortifications in Britain, built after the conquest of the Royalist Scillies in 1651.

OPENING TIMES
Any reasonable daylight hours

VISIT US
Direction: On the shoreline, approach with care, ¾ mile NW of New Grimsby

ACQ.1950

MAP Page 336 (4A)
OS Map 203, 101: SV882159

GARRISON WALLS
ST MARY'S, ISLES OF SCILLY

You can enjoy a two-hour walk alongside the ramparts of these defensive walls and earthworks, dating from the 16th to 18th centuries. Other remains include Elizabethan Star Castle and defences from both World Wars.

GARRISON WALLS

OPENING TIMES
Any reasonable daylight hours

VISIT US
Direction: Around the headland W of Hugh Town

ACQ.1973

MAP Page 336 (5A)
OS Map 203, 101: SV898104

HARRY'S WALLS
ST MARY'S, ISLES OF SCILLY

An unfinished artillery fort, built above St Mary's Pool harbour in 1552-53.

OPENING TIMES
Any reasonable daylight hours

VISIT US
Direction: ¼ mile NE of Hugh Town

ACQ.1950   P

MAP Page 336 (5B)
OS Map 203, 101: SV909109

INNISIDGEN LOWER AND UPPER BURIAL CHAMBERS
ST MARY'S, ISLES OF SCILLY

Two Bronze Age communal burial cairns of Scillonian type, with fine views. The upper cairn is the best preserved on the islands.

OPENING TIMES
Any reasonable daylight hours

VISIT US
Direction: 1¾ miles NE of Hugh Town

ACQ.1950

MAP Page 336 (5B)
OS Map 203, 101: SV922127

KING CHARLES'S CASTLE
TRESCO, ISLES OF SCILLY

The ruins of a mid 16th-century coastal artillery fort, later garrisoned – hence the name –

by Civil War Royalists. Reached from New Grimsby by footpath.

OPENING TIMES
Any reasonable daylight hours

VISIT US
Direction: Located ¾ mile NW of New Grimsby. Coastal location, approach with care

ACQ.1950

MAP Page 336 (4A)
OS Map 203, 101: SV882161

OLD BLOCKHOUSE
TRESCO, ISLES OF SCILLY

Substantial remains of a small 16th-century gun tower protecting Old Grimsby harbour, vigorously defended during the Civil War.

OPENING TIMES
Any reasonable daylight hours

VISIT US
Direction: Located on Blockhouse Point, at the S end of Old Grimsby harbour

ACQ.1950

MAP Page 336 (4A)
OS Map 203, 101: SV897155

PORTH HELLICK DOWN BURIAL CHAMBER
ST MARY'S, ISLES OF SCILLY

A large and imposing Scillonian Bronze Age entrance grave, with kerb, inner passage and burial chamber all clearly visible.

OPENING TIMES
Any reasonable daylight hours

VISIT US
Direction: 1¾ miles E of Hugh Town

ACQ.1950

MAP Page 336 (5B)
OS Map 203, 101: SV928108

DISCOUNTED ATTRACTIONS: **SOUTH WEST**

Use your membership to get exclusive discounts at these independent attractions in the South West. Please remember to show your card as proof of membership.

Discount applies to:

KEY	⚅ MEMBERS	OVP OVP HOLDERS	👪? NO. OF MEMBER'S CHILDREN

Terms and conditions may apply, so make sure you check the individual pages on our website or call the individual property for more details.

⚅ 👪1

AMERICAN MUSEUM
Bath BA2 7BD

Home to the finest collection of Americana outside the United States; features 17th-19th century Period Rooms, outstanding quilt collection, inspiring Folk Art and Native American craft.
www.americanmuseum.org
Tel. 01225 460503

⚅ OVP 👪3

THE ARTHURIAN CENTRE
Cornwall PL32 9TT

Beautiful walk to the unique, 1500-year-old 'King Arthur's Stone' on the site of Arthur and Mordred's last battle of 'Camlann'. Great visit for all ages. See website for details.
www.arthur-online.co.uk
Tel. 01840 213947

⚅

BATH ABBEY
Somerset BA1 1LT

There is nowhere else like Bath Abbey. Come and experience the special atmosphere of this holy and uplifting place.

www.bathabbey.org
Tel. 01225 422462

⚅ OVP 👪6

COLDHARBOUR MILL WORKING WOOL MUSEUM – Devon EX15 3EE

This 200-year old spinning mill still produces knitting yarns and weaves tartan cloth as it tells the story of the once flourishing West Country woollen industry.
www.coldharbourmill.org.uk
Tel. 01884 840960

OVP 👪2

DORSET COUNTY MUSEUM
Dorset DT1 1XA

Award-winning Museum of Dorset with galleries exploring all aspects of Dorset's history. Discover the Jurassic Coast, Thomas Hardy and artefacts excavated from Maiden Castle.
www.dorsetcountymuseum.org
Tel. 01305 262735

⚅ OVP

EDEN PROJECT
Cornwall PL24 2SG

Trek through steamy jungles and experience the largest rainforest in captivity. Meander through the fragrant Mediterranean and admire the splendour of the largest conservatories in the world.
www.edenproject.com
Tel. 01726 811911

DISCOUNTED ATTRACTIONS:

Use your membership to get exclusive discounts at these independent attractions in the South West. Please remember to show your card as proof of membership.

25% DISCOUNT ON ENTRY

⊞ OVP 🚹 6

FLEET AIR ARM MUSEUM
Somerset BA22 8HT

Get up close and personal with Europe's largest collection of naval aircraft and see the first British Concorde.

www.fleetairarm.com
Tel. 01935 840565

50% DISCOUNT ON ENTRY

⊞ OVP 🚹 6

KENTS CAVERN PREHISTORIC CAVES
Devon TQ1 2JF

Britain's oldest human fossil was found at Kents Cavern, making it one of the top Stone Age sites in the world.

www.kents-cavern.co.uk
Tel. 01803 215136

FREE ENTRY

⊞ OVP 🚹 6

LULWORTH CASTLE & PARK
Dorset BH20 5QS

Enjoy wide open spaces, historic buildings, stunning landscapes, park and woodland walks. Castle displays, children's activity room and unrivalled views.

www.lulworth.com
Tel. 0845 450 1054

DISCOUNT ON ENTRY

⊞ OVP

NATIONAL MARITIME MUSEUM CORNWALL
Cornwall TR11 3QY

Celebrating the sea, boats and Cornwall, this multi-award winning museum has 15 galleries of interactive exhibits over five floors.
www.nmmc.co.uk
Tel. 01326 313388

DISCOUNT ON ENTRY

⊞ OVP 🚹 6

POWDERHAM CASTLE
Devon EX6 8JQ

Family home of the Earl of Devon. Entertaining tours, stunning views, play area, animals, treasure trails, nature trails, shops, tearoom and Toby Buckland's plant centre.
www.powderham.co.uk
Tel. 01626 890243

TOWER TOURS

⊞ 🚹 3

SALISBURY CATHEDRAL & MAGNA CARTA
Wiltshire SP1 2EF

Britain's finest medieval cathedral, with the tallest spire, home to Magna Carta 1215, celebrating its 800th anniversary in 2015.
www.salisburycathedral.org.uk
Tel. 01722 555156

SOUTH WEST CONTINUED

Discount applies to:

KEY | ⊞ **MEMBERS** | OVP **OVP HOLDERS** | 🕅? **NO. OF MEMBER'S CHILDREN**

Terms and conditions may apply, so make sure you check the individual pages on our website or call the individual property for more details.

⊞ OVP 🕅6

SALISBURY AND SOUTH WILTSHIRE MUSEUM
Wiltshire SP1 2EN
Situated in the medieval King's House, within the glorious setting of Salisbury Cathedral Close. Fantastic collections, events and exhibitions.
www.salisburymuseum.org.uk
Tel. 01722 332151

⊞ OVP 🕅4

SHERBORNE CASTLE
Dorset DT9 5NR
Built by Sir Walter Raleigh in 1594, the castle displays magnificent state rooms, Raleigh's kitchen and a museum. Superb 'Capability' Brown lake landscape and gardens.
www.sherbornecastle.com
Tel. 01935 812072 – Ext 2

⊞ OVP 🕅1

STEAM – MUSEUM OF THE GREAT WESTERN RAILWAY
Wiltshire SN2 2EY
Climb aboard and follow the fantastic journey of the Great Western Railway; a great family day out! *Offer also applies on entry to nearby Lydiard House & Walled Garden.
www.steam-museum.org.uk
www.lydiardpark.org.uk

⊞ 🕅6

SUDELEY CASTLE
Gloucestershire GL54 5JD
England's only private castle to have a queen – Katherine Parr – buried within its award-winning grounds. NEW: admission to private rooms, some never opened to the public before.
www.sudeleycastle.co.uk
Tel. 01242 602308

⊞ OVP 🕅6

WHEAL MARTYN
Cornwall PL26 8XG
UK's only China Clay mining Museum, Cornwall's largest waterwheel, preserved Victorian clay works, woodland walks, vintage vehicles, mining in action, café, shop, dogs welcome.
www.wheal-martyn.com
Tel. 01726 850362

⊞ OVP 🕅6

WILTSHIRE MUSEUM
Wiltshire SN10 1NS
Dazzling new Prehistory display. Gallery features gold from the time of Stonehenge, including the ceremonial finds from Bush Barrow, Britain's richest Bronze Age burial.
www.wiltshiremuseum.org.uk
Tel. 01380 727369

EAST OF ENGLAND

Wrest Park

Keep up to date with
events, news and offers
www.english-heritage.
org.uk/newsletter

Framlingham Castle

33 25 •26
     24 22 Cromer

31
King's Lynn   •36   Norfolk
      29• •30
             •32
Wisbech   Downham Market   Norwich•   28
Peterborough   34• Great
8•   23• •27 Yarmouth
                                           •37
                                                  •Lowestoft

      41 •35
Cambridgeshire   40• •39
                    •38

      Ely 7   •Southwold
Huntingdon •5
         •5   47   Bury St Edmunds 49• •43   •45
Cambridge Newmarket •42
                          Suffolk   •Aldeburgh
Bedfordshire   •48
  •1
Bedford   •6   •46 Ipswich
•3   •Felixstowe
2• •4   9•Saffron Walden   15•   •44
      •16   Colchester 10 Harwich
Luton Stevenage   14•11
              Essex
         Hertford   •Clacton
19• 20• St Albans •Harlow Chelmsford
Hemel Hempstead 21
    •18 •13
Hertfordshire
         Basildon
              •12
         •17 Southend
Tilbury

Details of local public transport information in England are available from Traveline
www.traveline.org.uk or call 0871 200 2233.

HIGHLIGHTS FOR 2014/15 IN THE **EAST OF ENGLAND**

Audley End House & Gardens: newly-opened for 2014, the Nursery Suite and Coal Gallery join Audley's behind-the-scenes attractions.

Wrest Park: a garden-lovers' paradise, Wrest Park also offers a new 'Uncovered Treasures' tour of rarely-seen artefacts this year.

Framlingham Castle: an impressive medieval castle with Tudor connections, in an attractive East Anglian market town.

PROPERTIES

BEDFORDSHIRE
1 Bushmead Priory
2 De Grey Mausoleum, Flitton
3 Houghton House
4 Wrest Park

CAMBRIDGESHIRE
5 Denny Abbey and the Farmland Museum
6 Duxford Chapel
7 Isleham Priory Church
8 Longthorpe Tower

ESSEX
9 Audley End House and Gardens
10 Colchester, St Botolph's Priory
11 Colchester, St John's Abbey Gate
12 Hadleigh Castle
13 Hill Hall
14 Lexden Earthworks and Bluebottle Grove
15 Mistley Towers
16 Prior's Hall Barn, Widdington

17 Tilbury Fort
18 Waltham Abbey Gatehouse and Bridge

HERTFORDSHIRE
19 Berkhamsted Castle
20 Old Gorhambury House
21 Roman Wall, St Albans

NORFOLK
22 Baconsthorpe Castle
23 Berney Arms Windmill
24 Binham Market Cross
25 Binham Priory
26 Blakeney Guildhall
27 Burgh Castle
28 Caister Roman Fort
29 Castle Acre Priory
30 Castle Acre Priory, Castle and Bailey Gate
31 Castle Rising Castle
32 Cow Tower, Norwich
33 Creake Abbey

34 Great Yarmouth Row Houses & Greyfriars' Cloisters
35 Grime's Graves – prehistoric flint mine
36 North Elmham Chapel
37 St Olave's Priory
38 Thetford, Church of the Holy Sepulchre
39 Thetford Priory
40 Thetford Warren Lodge
41 Weeting Castle

SUFFOLK
42 Bury St Edmunds Abbey
43 Framlingham Castle
44 Landguard Fort
45 Leiston Abbey
46 Lindsey St James's Chapel
47 Moulton Packhorse Bridge
48 Orford Castle
49 Saxtead Green Post Mill

Remember to check opening times before you visit any of our properties
www.english-heritage.org.uk/daysout

BEDFORDSHIRE

BUSHMEAD PRIORY
BEDFORDSHIRE – MK44 2LD

A rare survival of the complete refectory of an Augustinian priory, with fine timber roof and notable 14th-century wall paintings.

NON-MEMBERS

Adult	£5.90
Concession	£5.30
Child	£3.50

OPENING TIMES
1 May-31 Aug, entry on the first Sat of the month only. Tel: 01525 860000 (Option 2) to book

VISIT US
Direction: Located off B660, 2 miles S of Bolnhurst

Train: St Neots 6 miles

Bus: Grant Palmer 29

ACQ.1974

MAP Page 340 (4E)
OS Map 153, 225: TL115607

CHURCH OF ST MARGARET OF ANTIOCH, KNOTTING
BEDFORDSHIRE
MK44 1AF

© CCT

This small rural church tucked into the landscape is quintessentially English. The spiked chancel gates were added in 1637 to stop cockfighting and betting, for which the rector of the day was de-frocked! In the churchyard stands a First World War memorial to the men of Knotting.

CHURCH OF ST MARGARET OF ANTIOCH, KNOTTING

Owned and managed by The Churches Conservation Trust.

OPENING TIMES
Open daily during daylight hours

VISIT US
Train: Wellingborough 6¾ miles

Bus: Grant Palmer 26

15 mins from Chichele College

MAP Page 340 (4E)
OS Map 153, 224: TL004636

DE GREY MAUSOLEUM, FLITTON
BEDFORDSHIRE – MK45 5EJ

Among the largest sepulchral chapels attached to any English church, this cruciform mausoleum houses a remarkable sequence of 17 sculpted and effigied monuments, spanning nearly 250 years (1614-1859), to the de Grey family of Wrest Park. You can download the audio tour prior to visiting from the English Heritage website.

OPENING TIMES
Weekends only. Contact the key keeper in advance: Mrs Stimson, 3 Highfield Road, Flitton MK45 5EB. Tel: 01525 860094

DE GREY MAUSOLEUM, FLITTON

VISIT US
Direction: Attached to Flitton church; through Flitton, on an unclassified road 1½ miles W of A6 at Silsoe

Train: Flitwick 2 miles

Bus: A limited service is provided by Flittabus (of Ampthill); Cedar service 146 (Fri only); Centrebus 20; Grant Palmer service 44 & 77 (Tue only)

Tel: 01525 860094 (weekends only)

ACQ.1979

MAP Page 340 (5E)
OS Map 153, 193: TL059359

HOUGHTON HOUSE
BEDFORDSHIRE – MK45 2EZ

The shell of a 17th-century mansion commanding magnificent views, reputedly the inspiration for the 'House Beautiful' in John Bunyan's *Pilgrim's Progress*. Built around 1615 for Mary, Dowager Countess of Pembroke, in a mixture of Jacobean and Classical styles; the ground floors of two Italianate loggias survive, possibly the work of Inigo Jones.

Information panels describe the house, its owners and the surrounding hunting estate. A free downloadable audio tour is available from the English Heritage website.

OPENING TIMES
Any reasonable daylight hours

VISIT US
Direction: 1 mile NE of Ampthill off B530, 8 miles S of Bedford

Train: Flitwick or Stewartby, both 3 miles

Bus: Stagecoach in Northants service 42; Grant Palmer service 42, 44, 197 & 200; Flittabus services

Tel: 01604 735464

ACQ.1938

MAP Page 340 (5E)
OS Map 153, 193: TL039395

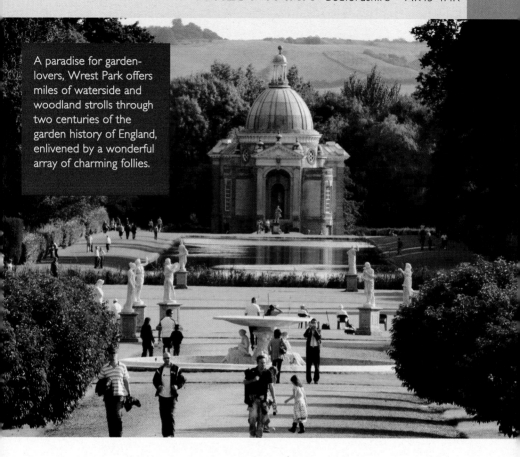

A paradise for garden-lovers, Wrest Park offers miles of waterside and woodland strolls through two centuries of the garden history of England, enlivened by a wonderful array of charming follies.

VISIT US

Address: Wrest Park, Silsoe, Luton, Bedfordshire

Direction: ¾ mile E of Silsoe off A6, 10 miles S of Bedford

Train: Flitwick 4 miles

Bus: Grant Palmer 44 & 77 (Tue only); Cedar 146 (Fri only); Flittabus

Tel: 01525 860000

NON-MEMBERS

Adult	£9.00
Concession	£8.10
Child	£5.40
Family	£23.40

OPENING TIMES

1 Apr-30 Sep, daily	10am-6pm
1 Oct-2 Nov, daily	10am-5pm
3 Nov-15 Feb, Sat-Sun	10am-4pm
16-20 Feb, daily	10am-4pm
21 Feb-29 Mar, Sat-Sun	10am-4pm
24-26 Dec, 31 Dec-1 Jan	Closed

Last entry one hour before closing. The house may be closed if an event is booked. Entry to the gardens may also be restricted earlier than the usual 'one hour before closing' time, although access to the gardens for those who have already arrived will continue until normal closing times. Please call to check

ACQ.1946

Mobility cart available for disabled visitors.

MAP Page 340 (5E)
OS Map 153, 193: TL091355

There is now even more to see at magnificent Wrest Park, English Heritage's latest star garden attraction. Wrest Park is among the most vastly impressive of all English gardens. Telling the story of England's love affair with landscape, it is a unique place displaying over two hundred years of garden history and design.

Wrest's 90-acre gardens were developed over more than two centuries by the aristocratic de Grey family,

CONTINUED ▶

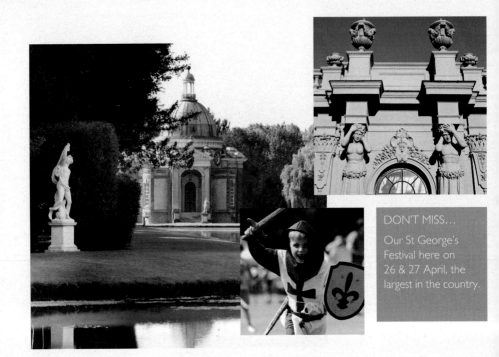

DON'T MISS...
Our St George's
Festival here on
26 & 27 April, the
largest in the country.

and have now been re-awakened in an
ambitious 20-year-long restoration project
supported by the Heritage Lottery Fund.

The gardens are enlivened throughout by
charming architectural features, unexpected
vistas and a wealth of statuary. More
sculptures, too delicate to remain outdoors,
are now displayed in the Dairy, a lovely 1830s
building now restored.

Visitors can stroll beside the Long Water to
the beautiful Baroque 'Archer Pavilion': the
focus of the main garden walks, it still retains its
outstanding interior decoration. The intricate
woodland paths of the 18th-century Great
Garden reveal Classical altars, a Chinese
Temple and a secluded Dogs' Cemetery for
de Grey family pets. And yet more walks
lead to the splendid 1830s Orangery; the
colonnaded Bowling Green House; and
Jemima, Marchioness Grey's enchanting Bath
House, disguised as a thatched Classical ruin.

Nearer the great mansion are the Rose
Garden and the vibrantly-planted Italian
Garden: while immediately below the terrace
the formal French Parterre has now been
restored to its appearance as at the turn
of the 20th century.

In addition to the gardens, some of the ground
floor of the French-style mansion, designed and
built by Thomas, Earl de Grey in 1834-39, is
open to visitors. Its unfurnished but opulently
decorated State Rooms include the Library
which served as the de Grey family's living
room, and the Drawing Room with its ceiling
paintings of wispily-draped 1830s ladies.

Countess Henrietta's Sitting Room, chintzily
furnished as it may have appeared in the
1840s, looks through to a lofty Conservatory,
unusually built as an integral part of the
mansion. An interactive exhibition traces the
history of the de Grey family and their estate.

One of the artefacts from the
Uncovered treasures tour.

NEW FOR 2014

Uncovered treasures:
Behind the scenes artefacts tour

English Heritage's archaeology collections
store at Wrest Park is home to thousands
of special and unique objects. Join our
collections team behind the scenes for
the opportunity to see some of our
treasures you don't normally get to see.
The collection spans over 2000 years of
England's history, from Roman tombstones
and Medieval cannon balls to 17th-century
brooches and Victorian fireplaces. We look
after these unique finds – great and small –
so that future generations can appreciate
them. Find out how English Heritage deals
with the challenges of caring for these
precious objects, and learn more about our
amazing sites. Tours take place on the first
Monday of every month – contact Visitor
Reception for details.

The Visitor Centre in the Walled
Garden also offers a spacious
café with indoor and outdoor
tables, overlooking a
children's play area inspired
by the house and
gardens.

Please note:
No flash
photography or
stiletto heels in
the house.

🆃 Available for
corporate and
private hire

🅰 Licensed for civil
wedding ceremonies

CAMBRIDGESHIRE

ALL SAINTS' CHURCH, CAMBRIDGE

CAMBRIDGESHIRE
CB5 8BP

© Paul Raeside
BBC Homes & Antiques magazine

The pale stone spire of All Saints' is a prominent landmark in the heart of Cambridge. The interior is a dramatic blast of colour and pattern – light gleams through stained-glass windows by leading Arts and Crafts artists and almost every surface has painted, stencilled or gilded decoration.

Owned and managed by The Churches Conservation Trust.

OPENING TIMES

Open daily during daylight hours

VISIT US

Train: Cambridge 1 mile

Bus: Stagecoach Routes 1, 2, 5 & 55

15 mins from Denny Abbey and the Farmland Museum

MAP Page 341 (4F)
OS Map 154, 209: TL453587

DENNY ABBEY AND THE FARMLAND MUSEUM CAMBRIDGESHIRE – CB25 9PQ

Founded in 1159 as a Benedictine monastery, Denny Abbey then became a retirement home for elderly Knights Templars. After the Templars' suppression for alleged heresy in 1308, it next passed to the Countess of Pembroke, who converted part into a house and established in the rest a convent of 'Poor Clare' Franciscan nuns. This in turn was dissolved by Henry VIII in 1539, whereafter the buildings became a farm until the 1960s, with the nuns' great refectory as its barn. Among its tenants was Thomas Hobson, the horse-hirer whose refusal to allow customers to select their mounts gave rise to the expression 'Hobson's choice'.

All these changes are still traceable in the building: they are now interpreted for visitors by graphic panels illustrated by local artist Anne Biggs, together with a time-line tracing the site's history from 4000 BC, a viewing platform and displays of site finds. Family-friendly activities include imaginative hands-on interactives about medieval tiles, stained glass and arches.

Denny's later farming story is continued by Walnut

Tree Cottage, furnished as a labourer's home of the 1940s. The site's Farmland Museum also features a fenman's hut, farrier's hut and wheelwright's workshops, a village shop display and many other aspects of Cambridgeshire rural life.

Managed by the Farmland Museum Trust.

NON-MEMBERS

Museum and Abbey

Adult	£5.00	Concession	£4.00
Child	£3.00	Family	£13.00

Free entry for children under 5

Museum charge

Adult	£4.00	Concession	£3.50
Child	£2.00	Family	£9.00

Free entry for children under 5

The abbey is free for members with reduced entry for the museum. There will be a premium payable by all visitors, including members, on special event days – please check www.dennyfarmlandmuseum.org.uk for details

OPENING TIMES

1 Apr-2 Nov, Mon-Fri	12pm-5pm
Sat-Sun & Bank Hols	10.30am-5pm

VISIT US

Direction: Located 6 miles N of Cambridge on A10

Train: Waterbeach 3 miles

Bus: Stagecoach Cambridge 9

Tel: 01223 860988

Disabled access (museum and abbey ground floor only).

Dogs on leads (restricted areas only).

Tearoom/restaurant (weekends and bank holidays only).

MAP Page 341 (4F)
OS Map 154, 226: TL492685

DUXFORD CHAPEL
CAMBRIDGESHIRE – CB2 4NL

A modest but complete and attractive 14th-century chantry chapel, perhaps originally a hospital.

OPENING TIMES
Any reasonable daylight hours

VISIT US
Direction: Adjacent to Whittlesford station off A505

Train: Whittlesford, adjacent

Bus: Stagecoach Cambridge Citi 7 & Whippet 7A. Also Myall service 101 (Tue only) & 132 (Sun only)

Tel: 01604 735464

MAP Page 341 (4F)
OS Map 154, 209: TL485473

ISLEHAM PRIORY CHURCH
CAMBRIDGESHIRE – IP28 7DP

The best example in England of a small Norman Benedictine priory church, surviving in a surprisingly unaltered state despite later conversion into a barn.

OPENING TIMES
Any reasonable daylight hours. Contact the key keeper, Mrs R Burton, 18 Festival Road, Isleham CB7 5SY – 5 min walk

VISIT US
Direction: Located in centre of Isleham, 16 miles NE of Cambridge on B1104

Train: Newmarket 8½ miles, Ely 9 miles

Bus: Freedom Travel service 203 (Tue and Sat only) & 204

Tel: 01604 735464

MAP Page 341 (4G)
OS Map 143, 226: TL642743

LONGTHORPE TOWER
CAMBRIDGESHIRE – PE3 6LU

Longthorpe Tower displays one of the most complete and important sets of 14th-century domestic wall paintings in northern Europe. This varied 'spiritual encyclopaedia' of worldly and religious subjects includes the Wheel of Life, the Nativity and King David.

Managed by Vivacity Culture & Leisure.

NON-MEMBERS

Adult	£3.00
Concession	£2.00
Child	£2.00
Family	£8.00

There will be a premium payable by all visitors, including members, on special event days – please visit www.vivacity-peterborough.com/museums-and-heritage/longthorpe-tower for details

OPENING TIMES

5 Apr-31 Jul, Sat-Sun & Bank Hols	10am-5pm
1-31 Aug, Thu-Sun & Bank Hols	10am-5pm
1 Sep-31 Oct, Sat-Sun	10am-5pm

Last admission 30 mins before closing

A guide or costumed interpreter will be on site on the first Sunday of the month, Apr-Oct

VISIT US
Direction: Located 2 miles W of Peterborough on A47

Train: Peterborough 1½ miles

Bus: Location is a short walk from Peterborough Bus Station. Centrebus service 9 & R47; Stagecoach Citi 2, Citi 4, 23 & X4

Tel: 01733 864663

LONGTHORPE TOWER

New guidebook.

Parking (not at site).

No wheelchair access.

MAP Page 340 (3E)
OS Map 142, 227/235: TL162984

ST PETER'S CHURCH, CAMBRIDGE
CAMBRIDGESHIRE
CB3 0AJ

© Cameron Newham

Tiny, tall-spired St Peter's is tucked into a quiet corner of Cambridge, a haven of tranquillity amid the busy streets around it. Mermen, carved into the stone font, may have an ancient link to St Peter, patron saint of fishermen.

Owned and managed by The Churches Conservation Trust.

OPENING TIMES
Open Mon-Fri during the morning; other times key available from Kettle's Yard Gallery next door

VISIT US
Train: Cambridge 2 miles

Bus: Drummer Street Bus Station 10 mins walk from church. Many buses pass close by

30 mins from Audley End House and Gardens

MAP Page 341 (4F)
OS Map 154, 209: TL445592

A noble Jacobean mansion amid lovely gardens, Audley End also provides unrivalled behind-the-scenes experiences of Victorian servants' lives in the kitchens, stables and nurseries of a great country house.

VISIT US

Address: Audley End House & Gardens, Off London Road, Saffron Walden, Essex

Direction: 1 mile W of Saffron Walden on B1383 (M11 exit 8 or 10)

Train: Audley End 1¼ miles. Note: Footpath is beside busy main road

Bus: Stephensons 6, 59 & 313; C.J. Myall service 101; 132 (Sun only); TGM 301; Viceroy 34, 59, 590; all pass within ¼ mile of entrance

Tel: 01799 522842 (info line)

Local Tourist Information
Saffron Walden: 01799 524002
Cambridge: 01223 464732

NON-MEMBERS

Adult	£15.40
Concession	£13.90
Child	£9.20
Family	£40.00

OPENING TIMES

House

1 Apr-30 Sep, daily	12pm-5pm
1 Oct-2 Nov, daily	12pm-4pm

Stables, Service Wing and Gardens

1 Apr-30 Sep, daily	10am-6pm
1 Oct-2 Nov, daily	10am-5pm
3 Nov-15 Feb, Sat-Sun	10am-4pm
16-20 Feb, daily	10am-4pm
21 Feb-29 Mar, Sat-Sun	10am-4pm
24-26 Dec, 31 Dec-1 Jan	Closed

Last entry to house one hour before closing. Gardens only prices available when house closed in winter (Nov-Mar)

The house will be accessible for guided tours only on certain days. Please call or check our website for more details

ACQ 1949

Disabled access (grounds, Great Hall, Stable Yard and Service Wing only. Please call for more information).

MAP Page 341 (5F)
OS Map 154, 195: TL525382

Among the most delightful of English Heritage's treasures, Audley End is the best place in the country to experience not only the sumptuous lifestyle enjoyed by the aristocratic owners of a great country house – but also how their indoor and outdoor servants made it happen.

The house takes its name from Sir Thomas Audley, Henry VIII's Lord Chancellor, who adapted suppressed Walden Abbey as his mansion. His grandson Thomas Howard, first Earl of Suffolk and James I's Lord Treasurer, rebuilt the house on a massive scale between 1603 and 1614. This immense double courtyard 'Palace of Audley End' was three times its present size, and one of the largest mansions in England: 'too big for a king', quipped James during a visit, 'though it might suit a Lord Treasurer'. But in 1618 Suffolk fell from favour, and his vast mansion went into decline.

Charles II bought Audley End in 1668 as a base for attending Newmarket races: his Queen Catherine of Braganza held court here that autumn. When repairs proved ruinously costly, William III returned Audley End to the Suffolk family in 1701. The witty and accomplished Henrietta Howard lived here, before leaving her 'obstinate, drunken and brutal' husband for a royal lover and her new Thames-side villa, Marble Hill House (see p.38).

After the Suffolk line died out in 1745, the estate was bought by the Countess of Portsmouth for her heir, later first Baron Braybrooke. He added a suite of neo-Classical rooms designed by Robert Adam and a Gothick chapel. Meanwhile, 'Capability' Brown was employed to remodel the grounds. Today the house's interior largely represents the taste of the third Baron Braybrooke, who redecorated many of its rooms in the Jacobean style during the 1820s. He installed his extensive picture collection and filled the rooms with inherited furnishings.

The Service Wing

The Victorian Service Wing gives a unique insight into the 'below stairs' working of this great household during the 1880s. The kitchens, dairy,

NEW FOR 2014

Even more 'behind-the-scenes' areas of Audley End, never before seen by visitors, will be opened up in 2014.

The Nursery Suite, the private domain of the 3rd Lord Braybrooke's eight children and their entourage of nursemaids and governesses, will be recreated as it was in the 1830s. Household accounts, diaries and watercolours painted by the Braybrooke girls will reveal the sheltered world of aristocratic children. Hands-on features, including replica period toys and children's dressing-up clothes, will help families explore their nursery life.

Discreet devices ensured aristocratic residents' comfort without troubling their tranquillity. Audley End's unique Coal Gallery, which fuelled warmth and hot water for the mansion's upper floors, will also re-open for the very first time in 2014.

Many of the State Rooms will be re-presented, including the magnificent State Bed made for a royal visit by George III which never happened, and afterwards slept in by especially honoured guests. A piano will enliven the Library, and a roaring fire will burn in the Great Hall.

CONTINUED ▶

dry larder and laundries are fully equipped with original and reproduction Victorian fixtures and fittings, and vividly animated with lifelike sights and sounds, film projection and even examples of foods eaten in the era. They provide a strikingly atmospheric picture of daily life for the people who once toiled here – from butler down to dairy maid and lowly houseboy. Incorporating research into the real lives of the servants employed here, the Service Wing illustrates how familiar household tasks were conducted on a near-industrial scale for the Braybrooke family. Watch out for special days when visitors can see and hear from costumed interpreters cooking, washing and ironing in traditional ways (Every weekend, June-September plus other days throughout the year).

The Stables

The lovely gabled red-brick early 17th-century stables are another of Audley End's many attractions. Once housing the horses, grooms, coaches, and other equipment needed to service the demands of this great country house, they are now set as in the 1880s. The horses are back, and there are daily riding displays, plus talks, stables tours and hands-on demonstrations of grooming and horse-care, in which children can take part. Lively interactive displays trace the development of the estate, and allow visitors to 'virtually' meet its Victorian outdoor staff.

The Gardens

Audley End's park and fine gardens also offer a series of varied delights. Visitors can stroll by the lake through the cascaded Elysian Garden; walk up to the Classical Temple of Concord to view the house in its wonderful setting; visit the memorial to Polish 'underground' resistance soldiers who trained here in the Second World War; or admire the restored 19th-century formal parterre garden. For practical gardeners, Audley End's massive and renowned walled organic kitchen garden, growing fruit and vegetable varieties from Victorian times, is an unmissable attraction. Next to it are the children's play area and Cart Yard Café.

Please note: in some rooms, light levels are reduced to preserve vulnerable textiles and other collections. No photography or stiletto heels allowed in the house.

HOLIDAY COTTAGE AT AUDLEY END HOUSE AND GARDENS

Book a relaxing break in **Cambridge Lodge** here. Enjoy stunning views of the tranquil lake and manicured lawns, and stroll through the grounds in private once the gates have closed to the public.

COLCHESTER, ST BOTOLPH'S PRIORY
ESSEX – CO2 7EE

The remains of one of the first Augustinian priories in England, founded c. 1100. An impressive example of early Norman architecture, built in flint and re-used Roman brick, the church displays massive circular pillars and round arches and an elaborate west front. Later badly damaged by cannon fire during the Civil War siege of 1648.

Managed by Colchester Borough Council.

OPENING TIMES
Any reasonable daylight hours

VISIT US
Direction: Nr Colchester Town station

Train: Colchester Town, adjacent

Bus: Bus services to/from Colchester are provided by Beestons (of Hadleigh) Chambers (of Bures), First Essex, Hedingham Omnibuses, Regal Busways, Stephensons of Essex and Network Colchester. Priory is 2 minutes walk from the bus station

Tel: 01206 282929

ACQ.1912

MAP Page 341 (5H)
OS Map 168, 184: TL999249

COLCHESTER, ST JOHN'S ABBEY GATE
SEE FEATURE – PAGE 158

HADLEIGH CASTLE ESSEX – SS7 2AP

The romantic ruins of a royal castle, on a ridge overlooking the Essex marshes and the Thames estuary. The first castle was begun in about 1215 by Hubert de Burgh, King John's powerful Justiciar, probably as a towered octagonal enclosure. But in 1239 it was confiscated by Henry III, and thereafter remained in royal ownership or gift for over three centuries.

Conveniently accessible from London by royal barge, Hadleigh Castle was extensively rebuilt by Edward III during the 1360s, to which period most of the surviving remains belong. Edward's refurbished castle was intended partly to reinforce the defences of the Thames Estuary against French invasion: the towers looking towards the estuary would have presented a strong impression of power and security. Yet the now ageing king's main use of the castle was probably as a personal retreat, where he could stay in privacy and comfort: excavated remains of Edward's great hall, with its 'solar' or private withdrawing room, can still be seen here.

After Edward III's death in 1377 his successors took little interest in Hadleigh, whose tenancy passed to a series of mainly absentee royal relations, including three of Henry VIII's queens. Eventually the castle was sold in 1551, and substantially demolished for building materials. Yet Edward III's two big eastern drum towers still remain, the south-east tower – allegedly used by Georgian revenue men looking out for smugglers – still commandingly standing three storeys high.

OPENING TIMES
Any reasonable daylight hours

VISIT US
Direction: ¾ mile S of A13 at Hadleigh

Train: Leigh-on-Sea 1½ miles by footpath

Bus: Arriva service 1 & 5; Regal Busways 3, 3A, 3B; First 21, 21A, 21B, 25B, 26, 27, 27A, 27X & 28; all within ½ mile

Tel: 01604 735464

ACQ.1948

Castle access is restricted as entry is via a 'kissing gate' only.

MAP Page 341 (7G)
OS Map 178, 175: TQ810860

COLCHESTER, ST JOHN'S ABBEY GATE
ESSEX – CO1 1RQ

This pinnacled gatehouse, elaborately decorated in East Anglian 'flushwork', is the sole survivor of the wealthy Benedictine abbey of St John. It was built c. 1400 to strengthen the abbey's defences following the Peasants' Revolt. Later part of the mansion of the Royalist Lucas family, the gatehouse was bombarded and stormed by Parliamentarian soldiers during the Civil War siege.

Managed by Colchester Borough Council.

OPENING TIMES
Any reasonable daylight hours

VISIT US
Direction: S side of central Colchester

Train: Colchester Town ¼ mile

Bus: Bus services to/from Colchester are provided by Beestons (of Hadleigh) Chambers (of Bures), First Essex, Hedingham Omnibuses, Regal Busways, Stephensons of Essex and Network Colchester

Tel: 01206 282929

ACQ.1983

MAP Page 341 (5H)
OS Map 168, 184: TL998248

HILL HALL ESSEX – CM16 7QQ

Built in 1568-77 for the scholar, diplomat and politician Sir Thomas Smith, this splendid Elizabethan mansion is among the earliest Renaissance houses in England. Its multi-columned Classical-style exterior follows examples Smith had admired on his ambassadorial travels in France and Flanders.

Its interior is adorned with very rare survivals of high quality figurative wall paintings, which despite damage while the Hall was a prison in 1947-52 and by fire in 1969 remain among the gems of English Heritage's collection. Now mainly visible in two rooms, they seemingly once extended throughout the house. One series depicts the Old Testament story of Hezekiah and the other (which imitates contemporary tapestries) the Classical legend of Cupid and Psyche. Expertly painted, they may be by Flemish artists, or English imitators:

Sir Thomas himself may have overseen their design.

Hill Hall has now been divided into private houses, but parts remain open to the public by prior arrangement.

NON-MEMBERS
Adult	£5.90
Concession	£5.30
Child	£3.50

OPENING TIMES
1 Apr-30 Sep. Pre-booked guided tours only

Tel: 01799 522842 to book

VISIT US
Direction: 3 miles SE of Epping. Entrance ½ mile N of Theydon Mount Church

Bus: Closest bus services are Arriva 375; Go Ahead Blue Triangle 575 to Passingford Bridge (2¾ miles)

Train: Epping or Theydon Bois 2½ miles

ACQ.1976

MAP Page 341 (6F)
OS Map 167/177, 174: TQ489995

LEXDEN EARTHWORKS
– CO3 5EF BLUEBOTTLE GROVE – CO3 4DU ESSEX

The banks and ditches of a series of late Iron Age defences protecting the western side of Camulodunum – pre-Roman Colchester. There are also many pre-Roman graves hereabouts, including excavated Lexden Tumulus, the burial place of a wealthy British chieftain.

Managed by Colchester Borough Council.

OPENING TIMES
Any reasonable daylight hours

VISIT US
Direction: 2 miles W of Colchester off A604. Lexden Earthworks are on Lexden Straight Rd. To visit Bluebottle Grove from Lexden, turn left into Heath Rd, left into Church Lane, right into Beech Hill and follow the signs to the site

Train: Colchester or Colchester Town, both 2½ miles

Bus: Hedingham 4 and 15

Tel: 01206 282929

ACQ.1925 🐕

MAP Page 341 (5H) OS Map 168,184
Lexden Earthworks: TL965246
Bluebottle Grove: TL975245

MISTLEY TOWERS
ESSEX – CO11 1HB

MISTLEY TOWERS

Two porticoed Classical towers, which stood at each end of a grandiose but highly unconventional Georgian church, designed by Robert Adam in 1776.

Managed by Mistley Thorn Residents' Association.

OPENING TIMES
Daily   10am-4pm
Key available from Mistley Quay Workshops: 01206 393884
Please call in advance

VISIT US
Direction: Located on B1352, 1½ miles E of A137 at Lawford, 9 miles E of Colchester

Train: Mistley ¼ mile

Bus: Hedingham service 2, 85 (Wed only); Carters 92, 93C, 96 & 101; First 103, 104, 193; Network Colchester 102

Tel: 01206 393884

ACQ.1958 🐕 ♿

Disabled access (exterior only).
Dogs on leads (restricted areas).

MAP Page 341 (5H)
OS Map 168/169,184/197: TM116320

PRIOR'S HALL BARN, WIDDINGTON
ESSEX – CB11 1SB

One of the finest surviving medieval barns in eastern England, tree-ring dated to the mid-15th century, with a breathtaking aisled interior and crown-post roof, the product of some 400 oaks.

OPENING TIMES
1 Apr-30 Sep, Sat-Sun   10am-6pm

VISIT US
Direction: In Widdington, on unclassified road 2 miles SE of Newport, off B1383

Train: Newport 2 miles

Bus: TGM Stansted 301; Regal 322

PRIOR'S HALL BARN, WIDDINGTON

Tel: 01604 735464

ACQ.1976 🐕 ♿

MAP Page 341 (5F)
OS Map 167, 195: TL537318

ST BOTOLPH'S PRIORY
ESSEX: SEE COLCHESTER, ST BOTOLPH'S PRIORY – PAGE 157

ST JOHN'S ABBEY GATE
ESSEX: SEE COLCHESTER, ST JOHN'S ABBEY GATE – PAGE 158

WALTHAM ABBEY GATEHOUSE AND BRIDGE
ESSEX – EN9 1XQ

A fine 14th-century gatehouse, bridge and other remains of the abbey refounded by Harold, last Saxon King of England.

Managed by Lee Valley Regional Park Authority.

OPENING TIMES
Any reasonable daylight hours

VISIT US
Direction: In Waltham Abbey off A112

Train: Waltham Cross 1¼ miles

Bus: Regal 211, 212, 213 & 240; Regal/Arriva 250 & 251; Network Harlow 505; Roadrunner 255; TWH 555

Tel: 0845 677 0600

ACQ.1976 🐕 ♿

Sensory trail guide.

MAP Page 341 (6F) OS Map 166,174
Gatehouse: TL381007
Harold's Bridge: TL382009

VISIT US

Direction: Located ½ mile E of Tilbury off A126, close to the Port of Tilbury

Train: Tilbury Town 1½ miles

Bus: Ensignbus service 99 connects with trains at Tilbury Town and passes the fort

Ferry: Gravesend – Tilbury Ferry, then ¼ mile walk

Tel: 01375 858489

NON-MEMBERS

Adult	£4.70
Concession	£4.20
Child	£2.80
Family	£12.20

OPENING TIMES

1 Apr-30 Sep, Wed-Sun & Bank Hols	10am-6pm
1 Oct-2 Nov, Wed-Sun & Bank Hols	10am-5pm
3 Nov-29 Mar, Sat-Sun & Bank Hols	10am-4pm
24-26 Dec, 31 Dec-1 Jan	Closed

Last admission 30 mins before closing

ACQ.1948

Disabled access (exterior, magazines and fort square).

Dogs on leads (restricted areas).

MAP Page 341 (7G)
OS Map 177/178,162/163:
TQ651753

Tilbury Fort on the Thames estuary has defended London's seaward approach from Tudor times to World War II. Henry VIII built the first permanent fort here, and Queen Elizabeth I famously delivered her Armada Speech at nearby Tilbury in 1588. King Charles II ordered his chief engineer Sir Bernard de Gomme to build the great artillery fort we see today, with work beginning in 1670. It is considered the best example of a 17th-century bastioned fortress in England, with its complete circuit of moats and outworks still substantially surviving.

Visitors enter the fort through the monumental Watergate, and access is now also possible through the historic Landport gate. The east gunpowder magazine houses an exhibition which traces the fort's role in the defence of London and provides information on advances in military engineering. The atmospheric Victorian magazine tunnels in the north-east bastion provide an insight into the life of a gunner in the 19th century. There are impressive views of the Thames and the historic riverside town of Gravesend from the fort ramparts.

Sharpe, the TV historical drama set during the Napoleonic Wars.

HERTFORDSHIRE

BERKHAMSTED CASTLE
HERTFORDSHIRE – HP4 1HH

The substantial remains of a strong and important motte and bailey castle dating from the 11th to 15th centuries, with surrounding walls, ditches and earthworks. Lived in by Thomas Becket in the 12th century: Richard Earl of Cornwall added a 13th-century palace complex.

OPENING TIMES

Summer, daily	10am-6pm
Winter, daily	10am-4pm
25 Dec & 1 Jan	Closed

VISIT US

Direction: Near ⬛ Berkhamsted

Train: Berkhamsted, adjacent

Bus: Arriva The Shires service 354 and Little Jim's service 532 pass the castle

Tel: 01604 735464

ACQ.1929

MAP Page 340 (6D)
OS Map 165, 181: SP995082

CHURCH OF ST MARY THE VIRGIN, LITTLE HORMEAD
HERTFORDSHIRE
SG9 0LS

© CCT

A 1000-year-old haven of tranquillity set in a churchyard encircled by trees. Atmospheric St Mary's is a rare and precious

survival with a rare Norman chancel arch, and some wonderful craftsmanship in wood and ironwork, including an original Norman door.

Owned and managed by The Churches Conservation Trust.

OPENING TIMES

Presently closed for conservation – see website for details
www.visitchurches.org.uk

VISIT US

Train: Bishop's Stortford 7½ miles, Stansted Airport 7¾ miles, Royston 8 miles

Bus: Richmonds Coaches 27 (Wed only), 28 (Mon only), 334 (Fri only) or 386 (Thu only) and Arriva The Shires 331

25 mins from Audley End House and Gardens

MAP Page 341 (5F)
OS Map 166, 194: TL398291

OLD GORHAMBURY HOUSE
HERTFORDSHIRE – AL3 6AH

The remains of a once immense mansion built in 1563-68 by Sir Nicholas Bacon, Queen Elizabeth's Lord Keeper, and visited by the queen on at least four occasions. Its elaborately

decorated Classical two-storey porch survives, with parts of the hall, chapel and clock-tower.

OPENING TIMES

All year during any reasonable daylight hours (except 1 Jun & every Sat 1 Sep-1 Feb). Pedestrian access via a 2 mile walk from nearest car park on all days when site is open. Closer access by car followed by a ½ mile walk, Thu only, May-Sep 2pm-5pm.

VISIT US

Direction: Just off A4147 on western outskirts of St Albans. Walk up 2 mile drive on permissive path. Access by car is limited

Train: St Albans Abbey 3 miles, St Albans 3½ miles

Bus: Arriva/Uno services 300 & 301 pass start of drive

Tel: 01604 735464

ACQ.1959

MAP Page 340 (6E)
OS Map 166, 182: TL110076

ROMAN WALL, ST ALBANS
HERTFORDSHIRE – AL3 4BL

A section of the two-mile-long wall built between AD 265 and 270 to defend the Roman city of Verulamium, including the foundations of towers and the London Gate.

OPENING TIMES

Any reasonable daylight hours

VISIT US

Direction: Located on the S side of St Albans, ½ mile from the centre, off the A4147

Train: St Albans Abbey ½ mile, St Albans 1¼ miles

Bus: Uno services S8 & S9 operate close to the Roman Wall site

Tel: 01604 735464

ACQ.1931

MAP Page 340 (6E)
OS Map 166, 182: TL137066

NORFOLK

BACONSTHORPE CASTLE
NORFOLK – NR25 6LE

Surrounded by a reedy moat and a wildfowl-haunted mere, the evocative ruins of this fortified manor house chronicle the rise and fall of the ambitious Heydon family over two centuries. The wealthy but 'crafty and quarrelsome' John Heydon built the imposing inner gatehouse and first castle in the 1450s, during the troubled Wars of the Roses period, and his son Sir Henry extended the gunport-defended castle to include a garden court. Subsequent generations converted part of the site into a textile factory, and added the turreted Elizabethan outer gatehouse. But the family eventually succumbed to bankruptcy, and sold their mansion for salvage.

The castle stands astride walking and cycle trails. Download a free audio tour from our website before you visit.

OPENING TIMES
Any reasonable daylight hours

VISIT US
Direction: ¾ mile N of village of Baconsthorpe off unclassified road, 3 miles E of Holt

Train: Sheringham 4½ miles

Bus: Sanders service 16 (Tue and Fri only) or 17 (Thu only); Aldborough Community Bus 8 (Fri only); NS2 (Wed only) serve the village

Tel: 01604 735464

ACQ.1966

MAP Page 341 (1H)
OS Map 133, 252: TG121382

BERNEY ARMS WINDMILL
NORFOLK

One of Norfolk's best and largest extant marsh mills, built to grind a constituent of cement and in use until 1951, finally pumping water to drain surrounding marshland.

Access to Berney Arms Windmill is by pre-booked tours, for further information please call the Great Yarmouth Row Houses on 01493 857900.

OPENING TIMES
Access by pre-arranged booking – please ring 01493 857900 for details

VISIT US
Direction: 3½ miles NE of Reedham on the N bank of River Yare. Accessible by hired boat, or by footpath from Halvergate (3½ miles)

Train: Berney Arms ¼ mile

Tel: 01493 857900

ACQ.1950

MAP Page 341 (3K)
OS Map 134, OL40: TG465049

BINHAM MARKET CROSS
NORFOLK – NR21 0DW

The tall shaft of a 15th-century cross, on the site of an annual fair held from the 1100s until the 1950s.

Managed by Binham Parochial Church Council.

OPENING TIMES
Any reasonable daylight hours

BINHAM MARKET CROSS

VISIT US
Direction: Located on the Binham village green adjacent to the Priory

Bus: Sanders service 13 (Thu only) & 46

Tel: 01604 735464

ACQ.1949

MAP Page 341 (1H)
OS Map 132, 251: TF984396

BINHAM PRIORY
NORFOLK – NR21 0DQ

Among the most impressive monastic sites in East Anglia, Binham Priory retains its nave – now the parish church – virtually complete, with a striking 13th-century west front and triple tiers of late Norman arches within, along with screens revealing medieval saints peeping through later overpainting. The extensive ruins beyond, notably the massive piers of the fallen church tower, emphasise the original size of this Benedictine priory.

Major recent enhancements, carried out by local initiatives with English Heritage support, make a visit even more worthwhile. They include much improved disabled access, a fascinating display of site finds, and a children's activity area.

Managed by Binham Parochial Church Council.
www.binhampriory.org

OPENING TIMES
Binham Priory (monastic ruins): Any reasonable daylight hours

Priory Church:

Summer, daily	9am-6pm
Winter, daily	9am-4pm

VISIT US
Direction: ¼ mile NW of village of Binham on road off B1388

Bus: Sanders service 13 (Thu only) & 46

BINHAM PRIORY

Tel: 01328 830362

ACQ.1933 E ♿ ♿ P ♿
Toilets available in Church.

MAP Page 341 (1H)
OS Map 132, 251: TF982399

BLAKENEY GUILDHALL
NORFOLK – NR25 7NA

A relic of Blakeney's medieval prosperity, the remains of a flint 15th-century merchant's house with complete brick-vaulted undercroft. Later the Guildhall of the port's fish merchants.

Managed by Blakeney Parish Council.

OPENING TIMES
Any reasonable daylight hours

VISIT US
Direction: In Blakeney off A149

Train: Sheringham 9 miles

Bus: Norfolk Green Coasthopper service (CH3), Sanders service 13 (Thu only) & 46

Tel: 01263 741106

ACQ.1956 ♿

MAP Page 341 (1H)
OS Map 133, 251: TG028441

BURGH CASTLE
NORFOLK – NR31 9QB

The imposing stone walls, with added towers for catapults, of a Roman 3rd-century 'Saxon Shore' fort. Panoramic views over Breydon Water, into which the fourth wall long since collapsed.

A free podcast is available on our website **www.english-heritage.org.uk/burghcastle**

Managed by Norfolk Archaeological Trust.
www.norfarchtrust.org.uk

OPENING TIMES
Any reasonable daylight hours

BURGH CASTLE

VISIT US
Direction: At far W end of Breydon Water on unclassified road, 3 miles W of Great Yarmouth

Train: Great Yarmouth 5 miles

Bus: First 5 or 7 from Great Yarmouth then a short walk

Tel: 01604 735464

ACQ.1929 ♿

MAP Page 341 (3K)
OS Map 134, OL40: TG475047

CAISTER ROMAN FORT
NORFOLK – NR30 5JS

The partial excavated remains of a Roman 'Saxon Shore' fort, including wall and ditch sections and building foundations. Built around AD 200 for a unit of the Roman army and navy, and occupied until the end of the 4th century.

Managed by Great Yarmouth Borough Council.

OPENING TIMES
Any reasonable daylight hours

VISIT US
Direction: From Great Yarmouth, follow the A149 northbound and then the A149 Caister Bypass. Follow brown tourist signs for Caister Roman Fort. From other directons follow signs for Great Yarmouth and then brown tourist signs from the Caister Bypass roundabout. Parking and the entrance to the Fort are situated off a lay-by on Norwich Road ¼ mile from the roundabout

Train: Great Yarmouth 3 miles

Bus: First services 1, 1A, 4 & 8 pass the site; Sanders 6; Anglian 63 pass within ½ mile

Tel: 01493 846534

ACQ.1954 ♿

MAP Page 341 (2K)
OS Map 134, OL40: TG517123

CASTLE RISING CASTLE
NORFOLK – PE31 6AH

One of the biggest, most complete and most lavishly decorated Norman keeps in England, with an impressive entrance forebuilding, surrounded by stupendous earthworks. Begun in 1138 by William d'Albini for his wife, the widow of Henry I, in the 14th century it became the luxurious prison of Queen Isabella, widow (and alleged murderess) of Edward II.

Owned and managed by Lord Howard of Rising.

www.castlerising.co.uk

NON-MEMBERS

Adult	£4.00
Concession	£3.30
Child	£2.50
Family (2+2)	£12.00

There will be a premium payable by all visitors, including members, on special event days – please check website for details

OPENING TIMES

1 Apr-1 Nov, daily (or dusk if earlier in Oct)	10am-6pm
2 Nov-29 Mar, daily	10am-4pm
24-26 Dec	Closed

VISIT US
Direction: Located 4 miles NE of King's Lynn off A149

Train: King's Lynn 4½ miles

Bus: Norfolk Green 11 to Castle Rising

Tel: 01553 631330

ACQ.1958 ♿ ♿ ♿ P ♿ ♿ ⚠
Disabled access (exterior only, toilets).
Dogs on leads (restricted areas).

MAP Page 341 (2G)
OS Map 132, 250: TF666246

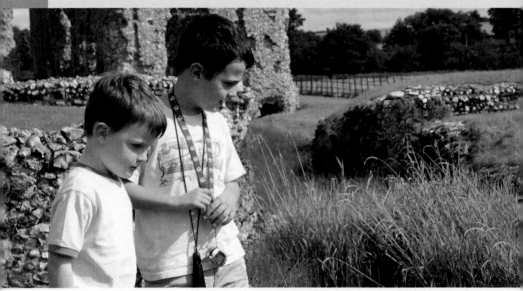

The delightful village of Castle Acre boasts an extraordinary wealth of history.

Situated on the Peddar's Way, a major trade and pilgrim route to Thetford, Bromholm Priory and Walsingham, it is a very rare and complete survival of a Norman planned settlement, including a castle, town, fine parish church and associated monastery. All this is the work of a powerful Norman baronial family, the Warennes, mainly during the 11th and 12th centuries.

First came the castle, founded soon after the Conquest by the first William de Warenne, probably as a stone 'country house'. During the first half of the 12th century, however, more disturbed conditions prompted its progressive conversion into a strong keep, further defended by stone walls and an immense system of earthworks. These massive ramparts and ditches are perhaps the finest castle earthworks anywhere in England.

Meanwhile, the 'planned town', deliberately established outside the castle, was also protected by ditched earthwork defences with stone gates. The north or Bailey Gate survives, with the main road into the village still running between its towers.

Visitors to Castle Acre can likewise trace the ancient street layout of this now peaceful village, lined with attractive flint or brick houses, before exploring both the great castle earthworks and the extensive priory remains. A village and castle trail can be downloaded from the Castle Acre Priory page of the English Heritage website.

CASTLE ACRE CASTLE AND BAILEY GATE
NORFOLK

VISIT US

Direction: Castle (PE32 2XB) located at SE edge of Castle Acre, 5 miles N of Swaffham. Parking in Pye's Lane. Bailey Gate (PE32 2AG) located in the centre of Castle Acre at the top of Bailey St

Bus: West Norfolk Community Transport 32 (weekdays); Peelings service 1 (Tue only)

Tel: 01604 735464

OPENING TIMES
Any reasonable daylight hours

ACQ.1970 Castle ACQ.1938 Bailey Gate (Castle only)

MAP Page 341 (2G) OS Map 132, 236/238
Bailey Gate: TF819152 Castle: TF819152

CASTLE ACRE PRIORY
NORFOLK

VISIT US

Direction: ¼ mile W of village of Castle Acre, 5 miles N of Swaffham

Bus: West Norfolk Community Transport 32 (weekdays); Peelings service 1 (Tue only)

Tel: 01760 755394

NON-MEMBERS

Adult	£6.00
Concession	£5.40
Child	£3.60
Family	£15.60

OPENING TIMES

1 Apr-30 Sep, daily	10am-6pm
1 Oct-2 Nov, daily	10am-5pm
3 Nov-29 Mar, Sat-Sun	10am-4pm
24-26 Dec, 31 Dec-1 Jan	Closed

Disabled access (ground floor and grounds only).

Toilets (a short walk. Not accessible for wheelchairs; 50 metres from entrance, with single step for access).

MAP Page 341 (2G)
OS Map 132, 236/238: TF814148

Among the largest and best-preserved monastic sites in all England, Castle Acre Priory often surprises new visitors by its immense size and variety. Its foundation in about 1090 by William de Warenne II reflected his family's devotion to the famous French monastery of Cluny: the Cluniac order's love of architectural decoration is displayed in the beautiful west front of the great 12th-century priory church, bedecked with tiers of intersecting round arches. Beyond extend the impressive remains of the cloister and monks' living quarters, including a gigantic, two-storey, 24-seater toilet block.

Best preserved of all is the west range, virtually complete and fully roofed. Its timber-framed and flint-chequered porch and oriel-windowed prior's lodging form an outstandingly attractive grouping with the church's west front. A mansion in itself, the lodging includes a chamber sumptuously revamped in early Tudor times for one of the last priors; with decorated fireplace, ceiling painted with Tudor roses, and two massive timber chests still in place. The adjacent prior's chapel was once even more elaborately adorned, with traces of medieval wall paintings still visible.

There is much more to see, including our exhibition and display of archaeological finds, site model and audio tour featuring a 15th-century chant from a Castle Acre song book. The recreated herb garden grows plants the monks would have used for medicinal and culinary purposes. A priory terrain guide can be downloaded from the Castle Acre Priory page of the English Heritage website.

CHURCH OF ST JOHN, MADDERMARKET, NORWICH
NORFOLK – NR2 1DS

© CCT

500-year-old St John's, which survived a gas explosion in 1876, is squeezed ingeniously into a cramped site. The almost square, light-filled interior is crowded with marvellous monuments, furnishings and rich stained glass. One of three CCT churches in Norwich.

Owned and managed by The Churches Conservation Trust.

OPENING TIMES
Apr-Mar, Wed   10.30am-1pm

Please contact our regional office to check opening arrangements at other times. Tel: 01223 324442

VISIT US
Train: Norwich ½ mile

Bus: Many bus services pass nearby

1 mile from Cow Tower

MAP Page 341 (2J)
OS Map 134, 237: TG229087

CHURCH OF THE HOLY SEPULCHRE, THETFORD, NORFOLK:
SEE THETFORD, CHURCH OF THE HOLY SEPULCHRE – PAGE 169

COW TOWER, NORWICH
NORFOLK – NR1 4AA

One of the earliest purpose-built artillery blockhouses in England, this brick tower was built in c.1398-99 to command a strategic point in Norwich's city defences. External viewing only.

Managed by Norwich City Council.

OPENING TIMES
Any reasonable daylight hours

VISIT US
Direction: In Norwich, near cathedral (approx. 1 mile walk)

Train: Norwich ½ mile

Bus: From surrounding areas

Tel: 01603 706229

ACQ.1950

MAP Page 341 (2J)
OS Map 134, OL40/237: TG240092

CREAKE ABBEY
NORFOLK – NR21 9LF

Tranquil ruins of an Augustinian abbey church, unusual because visibly reduced in size after a serious fire in the 15th century.

Managed by Mr and Mrs A C Scott.

www.creakeabbey.co.uk

OPENING TIMES
Any reasonable daylight hours

VISIT US
Direction: N of North Creake off B1355

CREAKE ABBEY

Bus: Sanders service 27

Tel: 01604 735464

ACQ.1950

MAP Page 341 (1H)
OS Map 132, 251: TF856395

GRIME'S GRAVES
SEE FEATURE – PAGE 168

NORTH ELMHAM CHAPEL
NORFOLK – NR20 5JU

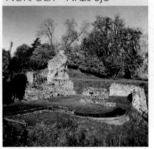

A place with an unusual story, illustrated on graphic panels. The small Norman chapel here stands on the site of an earlier timber church, probably the Saxon cathedral of East Anglia. In the 14th century it was converted into a fortified manor house by Henry Despenser, the unpopular Bishop of Norwich who brutally suppressed the Peasants' Revolt of 1381.

Managed by North Elmham Parish Council.

OPENING TIMES
Any reasonable daylight hours

VISIT US
Direction: Located 6 miles N of East Dereham on B1110

Bus: Konectbus service 18 & 21

Tel: 01604 735464

ACQ.1948

MAP Page 341 (2H)
OS Map 132, 238: TF988216

VISIT US

Direction: Great Yarmouth, follow signs for Historic Quay. The houses are directly behind the Norfolk Nelson Museum on the Historic South Quay

Train: Great Yarmouth ½ mile

Bus: Bus services to Great Yarmouth are operated by Anglian (of Beccles), Ambassador Travel and First in Suffolk & Norfolk and Sanders of Holt

Tel: 01493 857900

NON-MEMBERS

Adult	£4.40
Concession	£4.00
Child	£2.60
Family	£11.40

OPENING TIMES

1 Apr–30 Sep, Mon–Fri	11am–4pm
1 Oct–29 Mar	Closed

Access to Greyfriars' Cloisters is by pre-booked tours, please contact Great Yarmouth Row Houses on 01493 857900 for details

ACQ.1950 ♨ ⌂ ♿ ✗ ⌂ ⚠ OVP

Living space was very much at a premium in early 17th-century Great Yarmouth, then among the most prosperous fishing ports in England. Hence the inhabitants crowded into the town's distinctive 'Rows', a network of narrow alleyways linking Yarmouth's three main thoroughfares. Many 'Row houses' were damaged by the Second World War bombing or demolished during post-War clearances, but two surviving properties in the care of English Heritage show what these characteristic dwellings looked like at various stages in their history.

Both Row 111 and the Old Merchant's House were originally built in the early 17th century as wealthy merchants' residences, but later sub-divided into tenements. The Old Merchant's House, which has spectacular Jacobean plaster ceilings in two of its rooms, is presented as it was in the 1850s, when fish merchant Simon Fleet and his wife occupied one half of the property, and in the 1890s when the other half was occupied by Martha King and her family – represented here by models. Adjacent Row 111 house is shown as it was in about 1942 (just before it received a direct hit from an incendiary bomb), likewise with figures of the three families which then occupied parts of it. Both houses also display a wonderful collection of fixtures and fittings – including painted panels, elaborate wall-ties and door-knockers – rescued from other now-demolished Row dwellings, a treasure trove for lovers of period decoration.

Nearby stands Greyfriars' Cloisters, the remains of a 13th-century friary of Franciscan 'grey friars', later swallowed up by Row development and converted into a number of dwellings large and small. Traces of their interior features can still be seen on the brick-built walls of parts of the cloister and church, laid bare by wartime bombing. Early 14th-century wall-paintings were discovered here in the 1960s. Access to Greyfriars' Cloisters is by pre-booked tours.

MAP Page 341 (2K)
OS Map 134, OL40
Houses: TG525072
Cloisters: TG524073

VISIT US

Direction: Located 7 miles NW of Thetford off A134

Train: Brandon 3½ miles

Bus: The only public transport is Coach Services of Thetford service 40. Ask driver to set you down at Lynford

Tel: 01842 810656

NON-MEMBERS

Adult	£3.60
Concession	£3.20
Child	£2.20
Family	£9.40

No entry to the mines for children under 5 years of age

OPENING TIMES

1 Apr-30 Sep, daily	10am-6pm
1-31 Oct, Wed-Sun	10am-5pm
1 Nov-29 Mar	Closed

ACQ.1931

Disabled access (exhibition area only; access track rough).

Dogs on leads (restricted areas).

Visitors intending to descend the shaft should wear flat shoes.

Grime's Graves is the only Neolithic flint mine open to visitors in Britain. A grassy lunar landscape of over 400 shafts, pits, quarries and spoil dumps, they were first named Grim's Graves by the Anglo-Saxons – meaning the pagan god Grim's quarries, or 'the Devil's holes'.

It was not until one of them was excavated by Canon Greenwell in 1870 that they were identified as flint mines dug over 5000 years ago, during the later Neolithic and Early Bronze Ages.

What the prehistoric miners sought here was the fine quality, jet-black flint floorstone, which occurs some nine to twelve metres below surface level. Digging with red-deer antler picks, they sank shafts and dug radiating galleries which followed the seams of flint. Today visitors can descend 9 metres (30 ft) by ladder into one excavated shaft – an unforgettable experience.

Grime's Graves flint was prized for its distinctive colour and easily 'knapped' qualities. Rough-outs of axes and other tools were made on site, but then traded on and finished elsewhere.

Set amid the distinctive Breckland heath landscape, Grime's Graves is also a Site of Special Scientific Interest: the habitat of a variety of rare and distinctive plants and animals. The Breckland flora are especially attractive from April to July.

A small introductory exhibition in the visitor centre includes information about Neolithic mining, a virtual tour of the mines and landscape, and touchable reproduction Neolithic tools. A trail leaflet guides visitors round the multi-period site, explaining features from the earliest times until today.

The family explorer kit will enable you to read vital clues about the site.

See the Neolithic mine, and the plants and creatures which thrive in this unique landscape.

MAP Page 341 (3G)
OS Map 144, 229: TL817899

ST MARY'S CHURCH, EAST BRADENHAM
NORFOLK – IP25 7QL

This simple church has a powerful tower and stands at the end of an avenue of lime trees. The bold, buttressed exterior in its grassy graveyard setting is striking. Inside, it is plainly furnished and gloriously lit, with several lovely memorials to local people.

Owned and managed by The Churches Conservation Trust.

OPENING TIMES
Open during daylight hours summer Sat & Sun

At other times keyholder nearby

VISIT US
Train: Attleborough 11¼ miles

Bus: Konectbus service 17 (Tue and Fri only)

20 mins from Castle Acre Priory and Castle Acre Castle

MAP Page 341 (2H)
OS Map 144, 237: TF931084

ST NICHOLAS' CHAPEL, KING'S LYNN
NORFOLK – PE30 1NH

Nine centuries of dazzling treasures can be found in England's largest chapel. Startlingly life-like painted figures celebrate Kings Lynn's seamen, merchants, mayors and shopkeepers, and stunning carved woodwork adorns the interior, including the earliest known portrayal of an instrument in a church carving.

Owned and managed by The Churches Conservation Trust.

OPENING TIMES
Mid Jun-end Sep,
Tue & Sat   10.30am-4.30pm

VISIT US
Train: King's Lynn 10 mins walk

ST NICHOLAS' CHAPEL, KING'S LYNN

Bus: Bus station in Vancouver Centre by Sainsbury's 10 mins walk. Main bus services in Kings Lynn are operated by Norfolk Green, Konectbus and First

30 mins from Castle Rising Castle

MAP Page 341 (2G)
OS Map 132, 236/249/250: TF618204

ST OLAVE'S PRIORY
NORFOLK – NR31 9HE

The wonderfully complete, 14th-century, brick-vaulted refectory undercroft – later a cottage occupied until 1902 – of a small Augustinian priory.

OPENING TIMES
Any reasonable daylight hours

VISIT US
Direction: Located 5½ miles SW of the town of Great Yarmouth on A143

Train: Haddiscoe 1¼ miles

Bus: Ambassador service 577; Anglian services 81 & 81A

Tel: 01604 735464

ACQ.1921

Dogs on leads (restricted areas only).

MAP Page 341 (3K)
OS Map 134, OL40: TM459996

THETFORD, CHURCH OF THE HOLY SEPULCHRE
NORFOLK – IP24 3PW

The only surviving remains in England of a priory of Canons of the Holy Sepulchre, who aided pilgrims to Christ's tomb: the ruined nave of their 14th-century church, later used as a barn. Managed by Thetford Town Council.

OPENING TIMES
All year, daily   10am-5pm
(or dusk, whichever is earlier)

25 Dec   Closed

THETFORD, CHURCH OF THE HOLY SEPULCHRE

VISIT US
Direction: Located on the W side of Thetford on A134

Train: Thetford ¾ mile

Bus: Coach Services of Thetford 40, 81, 84, 86, 190, 200, 201, 332, T1, T1A, T2, T2A

Tel: 01842 754038

ACQ.1977

MAP Page 341 (3H)
OS Map 144, 229: TL865831

THETFORD PRIORY
NORFOLK – IP24 1AD

The extensive remains of one of the most important East Anglian monasteries, the Cluniac Priory of Our Lady of Thetford. Founded in the early 12th century, it owed much of its prosperity to a miraculous appearance of the Virgin Mary, whose statue here was discovered to conceal relics of saints, becoming a magnet for pilgrims. Survivals include the lower walls of the church and cloister, the impressive shell of the priors' lodging and, reached by a pathway from the main site, an almost complete 14th-century gatehouse.

The burial place of the earls and dukes of Norfolk for 400 years, it enjoyed their powerful protection. Hence it was almost the last monastery in England to be suppressed, in 1540 by Thomas Cromwell. Soon afterwards the vengeful Duke of Norfolk engineered Cromwell's downfall and execution, allegedly remarking: 'That's for Thetford!'

Managed by Thetford Town Council.

OPENING TIMES
1 Apr-30 Sep, daily   8am-6pm

1 Oct-29 Mar, daily   8am-4pm

25 Dec   Closed

THETFORD PRIORY

VISIT US
Direction: Near Thetford station

Train: Thetford ¼ mile

Bus: Coach Services of Thetford 40, 81, 84, 86, 190, 200, 201, 332, T1, T1A, T2, T2A

Tel: 01842 754038

ACQ.1932

MAP Page 341 (3G)
OS Map 144, 229: TL865831

THETFORD WARREN LODGE NORFOLK

Probably built c. 1400 by the Prior of Thetford, this defensible lodge protected gamekeepers and hunting parties against armed poachers. Much later used by the local 'warreners' who harvested rabbits here.

OPENING TIMES
Any reasonable daylight hours

VISIT US
Direction: Located 2 miles W of Thetford off B1107

Train: Thetford 2½ miles

Bus: Coach Services of Thetford 40, 86, 200

Tel: 01604 735464

ACQ.1948

MAP Page 341 (3G)
OS Map 144, 229: TL839984

WEETING CASTLE NORFOLK – IP27 0RQ

The ruins of a substantial early medieval moated manor house, built in local flint.

OPENING TIMES
Any reasonable daylight hours

VISIT US
Direction: Located 2 miles N of Brandon off B1106

Train: Brandon 1¼ miles

Bus: Coach Service 40

Tel: 01604 735464

ACQ.1926

MAP Page 341 (3G)
OS Map 144, 229: TL778891

SUFFOLK

BURY ST EDMUNDS ABBEY
SUFFOLK – IP33 1UZ

The extensive remains of the wealthiest and most powerful Benedictine monastery in England, shrine of St Edmund. They include the complete 14th-century Great Gate and Norman Tower, and the impressive ruins and altered west front of the immense church.

Managed by St Edmundsbury Borough Council.

OPENING TIMES
Any reasonable daylight hours

VISIT US
Direction: E end of town centre

Train: Bury St Edmunds 1 mile

Bus: Services to the town are operated by H.C.Chambers, Coach Services of Thetford, Galloway European, High Suffolk Community Transport, Mulley's Motorways, Stagecoach in Cambridge, Simonds of Diss, Stephensons of Essex and Suffolk Norse

Tel: 01284 764667

ACQ.1955

MAP Page 341 (4G)
OS Map 155, 211: TL857642

CHURCH OF ST MARY THE VIRGIN, STONHAM PARVA
SUFFOLK – IP14 5JL

© CCT

Spectacular and airy, this medieval flint-work church lies behind the village and beside the Old Hall. The nave and chancel are impressively high, and the double hammerbeam roof is a splendid example of medieval craftsmanship.

Owned and managed by The Churches Conservation Trust.

OPENING TIMES
Open daily during daylight hours

VISIT US
Train: Needham Market 3½ miles

Bus: Simonds service 113 & 114 to Little Stonham

30 mins from Framlingham Castle

MAP Page 341 (4H)
OS Map 155, 211: TM115601

FRAMLINGHAM CASTLE
SEE FEATURE – PAGE 172

LANDGUARD FORT SUFFOLK – IP11 3TW

The site of the last opposed seaborne invasion of England in 1667 and the first land battle of the Royal Marines. The current fort was built in the 18th century and modified in the 19th century, with substantial additional 19th/20th-century outside batteries.

Guided tours and audio tours of the fort are supplemented by an audio-visual presentation of the site's history, and by guided tours of the outside batteries.

Managed by Landguard Fort Trust.

The nearby submarine mining building houses Felixstowe Museum's collections of local interest. (For museum opening times and prices see felixstowemuseum.org, or call 01394 674355.)

NON-MEMBERS

Adult	£4.00
Concession	£3.00
Child	£1.50

Free entry for children under 5 and wheelchair users

There may be a premium payable by all visitors, including members, on event days – please check www.landguard.com for details

OPENING TIMES

1 Apr-2 Nov, daily	10am-5pm
3 Nov-29 Mar	Closed

Last admission 1 hour before closing

VISIT US

Direction: 1 mile S of Felixstowe town centre – follow signs to Landguard Point

Train: Felixstowe 2½ miles

Bus: First in Suffolk services 77 & 77

Tel: 01394 675900

ACQ.1975 🎧 🐕 🎒 💻 🖥 P 📷 ⚠

Route 51 cycle route comes to site.

MAP Page 341 (5J)
OS Map 169, 197: TM284319

LEISTON ABBEY
SUFFOLK – IP16 4TD

The mainly 14th-century remains of an abbey of Premonstratensian canons. Among Suffolk's most impressive monastic ruins, with some spectacular architectural features.

Managed by Pro Corda Trust.

OPENING TIMES

Any reasonable daylight hours

VISIT US

Direction: N of Leiston off B1069

Train: Saxmundham 5 miles

Bus: Stowmark Minibus Coach Hire 196 passes the site; First services 64; Anglian service 165 and Nightingales of Beccles service 521 all serve Leiston (1½ mile walk)

Tel: 01728 831354

ACQ.1964 🎒 P 🔏 ♿

MAP Page 341 (4K)
OS Map 156, 212: TM445642

LINDSEY ST JAMES'S CHAPEL
SUFFOLK – IP7 6QA

A pretty, thatched, 13th-century chapel with lancet windows.

OPENING TIMES

All year, daily	10am-4pm

VISIT US

Direction: Located on an unclassified road ½ mile E of Rose Green and 8 miles E of Sudbury

Train: Sudbury 8 miles

Bus: Hadleigh Community Transport 'Suffolk Links Cosford' demand-responsive bus service: telephone 01473 828202 to book

Tel: 01604 735464

ACQ.1930 🎒 ♿

Disabled access (single step).

MAP Page 341 (5H)
OS Map 155, 196: TL9784444

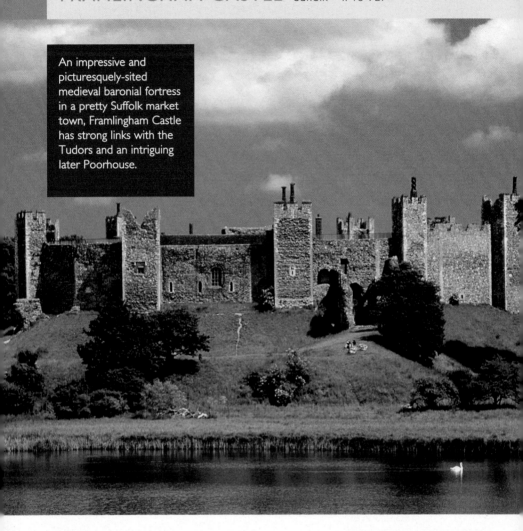

An impressive and picturesquely-sited medieval baronial fortress in a pretty Suffolk market town, Framlingham Castle has strong links with the Tudors and an intriguing later Poorhouse.

VISIT US

Address: Framlingham Castle, Church Street, Framlingham, Suffolk

Direction: In Framlingham on B1116

Train: Wickham Market 6½ miles; Saxmundham 7 miles

Bus: Galloway European 118, 119; Nightingales 482; PF Travel 62

Tel: 01728 724922

Local Tourist Information
Woodbridge: 01394 382240

NON-MEMBERS

Adult	£6.90
Concession	£6.20
Child	£4.10
Family	£17.90

OPENING TIMES

1 Apr-30 Sep, daily	10am-6pm
1 Oct-2 Nov, daily	10am-5pm
3 Nov-28 Dec, Sat-Sun	10am-4pm
29-31 Dec, daily	10am-4pm
2 Jan-15 Feb, Sat-Sun	10am-4pm
16-20 Feb, daily	10am-4pm
21 Feb-29 Mar, Sat-Sun	10am-4pm
24-26 Dec & 1 Jan	Closed

Disabled access (grounds and ground floor only).

Parking charge, refundable to EH members and paying visitors on admission.

MAP Page 341 (4J)
OS Map 156, 212: TM287637

Framlingham is a magnificent example of a late 12th-century castle. Built by Roger Bigod, Earl of Norfolk, one of the most influential people at the court of the Plantagenet kings, the castle, together with Framlingham Mere, was designed both as a stronghold and a proclamation of power and status. Architecturally, the fortress is notable for its curtain wall with regular mural towers, being an early example of this style.

The castle has fulfilled a number of roles. It was at the centre of the struggle between the Bigod barons and the Crown, and Mary Tudor mustered her supporters here in 1553, before being crowned Queen. At the end of the 16th century it was used to imprison enemies of the monarch; later still a Poorhouse was built within the walls. Today the imposing stone walls and crenellated towers with their ornate Tudor chimneys dominate, while the grassy earthworks around the castle are subdued reminders of its outer defences. To the west, the Mere provides a stunning setting.

Visitors can explore over 800 years of life at Framlingham Castle in an introductory

exhibition in the Poorhouse, which tells the story of the people who lived in the castle during its long and varied history. The displays illustrate the struggle for power between monarchs and the lords of Framlingham, including Thomas Howard, 3rd Duke of Norfolk and uncle to Anne Boleyn and Catherine Howard, both married to and beheaded by Henry VIII; the accession of Queen Mary Tudor; and the Poorhouse, still in use until 1839.

The Poorhouse Kitchen provides an area where visitors can enjoy a selection of factual and fictional books relating to Framlingham Castle. Entry also includes access to the Lanman Trust's Museum of Local History.

Embark on a self-guided journey of discovery around the site with our lively audio tour, and explore the Mere, the castle's outer courts and the wall-walk with its spectacular views over the surrounding landscape. Younger visitors can discover more about life in the castle with a variety of themed games and interactives.

MOULTON PACKHORSE BRIDGE SUFFOLK – CB8 8SR

A pretty, four-arched, late medieval bridge spanning the River Kennet on the old route from Cambridge to Bury St Edmunds.

OPENING TIMES
Any reasonable daylight hours

VISIT US

Direction: In Moulton off B1085, 4 miles E of Newmarket

Train: Kennett 2 miles

Bus: Stephensons 16, 16A, 16B & 17; Suffolk Norse services 310, 311A & 311B; Mulleys service 312

Tel: 01604 735464

ACQ.1977 🐾 P ♿

MAP Page 341 (4G)
OS Map 154, 210/226: TL698645

ST PETER'S CHURCH, CLAYDON SUFFOLK – IP6 0EQ

This originally Saxon church has wonderful views over the Gipping Valley, and is full of stunning, vibrant stained glass and extravagant carvings. A rector was responsible for the design of some of the stained glass, and it is possible he carved some of the stonework too.

Owned and managed by The Churches Conservation Trust.

OPENING TIMES
Open daily during daylight hours

VISIT US

Train: Westerfield 2¾ miles, Ipswich 4 miles

Bus: First 88/88a; Galloway 87 (Sun & Bank Hols only), 110; Simonds 113/114

35 mins from Framlingham Castle

MAP Page 341 (4J)
OS Map 169, 197: TM137499

SAXTEAD GREEN POST MILL
SUFFOLK – IP13 9QQ

This fine four-sailed corn-grinding 'post mill', whose whole body – turned by a secondary windmill or 'fantail' – revolves on its three-storey roundhouse base, is of a type characteristic of Suffolk since around the 13th century. It originates from about 1796, but has been three times rebuilt and raised: in 1854 it was given a full set of new cast-iron machinery. Though commercial milling ceased when the last miller died in 1947, the mill is still in full working order. Climb the stairs to the various floors, which are full of fascinating mill machinery. Framlingham Castle is nearby.

NON-MEMBERS

Adult	£3.70
Concession	£3.30
Child	£2.20

OPENING TIMES

1 Apr–29 Sep, Fri-Sat & Bank Hols	12pm-5pm
30 Sep–29 Mar	Closed

VISIT US

Direction: 2½ miles NW of Framlingham on A1120

Train: Wickham Market 9 miles

Bus: Galloway European 119; High Suffolk Community Transport (Tue only)

Tel: 01728 685789

ACQ.1951 ✉ ✖ 📷 ⚠ OVP

MAP Page 341 (4J)
OS Map 156, 212: TM253644

VISIT US

Direction: In Orford on B1084, 20 miles NE of Ipswich

Train: Wickham Market 8 miles

Bus: PF Travel service 71

Tel: 01394 450472

Local Tourist Information
Woodbridge: 01394 382240

NON-MEMBERS

Adult	£6.20
Concession	£5.60
Child	£3.70
Family	£16.10

OPENING TIMES

1 Apr-30 Sep, daily	10am-6pm
1 Oct-2 Nov, daily	10am-5pm
3 Nov-29 Mar, Sat-Sun	10am-4pm
27-31 Dec, daily	10am-4pm
24-26 Dec, 1 Jan	Closed

ACQ.1962 🏠 ♿ 🛍 P 📷 ⚠ OVP

MAP Page 341 (4J)
OS Map 169, 212: TM419499

The unique polygonal tower keep of Orford Castle stands beside the pretty town and former port, which Henry II also developed here in the 1160s. His aim was to counterbalance the power of turbulent East Anglian barons like Hugh Bigod of Framlingham, and to guard the coast against foreign mercenaries called to their aid.

An 18-sided drum with three square turrets and a forebuilding reinforcing its entrance, the keep was built to a highly innovative design. The progress of its construction between 1165 and 1173 is extensively recorded in royal documents. Both exterior and interior survive almost intact, allowing visitors to explore the basement, with its vital well, and the lower and upper halls – the latter the principal room of the castle. Around these polygonal rooms is a maze of passages leading to the chapel, kitchen and other chambers in the turrets. From the roof there are magnificent views seaward to Orford Ness.

Recent archaeological work has provided a clearer understanding of how the castle worked, and a painting by Frank Gardiner shows how the keep and its vanished outer defences looked in their heyday. The upper hall now houses a display by the Orford Museum Trust, including local finds of Roman brooches, medieval seals and coins and some of the borough's regalia. Graphic panels display maps, documents, pictures and photographs, illustrating Orford's history up to the 20th century.

DISCOUNTED ATTRACTIONS:

Use your membership to get exclusive discounts at these independent attractions in the East of England. Please remember to show your card as proof of membership.

FELIXSTOWE MUSEUM
Suffolk IP11 3TW
Fourteen display rooms, local, social and military history, housed within 1878-built Submarine Mining Establishment. Shop, tearoom. First World War exhibition for 2014.
www.felixstowemuseum.org
Tel. 01394 674355

HOLKHAM HALL
Norfolk NR23 1AB
Surrounded by acres of rolling parkland, this grand 18th-century Palladian Hall is full of stunning architecture and art, original furniture and classical statuary.
www.holkham.co.uk
Tel. 01328 710227

*Terms & conditions apply.

IWM DUXFORD
Cambridgeshire CB22 4QR
Discover the history of aviation in times of war and peace in one of the world's finest aviation heritage sites; explore over 200 aircraft including Spitfire and Concorde.
www.iwm.org.uk
Tel. 01223 835000

KELVEDON HATCH SECRET NUCLEAR BUNKER
Essex CM15 0LA
Visit this restored ex Government Cold War Bunker, to have been used in the event of a war. Open all year.
www.secretnuclearbunker.com
Tel. 01277 364883

LAYER MARNEY TOWER
Essex CO5 9US
England's tallest Tudor gatehouse, built in 1523. Climb the Tower, children's play areas, gardens, parkland, walks. Gift shop and tearoom. See website for events throughout the summer.
www.layermarneytower.co.uk
Tel. 01206 330784

NORWICH CASTLE MUSEUM & ART GALLERY
Norfolk NR1 3JQ
900-year-old Norwich Castle is packed with treasures to inspire and intrigue visitors of all ages. Models, computers, sound and video bring history vividly to life.
www.museums.norfolk.gov.uk
Tel. 01603 493625

EAST OF ENGLAND

Discount applies to:

KEY   ▦ **MEMBERS**   OVP **OVP HOLDERS**   👥? **NO. OF MEMBER'S CHILDREN**

Terms and conditions may apply, so make sure you check the individual pages on our website or call the individual property for more details.

▦ OVP 👥3

OLIVER CROMWELL'S HOUSE
Cambridgeshire CB7 4HF
Visit the former Lord Protector's family home. Experience what domestic life would have been like in the 17th century.
www.olivercromwellshouse.co.uk
Tel. 01353 662062

▦ OVP 👥4

RAF AIR DEFENCE RADAR MUSEUM
Norfolk NR12 8YB
Featuring the once Top Secret Cold War Ops Room, we cover the history of Air Defence from 1935 to today. A great day out!
www.radarmuseum.co.uk
Tel. 01692 631485

▦ OVP

SOMERLEYTON HALL & GARDENS
Suffolk NR32 5QQ
Twelve acres of landscaped gardens. Ancient yew hedge maze. Paxton glasshouses. Guided Hall tours. Excellent tearooms and giftshop.
www.somerleyton.co.uk
Tel. 0871 222 4244

▦ OVP

STOW MARIES AERODROME
Essex CM3 6RJ
An English Heritage Angel award winner, this unique aerodrome is the only First World War aerodrome with over 20 of its original buildings in their original context.
www.stowmaries.com
Tel. 01245 326040

▦ OVP 👥2

WOBURN ABBEY
Bedfordshire MK17 9WA
Home to the Duke of Bedford and birthplace of Afternoon Tea. Enjoy priceless art and treasures and beautiful gardens, all set in 3000 acres of deer park.
www.woburn.co.uk/abbey
Tel. 01525 290333

GIVE THE GIFT OF MEMBERSHIP

Give friends and family the opportunity to enjoy these fantastic discounts too!

- Free entry to over 400 historic properties
- Kids go free (up to six per adult in a family group)
- Free or discounted entry to hundreds of events
- Free handbook worth £10.95
- Exclusive Members' Magazine

See page 355 for full details.

EAST
MIDLANDS

Bolsover Castle

Keep up to date with events, news and offers www.english-heritage.org.uk/newsletter

Bolsover Castle

Glossop

7

Buxton
Bakewell
1
Chesterfield
5
8
2
3
6
4
9

Worksop

23
14
Gainsborough

Market Rasen

24

Mansfield

Lincolnshire

15
Lincoln

13
Skegness

17

16
Boston

Nottinghamshire

Nottingham

Derbyshire

Derby

Grantham

Spalding

10
Loughborough

Leicestershire

12
11
Leicester

Oakham

Rutland

25
21
18

Market
Harborough
22
20
Corby

Kettering

Northamptonshire

19

Daventry

Northampton

Brackley

Details of local public transport information in England are available from Traveline
www.traveline.org.uk or call 0871 200 2233.

HIGHLIGHTS FOR 2014/15 IN THE **EAST MIDLANDS**

p.184

p.183

p.193

Bolsover Castle: hilltop Stuart fantasy house, with intriguing new presentations of its Little Castle and Fountain Garden for 2014.

Hardwick Old Hall: the impressive shell of a formidable Elizabethan lady's mansion, set beside her even grander 'New Hall'.

Kirby Hall: extensive remains of an immense Elizabethan and Stuart country house, with fine gardens and some roofed apartments.

PROPERTIES

DERBYSHIRE
1   Arbor Low Stone Circle and Gib Hill Barrow
2   Bolsover Castle
3   Bolsover Cundy House
4   Hardwick Old Hall
5   Hob Hurst's House
6   Nine Ladies Stone Circle
7   Peveril Castle
8   Sutton Scarsdale Hall
9   Wingfield Manor

LEICESTERSHIRE
10   Ashby de la Zouch Castle
11   Jewry Wall
12   Kirby Muxloe Castle

LINCOLNSHIRE
13   Bolingbroke Castle
14   Gainsborough Old Hall
15   Lincoln Medieval Bishops' Palace
16   Sibsey Trader Windmill
17   Tattershall College

NORTHAMPTONSHIRE
18   Apethorpe Hall
19   Chichele College
20   Eleanor Cross, Geddington
21   Kirby Hall
22   Rushton Triangular Lodge

NOTTINGHAMSHIRE
23   Mattersey Priory
24   Rufford Abbey

RUTLAND
25   Lyddington Bede House

Remember to check opening times before you visit any of our properties
www.english-heritage.org.uk/daysout

DERBYSHIRE

ALL SAINTS' CHURCH, KEDLESTON
DERBYSHIRE – DE22 5JH

© CCT

All Saints' church is all that remains of the medieval village of Kedleston. A dazzling marble tomb, with life-size figures, floats on a sea of green translucent quartz, in its own chapel with spectacular stained glass windows. Carved monsters surround the Norman doorway.

Owned and managed by The Churches Conservation Trust.

OPENING TIMES
26 Mar-30 Oct, Mon-Wed during daylight hours;
Sat-Sun   11am-5pm

VISIT US
Train: Derby 5 miles

Bus: Arriva Derby Bus 109

30 mins from Wingfield Manor

MAP Page 342 (3E)
OS Map 119/128, 259: SK313404

ARBOR LOW STONE CIRCLE AND GIB HILL BARROW
DERBYSHIRE – DE45 1JS

The region's most important prehistoric site, Arbor Low is a Neolithic henge monument atmospherically set amid high moorland. Within an earthen bank and ditch, a circle of some 50 white limestone slabs, all now fallen, surrounds a central stone 'cove' – a feature found only in major sacred sites. Nearby is enigmatic Gib Hill, a large burial mound.

Please note: The farmer who owns access to the property will levy a charge for entry.

Managed by Peak District National Park Authority.

OPENING TIMES
Any reasonable daylight hours

Access charge of £1 per person to cross private land to the monument

VISIT US
Direction: ½ mile E of A515, 2 miles S of Monyash

Train: Buxton 10 miles

Bus: Infrequent High Peak bus 441; Clowes bus 446 and Warringtons 449 serve Parsley Hay which is within a 1 mile walk to the two locations

Tel: 01629 816200

ACQ.1884

MAP Page 342 (2E)
OS Map 119, OL24: SK160636

BOLSOVER CASTLE
SEE FEATURE – PAGE 184

BOLSOVER CUNDY HOUSE
DERBYSHIRE – S44 6BQ

This charming cottage-like 17th-century conduit house, with vaulted stone-slab roof, once supplied water to Bolsover Castle.

Managed by Bolsover Civic Society.

OPENING TIMES
Any reasonable daylight hours

VISIT US
Direction: Off M1 at junction 29A, follow signs for Bolsover Castle. Between junctions of Craggs Rd and Houfton Rd with Bolsover Hill, Bolsover, 6 miles E of Chesterfield on A362

Train: Chesterfield 6 miles or Langwith – Whaley Thorns 4½ miles

Bus: Stagecoach service 82 & TM Travel Bolsover town services B2 & B3 actually pass the property. Stagecoach services 53, 53A serve Hilltop Avenue a short walk from the Cundy House

Tel: 01246 822844 (Bolsover Castle)

ACQ.1945

MAP Page 343 (2F)
OS Map 120, 269: SK471709

HOLIDAY COTTAGE AT HARDWICK OLD HALL

East Lodge is a stunning 2-storey cottage that sleeps four comfortably. For more information and to book this, and other English Heritage cottages, visit www.english-heritage.org.uk/book-and-buy/holidaycottages

HARDWICK OLD HALL DERBYSHIRE S44 5QJ

The imposing shell of the remodelled family home of Bess of Hardwick, one of the most remarkable and most formidable women of Elizabethan England. Born on this site the daughter of an impoverished country squire, she rose via four increasingly advantageous marriages and much social manoeuvring to become Countess of Shrewsbury, and perhaps the richest woman in England. A friend and then enemy of Mary Queen of Scots, she was treated with respect even by Queen Elizabeth.

To celebrate her success and proclaim her status, Bess transformed her birthplace from a modest medieval manor house into a luxurious Elizabethan mansion. Completed by 1591, perhaps largely to Bess's own designs, the Old Hall was almost immediately superseded by her grander New Hall which stands beside it, becoming a guest and service wing to the newer mansion.

Though the Old Hall is now roofless, you can still ascend through four storeys to admire surviving decorative plasterwork and overmantels in the former staterooms, and view the kitchen and service rooms. An exhibition describes Bess's adventures in architecture, and on the ground floor there is a virtual tour of the first floor rooms (which are only accessible via steps).

Managed by English Heritage and owned by the National Trust.

NON-MEMBERS

Adult	£5.40
Concession	£4.90
Child	£3.20
Family	£14.00

National Trust members admitted free, but small charge at EH events. Tickets for the New Hall (the National Trust) and joint tickets for both properties available at extra cost

OPENING TIMES

1 Apr-30 Sep, Wed-Sun & Bank Hols	10am-6pm
1 Oct-2 Nov, Wed-Sun	10am-5pm
3 Nov-8 Feb, Sat-Sun	10am-4pm
9-13 Feb, daily	10am-4pm
14 Feb-29 Mar, Sat-Sun	10am-4pm
24-26 Dec, 31 Dec-1 Jan	Closed

VISIT US

Direction: 8 miles SE of Chesterfield, off A6175 (J29 of M1)

Train: Chesterfield 8 miles

Bus: Trent Barton/Stagecoach 'Pronto' service or G&J Holmes 'Hallmark' service 49 (alight Glapwell 'Young Vanish', then 2 mile walk) or Stagecoach/TM Travel service 96 to Hardstoft and 2 mile walk

Tel: 01246 850431

ACQ.1959

MAP Page 343 (2F)
OS Map 120, 269: SK462637

Holiday cottage available to let – see opposite

HOB HURST'S HOUSE
DERBYSHIRE – DE4 2NT

A square prehistoric burial mound with earthwork ditch and bank, amid remote moorland. Named after a local goblin.

Managed by the Peak District National Park Authority.

OPENING TIMES
Any reasonable daylight hours

VISIT US
Direction: On open moorland from unclassified road off B5057, 9 miles W of Chesterfield

Train: Chesterfield 9 miles

Bus: TM Travel services 218 (Mon-Sat only) & 215 (Sun only) to Beeley then walk 2 miles

Tel: 01629 816200

ACQ.1884

MAP Page 342 (2E)
OS Map 119, OL24: SK287692

NINE LADIES STONE CIRCLE
DERBYSHIRE – DE4 2LS

A small, early Bronze Age stone circle traditionally believed to represent nine ladies turned to stone as a penalty for dancing on Sunday. Their fiddler became the nearby King Stone. Part of an extensive complex of prehistoric remains on Stanton Moor.

Managed by Peak District National Park Authority.

OPENING TIMES
Any reasonable daylight hours

VISIT US
Direction: From an unclassified road off A6, 5 miles SE of Bakewell

Train: Matlock 4½ miles

Bus: Hulleys service 172 to Stanton in Peak (within 1 mile)

Tel: 01629 816200

ACQ.1883

MAP Page 342 (2E)
OS Map 119, OL24: SK249635

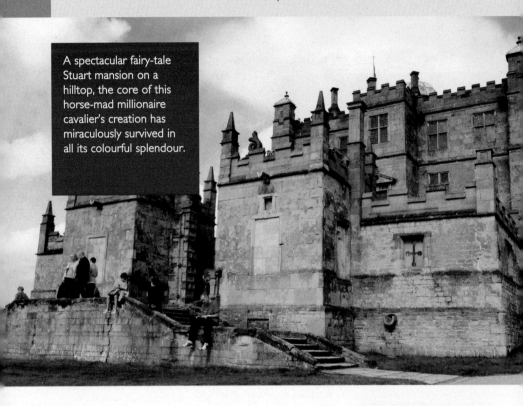

A spectacular fairy-tale Stuart mansion on a hilltop, the core of this horse-mad millionaire cavalier's creation has miraculously survived in all its colourful splendour.

VISIT US

Address: Bolsover Castle, Castle Street, Bolsover, Derbyshire

Direction: In Bolsover, 6 miles E of Chesterfield on A632. Off M1 at junction 29A (signposted)

Train: Chesterfield 6 miles

Bus: G&J Holmes service 49; TM Travel B2 & B3; Stagecoach services 53, 53A, 82 & 83 all pass close to the castle entrance

Tel: 01246 822844

Local Tourist Information (Chesterfield): 01246 345777

NON-MEMBERS

Adult	£9.50
Concession	£8.60
Child	£5.70
Family	£24.70

OPENING TIMES

1 Apr-30 Sep, daily	10am-6pm
1 Oct-2 Nov, daily	10am-5pm
3 Nov-8 Feb, Sat-Sun	10am-4pm
9-13 Feb, daily	10am-4pm
14 Feb-29 Mar, Sat-Sun	10am-4pm
24-26 Dec, 31 Dec-1 Jan	Closed

Part of the castle may close for 1 hour if an event is booked. Please call to check

New guidebook.

Parking (in castle car park, off main gate. Charge payable, refundable to EH members and paying visitors on admission). The coach drop-off point is in the council car park opposite.

There is good access to the grounds, but please note that the Little Castle is not accessible to wheelchairs.

MAP Page 343 (2F)
OS Map 120, 269: SK470707

🍸 Available for corporate and private hire

🏠 Licensed for civil wedding ceremonies

There is nothing else in Britain quite like Bolsover Castle. It is a unique survival of a Stuart 'prodigy house' in miniature; a rich man's toy designed for pleasure and extravagant display; a place to develop and show off learning and artistic sophistication; a place to entertain and impress the royal court.

Dominating the countryside from its hilltop, Bolsover occupies the site of a medieval

NEW FOR 2014

An ambitious new project for 2014 will reveal even more of the splendours of Bolsover Castle, evoking the world of extravagant Stuart courtly display for which it was created. The first floor rooms of the Little Castle will be dressed in the style of the 1630s, highlighting for the first time in centuries their original use and purpose.

For the first time in centuries, too, you will be able to enjoy the breathtaking views from the restored wall-walk round the Fountain Garden, where Stuart courtiers strolled to see and be seen. The Fountain Garden itself will likewise be lovingly recreated. Round its Venus Fountain will be arranged colourful Stuart-style borders, a period 'coloured earths' garden, and specimens of tulips and hyacinths – rare, fashionable and costly flowers in Cavendish's day. There will also be a brand-new play park for children.

castle. Sir Charles Cavendish, son of Bess of Hardwick, bought the old fortress in 1612 and began work on his playfully battlemented and pinnacled Little Castle.

His son William – playboy, poet, courtier and later Royalist general and first Duke of Newcastle – inherited the Little Castle in 1617 and set about its completion, decoration and furnishing, assisted by the architect John Smythson. The exquisitely carved fireplaces and richly-coloured murals and panelling of its interiors still take the visitor on an allegorical journey from earthly concerns to heavenly (and erotic) delights.

William also added the immense Terrace Range, now a dramatic roofless shell. To show off his achievement, in 1634 he invited King Charles I and his court to *Love's Welcome at Bolsover*, a masque specially written by Ben Jonson for performance in the Fountain Garden. Finally he constructed the cavernous Riding School, among the finest surviving indoor riding houses in the country.

An interactive exhibition in the Riding House stables introduces the site and celebrates the legacy of William Cavendish, his passion for horses and his contribution to the modern art of dressage. There are cavalier hats to try on and a replica 17th-century saddle children can sit on, discovery boxes to explore, plus an introductory film about the Little Castle and a lavish banquet held there in 1634.

Every weekend from April to September (excluding some event weekends, please see website for details) riders in 17th-century attire will give three spectacular performances of 'classical dressage', which takes horse and rider years to learn. Booking is highly recommended to avoid disappointment, call customer services on 0870 333 1183.

VISIT US

Direction: Via the market place in Castleton; 15 miles W of Sheffield on A6187

Train: Hope 2½ miles

Bus: Hulley's 68, 173, 174, 272, 273, 274, 276; First 272 to Castleton then short walk

Tel: 01433 620613

Local Tourist Information: 01629 816572

NON-MEMBERS

Adult	£4.70
Concession	£4.20
Child	£2.80
Family	£12.20

OPENING TIMES

1 Apr-30 Sep, daily	10am-6pm
1 Oct-2 Nov, daily	10am-5pm
3 Nov-8 Feb, Sat-Sun	10am-4pm
9-13 Feb, daily	10am-4pm
14 Feb-29 Mar, Sat-Sun	10am-4pm
24-26 Dec, 31 Dec-1 Jan	Closed

ACQ.1932 ⛰ 🗡 ♿ 🖼 🧒 🚻 🎁 🏠 ⚠ OVP

Parking (in town).

MAP Page 342 (2E)
OS Map 110, OL1: SK149826

Perched high above the pretty village of Castleton, the castle offers breathtaking views of the Peak District. Founded soon after 1066 by William Peverel, one of William the Conqueror's most trusted knights, it played an important role in guarding the Peak Forest.

Henry II made a number of additions to 'Castle Peak' (as it was known in the Middle Ages). Most notable is the great square keep, with its round-headed windows, built in 1176. Thirteenth-century developments included the great hall, and though by 1400 the fortress had ceased to be strategically important, its impregnability guaranteed its continued use as a prison.

Displays in the visitor centre tell the story of Peveril as the focal point of the Royal Forest of the Peak, a royal hunting preserve since the 11th century.

Wheelchair access is available to the visitor centre only via a steep slope.

SUTTON SCARSDALE HALL
DERBYSHIRE – S44 5UR

The imposing shell of a grandiose Georgian mansion built in 1724-29, with an immensely columned exterior. Roofless since 1919, when its interiors were dismantled and some exported to America: but there is still much to discover within, including traces of sumptuous plasterwork. Set amid contemporary garden remains, including a ha-ha ditch and parish church.

OPENING TIMES

Summer, daily	10am-6pm
Winter, daily	10am-4pm
24-26 Dec & 1 Jan	Closed

VISIT US

Direction: Between Chesterfield and Bolsover, 1½ miles S of Arkwright Town

Train: Chesterfield 5 miles

Bus: G&J Holmes 'Hallmark' service 48

Tel: 01604 735464

ACQ.1971 P ⌂ ♿

MAP Page 343 (2F)
OS Map 120, 269: SK442689

WINGFIELD MANOR DERBYSHIRE – DE55 7NH

The vast and immensely impressive ruins of a palatial medieval manor house arranged round a pair of courtyards, with a huge undercrofted Great Hall and a defensible High Tower 22 metres (72 feet) tall. This monument to late medieval 'conspicuous consumption' was built in the 1440s for the wealthy Ralph, Lord Cromwell, Treasurer of England and also builder of Tattershall Castle and College. Later the home of Bess of Hardwick's husband, the Earl of Shrewsbury, who imprisoned Mary Queen of Scots here in 1569, 1584 and 1585.

Please note: Wingfield Manor is part of a working farm and the owner's privacy should be respected at all times.

No access to the public except by pre-booked guided tours.

NON-MEMBERS

Adult	£5.70
Concession	£5.10
Child	£3.40

OPENING TIMES

Entry by pre-booked guided tours only, on the first Sat of the month from Apr-Sep. To book please call 0870 333 1181

Call for full details of opening times and other site facilities

VISIT US

Direction: 17 miles N of Derby; 11 miles S of Chesterfield on B5035; ½ mile S of South Wingfield. From M1 junction 28, W on A38, A615 (Matlock Road) at Alfreton, 1½ miles and turn onto B5035

Train: Alfreton 4 miles

Bus: Yourbus 140 & 142

Tel: 0870 333 1183 to book (Customer Services)

ACQ.1960 ✕ ⚠

Parking (none on site or in gateway).

MAP Page 342 (3E)
OS Map 119, 269: SK374548

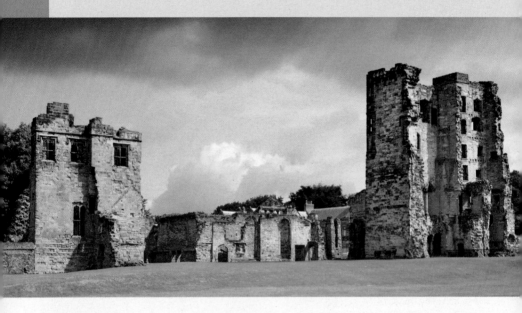

VISIT US

Direction: In Ashby de la Zouch, 12 miles S of Derby on A511. Restricted parking on site, please park in town car park

Train: Burton on Trent 9 miles

Bus: Macpherson Coaches 1, 2 & 3; Arriva 8, 9A; Roberts 7; Paul S. Winson Travel 129; Arriva/Midland Classic 9

Local Tourist Information: 01530 411767

Tel: 01530 413343

NON-MEMBERS

Adult	£4.70
Concession	£4.20
Child	£2.80
Family	£12.20

OPENING TIMES

1 Apr-30 Sep, Wed-Sun & Bank Hols	10am-6pm
1 Oct-2 Nov, Wed-Sun	10am-5pm
3 Nov-15 Feb, Sat-Sun	10am-4pm
16-20 Feb, daily	10am-4pm
21 Feb-29 Mar, Sat-Sun	10am-4pm
24-26 Dec, 31 Dec-1 Jan	Closed

Disabled access (grounds only).

Parking (restricted on site, please park in town car park – charge applies).

MAP Page 342 (4E)
OS Map 128, 245: SK361166

Ashby Castle forms the backdrop to the famous jousting scenes in Sir Walter Scott's classic novel of 1819, *Ivanhoe*. Now a ruin, the castle began as a manor house in the 12th century. It only achieved castle status in the 15th century, by which time the hall and buttery had been enlarged with a solar to the east and a large integral kitchen added to the west.

Between 1474 and his execution by Richard III in 1483, Edward IV's Chamberlain Lord Hastings added the chapel and the impressive keep-like Hastings Tower – a castle within a castle. Visitors can climb the 24 metre (78 feet) high tower, which offers fine views. Later the castle hosted many royal visitors, including Henry VII, Mary Queen of Scots, James I and Charles I.

A Royalist stronghold during the Civil War, the castle finally fell to Parliament in 1646, and was then made unusable. An underground passage from the kitchen to the tower, probably created during this war, can still be explored today. Archaeologists recently investigated the mysterious castle garden, famous for its elaborately shaped sunken features.

Interpretation boards include beautiful illustrations evoking the splendour of Lord Hastings' additions to the castle. The audio guide provides an amusing account of the castle's dramatic history, drawing upon a masque performed here for Alice Spencer, Countess of Derby, in the early 17th century.

JEWRY WALL
LEICESTERSHIRE – LE1 4LB

A length of Roman bath-house wall over 9 metres (30 feet) high, near a museum displaying the archaeology of Leicester and its region. Graphic panels describe the Roman baths.

Managed by Leicester City Council Parks and Gardens.

OPENING TIMES
Any reasonable daylight hours

Access to the adjacent garden with interpretation
1 Feb-31 Oct   11am-4.30pm

VISIT US
Direction: In St Nicholas St, W of Church of St Nicholas

Train: Leicester ¾ mile

Bus: Various services operated by First, Stagecoach, Arriva, Centrebus UHL service, NJ Travel, Kinch Bus, Leicester Truck & Bus & Roberts Coaches. Alight at St Nicholas Circle

Tel: 01604 735464

 ACQ.1920

Parking (by museum, within St Nicholas Circle).

MAP Page 343 (4F)
OS Map 140, 233: SK582045

KIRBY MUXLOE CASTLE
LEICESTERSHIRE – LE9 2DH

The picturesque moated remains – including the fine gatehouse and a complete corner tower – of this brick-built fortified mansion have recently been extensively conserved by English Heritage. Begun in 1480 by Lord Hastings, the castle was left unfinished after his execution by Richard III in 1483.

NON-MEMBERS
Adult	£3.70
Concession	£3.30
Child	£2.20

OPENING TIMES
1-30 Apr	Closed
1 May-1 Sep, Sat-Sun & Bank Hols	10am-5pm
2 Sep-29 Mar	Closed

Last admission 30 mins before closing

VISIT US
Direction: 4 miles W of Leicester off B5380; close to M1 junction 21A, northbound exit only

Train: Leicester 5 miles

Bus: NJ Travel service 13A to Kirby Corner; Arriva 153 to Kirby Muxloe then ½ mile walk

Tel: 01162 386886

 ACQ.1912 P OVP

MAP Page 343 (4F)
OS Map 140, 233: SK524046

LINCOLNSHIRE

BOLINGBROKE CASTLE
LINCOLNSHIRE – PE23 4HH

The remains of a 13th-century hexagonal castle, birthplace in 1367 of the future King Henry IV, with adjacent earthworks. Besieged and taken by Cromwell's Parliamentarians in 1643.

Managed by Heritage Lincolnshire.

OPENING TIMES
Any reasonable daylight hours

VISIT US
Direction: In Old Bolingbroke, 16 miles N of Boston off A16

Train: Thorpe Culvert 10 miles

Bus: Translinc Spilsby Call Connect (TC Minicoaches) service 6S will operate to Old Bolingbroke on request. To book telephone 0845 234 3344

Tel: 01529 461499

ACQ.1949

MAP Page 343 (2J)
OS Map 122, 273: TF349650

GAINSBOROUGH OLD HALL
LINCOLNSHIRE – DN21 2NB

Gainsborough Old Hall is among the biggest and best-preserved medieval manor houses in England, part timber-framed but mostly brick-built. Later 15th century with Elizabethan additions, it has

GAINSBOROUGH OLD HALL

an impressive kitchen with an enormous fireplace, a noble great hall, and an imposing lodgings tower. Many rooms are furnished as they may have appeared in the 15th century, and there is an exhibition tracing the Hall's later links with the Pilgrim Fathers.

Managed by Lincolnshire County Council.

www.gainsborougholdhall.com

NON-MEMBERS

Adult	£6.50
Child	£4.50
Family	£17.50
Free entry for children under 5	

OPENING TIMES

1 Mar-31 Oct, Mon-Fri	10am-5pm
Sat-Sun	11am-5pm
1 Nov-28 Feb, Mon-Fri	10am-4pm
Sat	11am-4pm
1-29 Mar, Mon-Fri	10am-5pm
Sat-Sun	11am-5pm
20 Dec-1 Jan	Closed

Last admission 30 mins before closure every day

The site may close occasionally for weddings between May and Sep – please phone site to check for latest details

VISIT US

Direction: In Parnell Road, Gainsborough, opposite the library

Train: Gainsborough Central ½ mile, Gainsborough Lea Road 1 mile

Bus: Stagecoach operate services to Gainsborough bus station from surrounding areas. It is a short walk from there to the Old Hall

Tel: 01427 677348

Disabled access (most of ground floor).

MAP Page 343 (1G)
OS Map 112/121, 280: SK813900

LINCOLN MEDIEVAL BISHOPS' PALACE
LINCOLNSHIRE – LN2 1PU

Standing almost in the shadow of Lincoln cathedral, with sweeping views over the ancient city and the countryside beyond, the medieval bishops' palace was once among the most important buildings in the country. The administrative centre of the largest diocese in medieval England, stretching from the Humber to the Thames, its architecture reflected the enormous power and wealth of the bishops as princes of the church.

Begun in the late 12th century, the palace's most impressive feature is the undercrofted East Hall, initiated by Bishop St Hugh and completed in the 1230s. The chapel range and entrance tower were built by Bishop William Alnwick, who modernised the palace in the 1430s. Having hosted visits from Henry VIII and James I, the palace was sacked by Royalist troops during the Civil War.

Built on hillside terraces, the palace also boasts a Contemporary Heritage Garden, designed by Mark Anthony Walker. Its form was inspired by the cathedral's medieval vaulting, with trees shaped to echo spires. Award-winning audio tour.

The site is also the home of a working vineyard, donated to Lincoln City Council in 1972 by Lincoln's twinned city, Neustadt an der Weinstrasse in Germany. The vineyard was re-established in 2012 with the landscaping of the contemporary garden. The vines are tended by an active group of volunteers using traditional methods. Visit the palace at different times of the year to see how the vines are progressing.

NON-MEMBERS

Adult	£4.70
Concession	£4.20
Child	£2.80
Family	£12.20

OPENING TIMES

1 Apr-30 Sep, Wed-Sun & Bank Hols	10am-6pm
1 Oct-2 Nov, Wed-Sun	10am-5pm
3 Nov-29 Mar, Sat-Sun	10am-4pm
24-26 Dec, 31 Dec-1 Jan	Closed

VISIT US

Direction: On the south side of Lincoln Cathedral. From the cathedral precinct gate, follow wall to your right to the gateway directly opposite cathedral south porch, then take tunnelled walkway (Chesney Gate). Entrance to the left down the pathway

Train: Lincoln 1 mile

Bus: From surrounding areas

Tel: 01522 527468

Parking (limited disabled parking on site).

MAP Page 343 (2H)
OS Map 121, 272: SK978717

SIBSEY TRADER WINDMILL
LINCOLNSHIRE – PE22 0SY

Built in 1877, this restored six-storey mill, with complete gear, sails and fantail, still works today. The award-winning tearoom sells produce made from the mill's organic, stone-ground flour.

Managed by Ian Ansell.

www.sibseytraderwindmill.co.uk

NON-MEMBERS

Adult	£2.50
Concession	£2.00
Child	£1.00

OPENING TIMES

1 Mar-30 Apr, Sat	10am-6pm	
Sun & Bank Hols	11am-6pm	
1 May-30 Sep, Tue, Sat	10am-6pm	
Sun & Bank Hols	11am-6pm	
1-31 Oct, Sat	10am-6pm	
Sun	11am-6pm	
1-30 Nov, Sat-Sun	11am-5pm	
1 Dec-28 Feb, Sat	11am-5pm	
27 Dec	Closed	

Group and education visits outside these hours by arrangement

VISIT US

Direction: ½ mile W of Sibsey off A16, 5 miles N of Boston

Train: Boston 5 miles

Bus: Brylaine 113 and Grayscroft 8 (Wed) to Sibsey, then ½ mile walk

Tel: 01205 460647/07718 320449

Disabled access (exterior only).

MAP Page 343 (3J)
OS Map 122, 261: TF345510

ST GEORGE'S CHURCH, GOLTHO
LINCOLNSHIRE LN8 5JD

© CCT

The charming red-brick chapel of St George is situated beside one of Lincolnshire's lost Saxon villages. The name 'Goltho' is said to be Saxon for 'where the marigolds grow'. Inside, this tranquil atmospheric church contains rustic painted wooden pews and a sense of time stood still.

Owned and managed by The Churches Conservation Trust.

OPENING TIMES

Presently closed see website for details www.visitchurches.org.uk

VISIT US

Train: Market Rasen 7½ miles

Bus: Stagecoach Lincolnshire service 6 or 10 to Rand, Village Lane end stop and then it is c. ½ mile walk

25 mins from Lincoln Medieval Bishops' Palace

MAP Page 343 (2H)
OS Map 121, 273: TF116775

TATTERSHALL COLLEGE
LINCOLNSHIRE – LN4 4LJ

Remains of a grammar school for church choristers, founded in the mid-15th century by Ralph, Lord Cromwell, the builder of Wingfield Manor (p.187) and nearby Tattershall Castle (National Trust).

The college is managed by Heritage Lincolnshire.

OPENING TIMES

Any reasonable daylight hours

VISIT US

Direction: In Tattershall, 14 miles NE of Sleaford on A153

Train: Ruskington 10 miles

Bus: Brylaine Interconnect service 5 and Translinc Call Connect (Kier) service 65

Tel: 01529 461499

ACQ 1972

MAP Page 343 (2H)
OS Map 122, 261: TF213578

NORTHAMPTONSHIRE

APETHORPE HALL
NORTHAMPTONSHIRE
PE8 5AQ

Among England's finest country houses, big and stately Apethorpe Hall was begun in the late 15th century. It contains one of the country's most complete Jacobean interiors, and hosted thirteen royal visits between 1565 and 1636.

While restoration work continues, English Heritage is pleased to offer access to visitors during 2014 on a limited, pre-booked and guided-tour basis only. For further details please visit our website or phone 0870 333 1181.

Please note: Apethorpe is still classed as a building site, and suitable footwear must be worn. There are lots of stairs, and no resting/seating points available. Children under 16 must be accompanied by an adult. We are unable to admit children under 5.

NON-MEMBERS
Please call for details

OPENING TIMES
By pre-booked guided tour only (charge applies) – please call 0870 333 1183 for details

VISIT US
Direction: Located off the A43 towards King's Cliffe. If entering Apethorpe via King's Cliffe Road, advance to Laundry Lane, not the High Street. If entering via Bridge St, pass the stone cross and turn left into Laundry Lane

Train: Stamford 11 miles or Peterborough 14 miles

APETHORPE HALL

Bus: CallConnect services 4P, 4S Mon-Sat (Tel: 0845 263 8153); or Centrebus service C24 (Tel: 0845 456 4474). Bus services must be booked in advance

Tel: 0870 333 1181

ACQ.2004 P

Access via narrow residential lane – please observe 10mph speed limit at all times.

MAP Page 343 (5H)
OS Map 141, 224/234: TL023954

CHICHELE COLLEGE
NORTHAMPTONSHIRE
NN10 8DZ

The chapel and other remains of a communal residence for priests serving the parish church, founded by locally-born Archbishop Chichele.

2014 marks the 600th anniversary of Henry Chichele's accession to the office of Archbishop of Canterbury, at the early age of 31: he held office for nearly 30 years.

The chapel is regularly used to display works of art.

Managed by Higham Ferrers Tourism, Business and Community Partnership. www.highamferrerstourism.org.uk

OPENING TIMES
Quadrangle – any reasonable daylight hours. Contact the keykeeper for the chapel: Mrs D Holyoak, 12 Lancaster St, Higham Ferrers NN10 8HY Tel: 01933 314157

CHICHELE COLLEGE

VISIT US
Direction: College Street, Higham Ferrers

Train: Wellingborough 5 miles

Bus: Stagecoach 49, 50, 51, X46, X47; Expresslines of Fenlake 'Rushden Higham Link'

Tel: 01933 314006

ACQ.1949

Dogs on leads (restricted areas only).

MAP Page 343 (6G)
OS Map 153, 224: SP960687

ELEANOR CROSS, GEDDINGTON
NORTHAMPTONSHIRE
NN14 1AD

In 1290 Eleanor of Castile, the beloved wife of Edward I and mother of his 14 children, died at Harby in Nottinghamshire. The places where her body rested on the journey south to its tomb in Westminster Abbey were marked by stone crosses. The stately triangular Geddington cross, with its canopied statues surmounted by a slender hexagonal pinnacle, is the best-preserved of only three intact survivors. Other crosses stand at Hardingstone near Northampton and Waltham Cross, Hertfordshire.

OPENING TIMES
Any reasonable daylight hours

VISIT US
Direction: Located in the village of Geddington, off A43 between Kettering and Corby

Train: Kettering 4 miles

Bus: Centrebus 8 to Geddington

Tel: 01604 735464

ACQ.1915

MAP Page 343 (5G)
OS Map 141, 224: SP894830

HOLIDAY COTTAGE AT KIRBY HALL

Peacock Cottage gives you direct access to the ruins and the grounds at any time. This means that in winter, when Kirby is only open to the public at weekends, you will have days of undisturbed pleasure.

VISIT US

Direction: On an unclassified road off A43, 4 miles NE of Corby

Train: Corby 4 miles

Bus: There are no bus services to the property. The closest is Centrebus 67. Alight at Kirby Lodge from there it is a 1 mile walk. Otherwise Stagecoach services 2, 2A, 2B, X1 and X4 to Priors Hall from there it is a 2 mile walk

Tel: 01536 203230

NON-MEMBERS

Adult	£6.00
Concession	£5.40
Child	£3.60
Family	£15.60

OPENING TIMES

1 Apr-30 Sep, Wed-Sun & Bank Hols	10am-6pm
1 Oct-2 Nov, Wed-Sun	10am-5pm
3 Nov-29 Mar, Sat-Sun	10am-4pm
24-26 Dec, 31 Dec-1 Jan	Closed

Disabled access (grounds, gardens and ground floor only).

Dogs on leads (restricted areas).

Kirby Hall is one of England's greatest Elizabethan and 17th-century houses. Begun by Sir Humphrey Stafford, it was purchased by Sir Christopher Hatton, one of Queen Elizabeth I's 'comely young men' and later her Lord Chancellor. Hatton hoped in vain to receive the Queen here during one of her annual 'progresses' around the country. Although this vast mansion is partly roofless, most of its walls survive to their full impressive height; as does the prodigious three-tier inner porch, begun following French pattern books and later embellished in the Classical style by the sculptor Nicholas Stone.

Kirby Hall's exceptionally rich decoration proclaims that its successive owners were always in the forefront of new ideas about architecture and design. The Great Hall and state apartments remain roofed and intact, with their interiors redecorated to authentic 17th- and 18th-century specifications.

Sir Christopher Hatton the Fourth added the great gardens (described as 'the finest garden in England') in the late 17th century. They have been recreated as they may have appeared at that time, with elaborate period style 'cutwork', statues, urns, seating, topiary and other features.

The gardens and ground floor of the mansion are easily accessible by wheelchair users.

An audio tour guides visitors through the house and gardens, accompanied by commentaries from experts in garden history, conservation and country houses.

Owned by the Earl of Winchilsea and managed by English Heritage.

MAP Page 343 (5G)
OS Map 141, 224: SP926927

VISIT US

Direction: 1 mile W of Rushton, on unclassified road; 1 mile from Desborough on A6

Train: Kettering 5 miles

Bus: Stagecoach in Northants service 19, stops outside property

Tel: 01536 710761

NON-MEMBERS

Adult	£3.40
Concession	£3.10
Child	£2.00

OPENING TIMES

1 Apr-31 Oct, Wed-Sun & Bank Hols	11am-5pm
1 Nov-29 Mar	Closed

ACQ.1951 🦮 📷 **P** 📷 OVP

Dogs on leads (restricted areas only).

Parking in lay-by on opposite side of road to entrance.

MAP Page 343 (5G)
OS Map 141, 224: SP830831

This delightful triangular building was designed by Sir Thomas Tresham (father of one of the Gunpowder Plotters) and constructed between 1593 and 1597. It is a testament to Tresham's Roman Catholicism: the number three, symbolising the Holy Trinity, is apparent everywhere. There are three floors, trefoil windows and three triangular gables on each side. On the entrance front is the inscription 'Tres Testimonium Dant' ('there are three that give witness'), a Biblical quotation from St John's Letters referring to the Trinity. It is also a pun on Tresham's name: his wife called him 'Good Tres' in her letters.

ST ANDREW'S CHURCH, CRANFORD
NORTHAMPTONSHIRE
NN14 4AD

© CCT

Sumptuous memorials to 300 years of the Robinson family fill medieval St Andrew's, which lies next to the Robinson seat of Cranford Hall. Structural additions, stained glass and furnishings from across the centuries give this church a rich and varied history.

Owned and managed by The Churches Conservation Trust.

OPENING TIMES
Keyholder nearby

VISIT US
Train: Kettering 4 miles

Bus: Centrebus Midlands service 16

10 mins from Eleanor Cross, 30 mins from Kirby Hall

MAP Page 343 (5G)
OS Map 141, 224: SP925773

ST PETER'S CHURCH, DEENE
NORTHAMPTONSHIRE
NN17 3EJ

© Steven Cole

Set in the estate of Deene Park, St Peter's is the family church of the Brudenells, who bought the estate in 1514. The church is a large building of local stone and Collyweston slate, with a tall west tower, a broach spire, and a number of family memorials.

Owned and managed by The Churches Conservation Trust.

OPENING TIMES
Keyholder nearby

VISIT US
Train: Kettering 10½ miles

Bus: Stamford & Welland Vale Call Connect service 4S will serve the village by request. Tel 0845 263 8153 to book

4 mins from Kirby Hall

MAP Page 343 (5G)
OS Map 141, 224: SP952928

ST PETER'S CHURCH, NORTHAMPTON
NORTHAMPTONSHIRE
NN1 1SR

© CCT

One of the most outstanding Norman churches in the county, this 900-year-old church in Northampton city centre is filled with glorious carved treasures. Inside, great stone arches rise and flow with zigzag waves of banded and plain stone, supported by carved capitals overflowing with foliage, scrollwork, birds and beasts.

Owned and managed by The Churches Conservation Trust.

OPENING TIMES
Mar-Oct, Wed-Sat	10am-4pm
Nov-Feb, Wed-Sat	11am-3pm

VISIT US
Train: Northampton ¼ mile

Bus: Multiple bus routes from town centre

30 mins from Chichele College

MAP Page 343 (6G)
OS Map 152, 207/223: SP7497160377

PROPERTY EVENTS NEAR YOU
Check our website for up-to-the-minute information on our year long programme of events.
www.english-heritage.org.uk/events

NOTTINGHAMSHIRE

MATTERSEY PRIORY
NOTTINGHAMSHIRE
DN10 5HN

The remains (mainly the 13th-century refectory and kitchen) of a small monastery for just six Gilbertine canons – the only wholly English monastic order.

OPENING TIMES
Any reasonable daylight hours

VISIT US
Direction: ¾ mile down rough drive, 1 mile E of Mattersey off B6045

Train: Retford 7 miles

Bus: Stagecoach East Midlands service 27, 27A; TM Travel 83 to village centre then ½ mile walk

Tel: 01604 735464

ACQ.1913

MAP Page 343 (1G)
OS Map 112/120, 280: SK703896

MILTON MAUSOLEUM, MARKHAM CLINTON
NOTTINGHAMSHIRE
NG22 0PJ

© James Darwin

This lovely Classical building with its domed tower was designed for the 4th Duke of Newcastle as a mausoleum for his wife. Inside there is an elegant Ionic reredos screen and some stunning marble effigies.

Owned and managed by The Churches Conservation Trust.

OPENING TIMES
May–Sep on
2nd and 4th Sun
of each month   2.30pm–4.30pm

At other times key holder nearby

VISIT US
Train: Retford 4¼ miles

Bus: Yourbus service 38 to Milton

20 mins from Rufford Abbey

MAP Page 343 (2G)
OS Map 120, 271: SK715730

RUFFORD ABBEY
NOTTINGHAMSHIRE
NG22 9DF

RUFFORD ABBEY

The best-preserved remains of a Cistercian abbey west cloister range in England, dating mainly from c. 1170. Incorporated into part of a 17th-century and later mansion, set in Rufford Country Park. Graphic panels show how the abbey was transformed into a great house.

Managed by Nottinghamshire County Council.

OPENING TIMES
1 Apr-31 Oct, daily	10am-5pm
1 Nov-29 Mar, daily	10am-4.30pm
25 Dec	Closed

See www.nottinghamshire.gov.uk/ ruffordcp for full details

VISIT US
Direction: 2 miles S of Ollerton off A614

Train: Mansfield 8 miles

Bus: 'The Sherwood Arrow' (Stagecoach) service Nottingham – Worksop; also Travelwright 227 (Wed and Fri only)

Tel: 01623 821338

ACQ.1959

Occasional charge for members on event days.

Parking (charge applies – not managed by English Heritage).

Shop – craft centre.

MAP Page 343 (2F)
OS Map 120, 270: SK646648

VISIT US

Direction: In Lyddington, 6 miles N of Corby; 1 mile E of A6003, next to the church

Train: Oakham 7 miles

Bus: Centrebus 'Rutland Flyer' service 1 Corby-Oakham (passes close to ⊞ Oakham)

Tel: 01572 822438

NON-MEMBERS

Adult	£4.50
Concession	£4.10
Child	£2.70
Family	£11.70

OPENING TIMES

1 Apr-30 Sep, Wed-Sun & Bank Hols	10am-6pm
1 Oct-3 Nov, Wed-Sun	10am-5pm
4 Nov-29 Mar	Closed

ACQ.1952 🏛 ✗ 🏠 🔒 ♿ ⚠ OVP
Disabled access (ground floor only).

MAP Page 343 (5G)
OS Map 141, 234: SP876970

Set beside the church in a picturesque ironstone village, Lyddington Bede House originated as the medieval wing of a palace belonging to the Bishops of Lincoln. By 1600 it had passed to Sir Thomas Cecil, son of Queen Elizabeth I's chief minister, who converted it into an almshouse for twelve poor 'bedesmen' over 30 years old and two women (over 45), all free of lunacy, leprosy or the French pox. It continued to serve as an almshouse until the 1930s. Visitors can wander through the bedesmen's rooms, with their tiny windows and fireplaces, and view the Bishops' Great Chamber with its beautifully carved early Tudor ceiling cornice.

Interpretation includes a case displaying a Bible and prayer book used at the Bedehouse, and audio boxes where you can hear letters read by the 'bedesmen'. One of the bedeswomen's rooms has been recreated as it may have appeared in late Victorian times. There is a small herb garden.

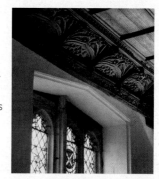

DISCOUNTED ATTRACTIONS:

Use your membership to get exclusive discounts at these independent attractions in the East Midlands. Please remember to show your card as proof of membership.

FREE ENTRY

ASHBY DE LA ZOUCH MUSEUM
Leicestershire LE65 1HU
2010/2007 County Museum of the year. Model of Ashby Castle. Temporary displays, archives, research/family history facilities, guided walks.
www.ashbydelazouchmuseum.org.uk
Tel. 01530 560090

20% DISCOUNT ON ENTRY

BOSWORTH BATTLEFIELD
Leicestershire CV13 0AD
Re-live the drama and excitement of the Battle of Bosworth in 1485 at the award-winning Bosworth Heritage Centre.
www.bosworthbattlefield.com
Tel. 01455 290429

25% OFF ADULT HOUSE AND GARDENS TICKETS

BURGHLEY HOUSE
Lincolnshire PE9 3JY
England's greatest Elizabethan House. Burghley was built and designed by William Cecil, Lord High Treasurer to Queen Elizabeth I.
www.burghley.co.uk
Tel. 01780 752451

25% OFF ICE AGE TOUR

CRESWELL CRAGS
Nottinghamshire and Derbyshire Border S80 3LH
Home to Britain's oldest cave art and remarkable archaeology, Creswell Crags provides a glimpse of life during the Ice Age.
www.creswell-crags.org.uk
Tel. 01909 720378

2 for 1 ENTRY

CRICH TRAMWAY VILLAGE
Derbyshire DE4 5DP
Travel through time on vintage trams along the period street and out into the open countryside.
www.tramway.co.uk
Tel. 01773 854321

25% DISCOUNT ON ENTRY

78 DERNGATE: THE CHARLES RENNIE MACKINTOSH HOUSE & GALLERIES
Northampton NN1 1UH
Style. Inspiration. Innovation. The only house in England designed by Charles Rennie Mackintosh.
www.78derngate.org.uk
Tel. 01604 603407

EAST MIDLANDS

Discount applies to:

KEY	⊞ MEMBERS	OVP OVP HOLDERS	👪? NO. OF MEMBER'S CHILDREN

Terms and conditions may apply, so make sure you check the individual pages on our website or call the individual property for more details.

£2 OFF ENTRY

⊞ OVP

GRIMSTHORPE CASTLE
Lincolnshire PE10 0LY
Grimsthorpe is a historic house, park and garden, open for adults and children to enjoy the countryside, nature and history.

www.grimsthorpe.co.uk
Tel. 01778 591205

2 for 1 ENTRY

⊞ OVP 👪 3

KELMARSH HALL & GARDENS
Northampton NN6 9LY
Original James Gibbs house set in renowned gardens with wonderful views and vistas.

www.kelmarsh.com
Tel. 01604 686543

25% DISCOUNT ON ENTRY

⊞ 👪 2

PAPPLEWICK PUMPING STATION
Nottinghamshire NG15 9AJ
Britain's finest working Victorian water pumping station, with woodland play area and miniature railway.

www.papplewickpumpingstation.org.uk
Tel. 0115 963 2938

2 for ON STANDARD TICKETS

⊞ OVP 👪 1

PEAK RAIL
Derbyshire DE4 3NA
Take a nostalgic journey back in time through the Derbyshire dales. Stations at Matlock, Darley Dale and Rowsley South.

www.peakrail.co.uk
Tel. 01629 580381

2 for 1 ENTRY

⊞ 👪 2

ROCKINGHAM CASTLE
Leicestershire LE16 8TH
A royal fortress for 450 years and a much-loved family home. Set in 18 acres of gardens with activities for children.

www.rockinghamcastle.com
Tel. 01536 770240

GIVE THE GIFT OF MEMBERSHIP

Give friends and family the opportunity to enjoy these fantastic discounts too!

- Free entry to over 400 historic properties
- Kids go free (up to six per adult in a family group)
- Free or discounted entry to hundreds of events, activities and other attractions
- Free handbook worth £10.95
- Exclusive Members' Magazine

WEST MIDLANDS

Goodrich Castle

Keep up to date with
events, news and offers
www.english-heritage.
org.uk/newsletter

Stokesay Castle

Stoke-on-Trent

23

Staffordshire

18
Oswestry
Shropshire

17

Burton upon Trent

Stafford

12

15

Shrewsbury

22
Telford
8

10
24

9 13
Tamworth

7
21

14
20

Wolverhampton

16

Nuneaton

Bishop's Castle

27
Birmingham

26
West
Midlands
Coventry

11
19

Kidderminster

Ludlow
25
Rugby

6
Worcestershire

29
Warwick

Leominster
Warwickshire

28
Worcester
Stratford-upon-Avon

Herefordshire

Great Malvern

Evesham

1

Hereford
5

4

Ross-on-Wye

3

Details of local public transport information in England are available from Traveline
www.traveline.org.uk or call 0871 200 2233.

HIGHLIGHTS FOR 2014/15 IN THE **WEST MIDLANDS**

p.218

Kenilworth Castle and Elizabethan Garden: lofty new platforms offer 'Queen's eye-views' of the great medieval and Elizabethan castle this year.

p.214

Stokesay Castle: England's finest and most original fortified medieval manor house, in a lovely Welsh Borders setting.

p.222

Witley Court and Gardens: spectacular remains of a palatial mansion amid lovely gardens, including an exciting Wilderness Play Area.

PROPERTIES

HEREFORDSHIRE

1 Arthur's Stone
2 Edvin Loach Old Church
3 Goodrich Castle
4 Longtown Castle
5 Rotherwas Chapel
6 Wigmore Castle

SHROPSHIRE

7 Acton Burnell Castle
8 Boscobel House and The Royal Oak
9 Buildwas Abbey

10 Cantlop Bridge
11 Clun Castle
12 Haughmond Abbey
13 Iron Bridge
14 Langley Chapel
15 Lilleshall Abbey
16 Mitchell's Fold Stone Circle
17 Moreton Corbet Castle
18 Old Oswestry Hill Fort
19 Stokesay Castle
20 Wenlock Priory
21 White Ladies Priory
22 Wroxeter Roman City

STAFFORDSHIRE

23 Croxden Abbey
24 Wall Roman Site

WARWICKSHIRE

25 Kenilworth Castle and Elizabethan Garden

WEST MIDLANDS

26 Halesowen Abbey
27 J.W. Evans Silver Factory

WORCESTERSHIRE

28 Leigh Court Barn
29 Witley Court and Gardens

Remember to check opening times before you visit any of our properties
www.english-heritage.org.uk/daysout

HEREFORDSHIRE

ARTHUR'S STONE
HEREFORDSHIRE

An atmospheric Neolithic burial chamber made of great stone slabs, in the hills above Herefordshire's Golden Valley.

OPENING TIMES
Any reasonable daylight hours

VISIT US
Direction: 7 miles E of Hay-on-Wye off B4348 near Dorstone

Bus: Stagecoach in South Wales service 39; Yeomans Canyon service 39A (Sun) ⬛ Hereford – Brecon to within ¾ mile

ACQ.1909 🐾 P

MAP Page 342 (7B)
OS Map 148/161, OL13/201: SO319431

CHURCH OF ST JOHN THE BAPTIST, LLANROTHAL
HEREFORDSHIRE
NP25 5QJ

© Nicholas Kaye

This remote whitewashed church, right on the Welsh border, sits in an idyllic valley by the River Monnow. The church is said to have been founded by a Celtic saint, St Ridol, and has a beautiful medieval interior.

Owned and managed by The Churches Conservation Trust.

OPENING TIMES
Any reasonable daylight hours

VISIT US
Train: Abergavenny 10¾ miles

Bus: Stagecoach service 36 to Welsh Newton (2¼ miles walk); Yeomans service 412 to Broad Oak (2¼ miles walk)

20 mins from Goodrich Castle

MAP Page 342 (7B)
OS Map 161, OL14: SO489169

EDVIN LOACH OLD CHURCH
HEREFORDSHIRE

EDVIN LOACH OLD CHURCH

The ruins of an 11th-century and later church built within the earthworks of a Norman motte and bailey castle, with a Victorian church nearby.

OPENING TIMES
Any reasonable daylight hours

VISIT US
Direction: Located 4 miles N of Bromyard on an unclassified road off B4203

Bus: The closest town is Bromyard (3½ miles). Bus services operated by Astons 405; First/DRM 420; DRM 469, 482, 673 & 674

ACQ.1980 🐾 P

MAP Page 342 (6C)
OS Map 149, 202: SO663584

GOODRICH CASTLE
SEE FEATURE – PAGE 206

LONGTOWN CASTLE
HEREFORDSHIRE

LONGTOWN CASTLE

Built within an earlier square earthwork, Longtown Castle is a powerful, thick-walled round keep of c. 1200, characteristic of the Welsh Borders, on a large earthen mound within a stone-walled bailey. Set in the beautiful Olchon valley, with magnificent views of the Black Mountains.

OPENING TIMES

Any reasonable daylight hours

VISIT US

Direction: Located in the centre of Longtown

Bus: Abbey Cars service 441 (Wed) & 442 (Tue); Roy Brown Coaches (summer service) B17

ACQ.1973 | P

Parking in lay-by.

MAP Page 342 (7B)
OS Map 161, OL13: SO321291

ROTHERWAS CHAPEL
HEREFORDSHIRE

The family chapel of the Roman Catholic Bodenham family. The originally simple medieval building has a fine Elizabethan timber roof, a rebuilt 18th-century tower, and striking Victorian interior decoration and furnishings by the Pugins.

OPENING TIMES

Any reasonable daylight hours. Key available at nearby Rotherwas Service Station. Tel: 01432 352978

ROTHERWAS CHAPEL

VISIT US

Direction: 1½ miles SE of Hereford on B4399, left into Chapel Road

Train: Hereford 3½ miles

Bus: First service 78, 78A then ½ mile walk

ACQ.1928 | P |

Disabled access via kissing gate only.

MAP Page 342 (7B)
OS Map 149, 189: SO536383

ST MICHAEL'S CHURCH, MICHAELCHURCH
HEREFORDSHIRE
HR2 8LD

© Nicholas Kaye

Said to have been founded by Bishop Herwald of Llandaff in 1056, this lovely church hugs the side of a remote valley. A Roman altar is built into a blocked doorway, and 13th-century paintings decorate the walls.

Owned and managed by The Churches Conservation Trust.

OPENING TIMES

Any reasonable daylight hours

VISIT US

Train: Hereford 9¼ miles

Bus: Stagecoach service 36 to Sandyway then 2 miles walk; Stagecoach 32 or 33 to Harewood End then 2 miles walk

60 mins from Goodrich Castle

MAP Page 342 (7B)
OS Map 162, 189: SO522255

WIGMORE CASTLE
HEREFORDSHIRE

Once the stronghold of the turbulent Mortimer family, Wigmore Castle was later dismantled to prevent its use during the Civil War. Now it is among the most remarkable ruins in England. The site has been excavated, but is largely buried up to first floor level by earth and fallen masonry. Yet many of its fortifications survive to full height, including parts of the keep on its towering mound. Graphic panels tell the story of this important medieval castle, now conserved for its wildlife habitats as well as its historic interest.

OPENING TIMES

Any reasonable daylight hours

VISIT US

Direction: Located 8 miles W of Ludlow on A4110. Accessible via footpath ¾ mile from the village on Mortimer Way

Train: Bucknell 6 miles, Ludlow 10 miles

Bus: Lugg Valley 489 (Tue, Fri only), 491 (1st, 3rd & 5th Wed only), 498 (2nd & 4th Wed only), 802 (Sun only); Roy Brown Coaches X11 (Mon only)

ACQ.1995 | P | ⚠

Toilets in the village hall are open from Easter to October half term, inclusive. There is a disabled toilet with ramp access from the village hall car park.

There are steep steps to the summit, which are hazardous in icy and wet conditions. Children must stay under close control. Do not climb on the walls or banks. Strong footwear is recommended.

MAP Page 342 (6B)
OS Map 137/148, 203: SO408693

GOODRICH CASTLE Herefordshire – HR9 6HY

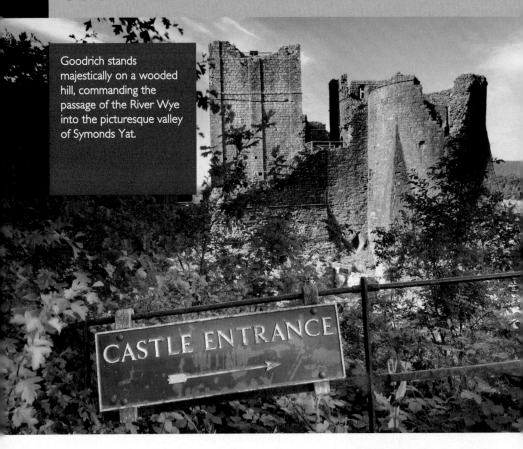

Goodrich stands majestically on a wooded hill, commanding the passage of the River Wye into the picturesque valley of Symonds Yat.

CASTLE ENTRANCE

VISIT US

Address: Goodrich Castle, Castle Lane, Goodrich, Ross-on-Wye, Herefordshire

Direction: 5 miles S of Ross-on-Wye off A40

Bus: H&H Coaches service 34 and 411 (Wed) to within ½ mile

Tel: 01600 890538

NON-MEMBERS

Adult	£6.40
Concession	£5.80
Child	£3.80
Family	£16.60

OPENING TIMES

1 Apr-30 Sep, daily	10am-6pm
1 Oct-2 Nov, daily	10am-5pm
3 Nov-15 Feb, Sat-Sun	10am-4pm
16-20 Feb, daily	10am-4pm
21 Feb-29 Mar, Sat-Sun	10am-4pm
24-26 Dec, 31 Dec-1 Jan	Closed

Last admission 30 mins before closing

ACQ.1920 🎧 ♿ 🐾 🎁 👕 🧥 📷 🚻 👶
🅿 🏠 📷 ☕ ⚠ OVP

A non-refundable car parking charge of £1 applies.

Dogs on leads.

Disabled access (limited, please call for details or ask the visitor centre on arrival).

The tearoom will close 30 minutes before the site closes.

Goodrich's delightful tearoom serves a fine selection of light refreshments made from locally-sourced Herefordshire ingredients.

MAP Page 342 (7C)
OS Map 162, OL14: SO577200

The castle was begun in the late 11th century by the English landowner Godric, who gave it his name. A generation later the splendidly preserved square keep that still forms its core was added, probably in the time of Richard 'Strongbow' de Clare, Earl of Pembroke and Lord of Goodrich 1148-76.

Under King Richard the Lionheart, Goodrich was granted along with the earldom of Pembroke to the famous William Marshal, a great castle builder who may have initiated work on the inner ward. Each of Marshal's five sons inherited the fortress in turn, the fourth son dying childless at Goodrich in 1245.

Thereafter the fortress and earldom passed to Henry III's half-brother, William de Valence, who rebuilt its defences and living quarters in the most up-to-date style.

Goodrich still boasts one of the most complete sets of medieval domestic buildings surviving in any English castle. William's widow Countess Joan frequently stayed here with an entourage of up to 200, entertaining her relations and friends in the most lavish style.

During the Civil War, Goodrich was held successively by both sides. Sir Henry Lingen's Royalists eventually surrendered in 1646 under threats of undermining and a deadly Parliamentarian mortar. Visitors can see the famous 'Roaring Meg', the only surviving Civil War mortar, which has returned to the castle after over 350 years, and a cache of Civil War cannonballs, found at Goodrich in the 1920s. The visitor centre features an exhibition exploring life at the castle from its late 11th-century origins until its dramatic fall in 1646, including Civil War artefacts.

SHROPSHIRE

ACTON BURNELL CASTLE
SHROPSHIRE

The impressive red sandstone shell of a battlemented tower house mansion, built c.1283-92 by Bishop Robert Burnell, Edward I's Lord Chancellor. Parliament was held nearby in 1283, when the king ratified a law for the protection of merchants, known as the Statute of Acton Burnell.

OPENING TIMES
Any reasonable daylight hours

VISIT US
Direction: Located in Acton Burnell, signposted from A49, 8 miles S of Shrewsbury

Train: Shrewsbury or Church Stretton, both 8 miles

Bus: Boultons (of Cardington) service 540

ACQ.1930 🐕 P ♿

MAP Page 342 (4B)
OS Map 126, 241: SJ534019

BOSCOBEL HOUSE AND THE ROYAL OAK
SEE FEATURE OPPOSITE

BUILDWAS ABBEY
SHROPSHIRE – TF8 7BW

Impressive ruins of a Cistercian abbey, including its unusually unaltered 12th-century church, beautiful vaulted and tile-floored chapter house and recently re-opened crypt chapel.

In a wooded Severn-side setting, not far from the Iron Bridge (p.211) and Wenlock Priory (p.213) – near the home of Dr William Penny Brookes, originator of the still-continuing Olympian Wenlock Games, a major inspiration for the modern International Olympics.

NON-MEMBERS
Adult	£3.70
Concession	£3.30
Child	£2.20

OPENING TIMES
1 Apr-30 Sep, daily	10am-5pm
1 Oct-29 Mar	Closed

Last admission 30 mins before closing

VISIT US
Direction: On S bank of River Severn on A4169, 2 miles W of Ironbridge

Train: Telford Central 6 miles

Bus: Arriva Midlands service 96

Tel: 01952 433274

ACQ.1925 🐕 ⌂ P 📷 🍴 ♿ ⚠ OVP

Disabled access is limited.

Nature trail (not managed by EH) including site of abbey fishponds.

MAP Page 342 (4C)
OS Map 127, 242: SJ643043

CANTLOP BRIDGE
SHROPSHIRE

A single-span, cast-iron road bridge over the Cound Brook. Possibly designed and certainly approved by the great engineer Thomas Telford, who was instrumental in shaping industrial Shropshire and the West Midlands.

OPENING TIMES
Any reasonable daylight hours

VISIT US
Direction: ¾ mile SW of Berrington on an unclassified road off A458

Train: Shrewsbury 5 miles

Bus: Boultons (of Cardington) service 540

ACQ.1977 ♿ 🐕 P

Parking in lay-by.

MAP Page 342 (4B)
OS Map 126, 241: SJ517062

VISIT US

Direction: On minor road from A41 to A5, 8 miles NW of Wolverhampton. 5 mins drive from M54 J3

Train: Cosford 3 miles

Bus: Coastal Liner 17 (Wed only); Arriva Midlands services 88/88A to Bishopswood then 1 mile walk

Tel: 01902 850244

NON-MEMBERS

Adult	£6.40
Concession	£5.80
Child	£3.80
Family	£16.60

OPENING TIMES

1 Apr-2 Nov, Wed-Sun & Bank Hols	10am-5pm
3 Nov-29 Mar, Sat-Sun Guided tours only	10am-4pm
24-26 Dec, 31 Dec-1 Jan	Closed

House will be closed for 1 hour at 11am and 2pm for guided tours. Guided tours are subject to availability and booking is advisable

Last entry to house at 3pm

NB. External conservation maintenance work on the house exterior may restrict views of the façade throughout 2014

Dogs on leads (grounds only).

Parking (coaches welcome).

Disabled access limited. Call for details.

MAP Page 342 (4C)
OS Map 127, 242: SJ838082

A pretty timber-framed house that played a brief but important role in English history, Boscobel was converted into a lodge by John Giffard in about 1630. The Giffards were Roman Catholics, and tradition holds that its real purpose was to serve as a secret refuge for persecuted Catholics at times of need.

Boscobel was destined for greater fame. Following the execution of King Charles I in 1649, his son made a brave though misguided attempt to regain the throne. Defeated in 1651 at Worcester, the final battle of the Civil War, young Charles fled for his life.

Initially Charles intended to cross the River Severn into Wales, but found his way blocked by Cromwell's patrols. He sought refuge instead at Boscobel, hiding first in a tree, known afterwards as 'The Royal Oak', and then in a priest-hole in the house's attic. The future King Charles II then travelled on in disguise via other safe houses before escaping to France.

Boscobel became a much-visited place, although it remained a working farm. Today's visitors can enjoy our audio and visual displays; take a guided tour of the lodge; see the garden and a descendant of The Royal Oak; and find out about Boscobel's past as a working Victorian farm.

There is a permissive path from Boscobel House to White Ladies Priory (p.213), another of Charles's hiding places.

Visit the education and family room, where you can try on armour and dress as a Roundhead or Cavalier.

CHURCH OF ST MARY THE VIRGIN, SHREWSBURY
SHROPSHIRE – SY1 1DX

© CCT

St Mary's is a gem on a grand scale. It has the tallest spire in England; glorious stained glass including a world-famous 14th-century 'Jesse window' and a Medieval cartoon strip featuring St Bernard; a stunning 15th-century carved oak ceiling and a wealth of rich colours and fascinating treasures.

Owned and managed by The Churches Conservation Trust.

OPENING TIMES

1 Apr-31 Oct, Mon-Sat	10am-5pm
1 Nov-29 Mar, Mon-Sat	10am-4pm
Sometimes open on Sundays	

VISIT US

Train: Shrewsbury 15 mins walk

Bus: Shrewsbury is served by many buses

10 mins from Haughmond Abbey

MAP Page 342 (4B)
OS Map 126, 241: SJ494126

CLUN CASTLE
SHROPSHIRE

CLUN CASTLE

The dramatic riverside ruins and extensive earthworks of a Welsh Border castle, its tall 13th-century keep unusually set on the side of its mound. Information panels tell the story of the castle and the adjacent town.

OPENING TIMES

Any reasonable daylight hours

VISIT US

Direction: In Clun, off A488, 18 miles W of Ludlow

Train: Hopton Heath 6½ miles; Knighton 6½ miles

Bus: Minsterley 745 (Mon & Fri only); M&J service 773 & 860 (Tue only)

ACQ.1991 ⚔ 🅿 🚻 ⚠

Toilets available near car park (not managed by English Heritage).

MAP Page 342 (5B)
OS Map 137, 201: SO299809

HAUGHMOND ABBEY
SHROPSHIRE – SY4 4RW

The extensive remains of an Augustinian abbey, including its abbots' quarters, refectory and cloister. The substantially surviving chapter house has a frontage richly bedecked with 12th and 14th-century carving and statuary and a fine timber roof of c. 1500. An introductory exhibition displays archaeological finds. Picnic area.

NON-MEMBERS

Adult	£3.70
Concession	£3.30
Child	£2.20

HAUGHMOND ABBEY

OPENING TIMES

1 Apr-30 Sep, Wed-Sun & Bank Hols	10am-5pm
1 Oct-29 Mar	Closed

VISIT US

Direction: Located 3 miles NE of Shrewsbury off B5062

Train: Shrewsbury 3½ miles

Bus: Arriva 519 Shrewsbury – Newport

Tel: 01743 709661

ACQ.1931 ⚔ 🍴 🅿 🚻 ♿ ⚠ OVP

Disabled access (not easy).

Light refreshments available

MAP Page 342 (4B)
OS Map 126, 241: SJ542152

IRON BRIDGE
SEE FEATURE OPPOSITE

LANGLEY CHAPEL
SHROPSHIRE

A small chapel tranquilly set all alone in charming countryside. Its atmospheric interior contains a perfect set of 17th-century timber furnishings, including a musicians' pew.

OPENING TIMES

1 Apr-2 Nov, daily	10am-6pm
3 Nov-29 Mar, daily	10am-4pm
24-26 Dec & 1 Jan	Closed

VISIT US

Direction: 1½ miles S of Acton Burnell, on an unclassified road off A49; 9½ miles S of Shrewsbury

Train: Shrewsbury 7½ miles

Bus: Boultons (of Cardington) service 540 (then 1¼ mile walk)

ACQ.1914 ⚔ 🅿

MAP Page 342 (5B)
OS Map 126/127/138, 217/241: SJ538001

VISIT US

Direction: Adjacent to A4169

Bus: Arriva 88, 88A 96, 99, 99A Gorge Connect service WH1 (summer Sat & Sun only)

OPENING TIMES

Any reasonable time

Members can also get a Passport discount at Ironbridge Gorge Museums. See p.224 for details.

ACQ.1975

Parking (charge applies). Car park not managed by English Heritage.

MAP Page 342 (4C)
OS Map 127, 242: SJ672034

The world's first iron bridge was erected over the River Severn here in 1779. Britain's best-known industrial monument, the bridge gave its name to the spectacular wooded gorge which, though now tranquil, was once an industrial powerhouse and the cradle of the Industrial Revolution. Ironbridge Gorge is now a World Heritage Site.

At the beginning of the 18th century, Abraham Darby I pioneered the process of using coke made from local coal to smelt local iron ore, but industrial expansion was hampered by the lack of a bridge over the Severn, which had to be a single span to allow for barge traffic. An iron bridge was first suggested by the Shrewsbury architect Thomas Pritchard: he designed a single-span bridge 30 metres long, but died as work began. The project was then taken over by Abraham Darby III, who cast the bridge in his Coalbrookdale foundry, using 378 tons of iron. Recent research shows that most parts were individually cast to fit, each being slightly different from the next: and that traditional woodworking-style joints were adapted to assemble them.

Costing over £6000, this proclamation of the achievements of Shropshire ironmasters was formally opened on New Year's Day 1781. It continued in full use by ever-increasing traffic until closed and designated an Ancient Monument in 1934. Massive strengthening works were later undertaken, and in 1999-2000 English Heritage assisted with a full survey of this revolutionary and iconic structure.

The Iron Bridge is the perfect place to begin a tour of the Gorge's many museums and the many other English Heritage sites nearby, including Buildwas Abbey, Wenlock Priory and Wroxeter Roman City.

LILLESHALL ABBEY
SHROPSHIRE

Extensive ruins of an Augustinian abbey, later a Civil War stronghold, in a deeply rural setting. Much of the church survives, unusually viewable from gallery level, along with the lavishly sculpted processional door and other cloister buildings. Graphic panels show how the abbey appeared in medieval times.

OPENING TIMES

1 Apr–2 Nov, daily	10am–6pm
3 Nov–29 Mar, daily	10am–4pm
24–26 Dec & 1 Jan	Closed

VISIT US

Direction: On an unclassified road off A518, 4 miles N of Oakengates

Train: Oakengates 4½ miles

Bus: Arriva service 481 Telford – Stafford (passes close to 🚃 Telford Central and Stafford) or Arriva 115/116 (Sat only passes close to Shinall station) to within 1 mile – alight between Sheriffhales and Heath Hill

ACQ.1950 🐕 Ｐ ♿

Disabled access via kissing gate only.

MAP Page 342 (4C)
OS Map 127, 242: SJ738142

MITCHELL'S FOLD STONE CIRCLE
SHROPSHIRE

A neolithic stone circle, the focus of many legends, set in dramatic moorland on Stapeley Hill. It once consisted of some 30 stones, 15 of which are still visible.

OPENING TIMES

Any reasonable daylight hours

VISIT US

Direction: 16 miles SW of Shrewsbury, on unclassified road off A488

Train: Welshpool 10 miles

Bus: Minsterley Motors service 553 Shrewsbury – Bishop's Castle (passes close to 🚃 Shrewsbury). Also Minsterley Motors 745 (Mon & Fri only) 775 (Wed only) – all to Pennerley Junction within 1 mile. Also Shropshire Link service Zone 1 area 1 (Wed & Fri only)
Tel: 0845 678 9068

ACQ.1915 🐕 Ｐ

MAP Page 342 (5B)
OS Map 137, 216: SO304984

MORETON CORBET CASTLE
SHROPSHIRE

The ruins of the medieval castle and Tudor manor house of the Corbets are dominated by the theatrical shell of an ambitious Elizabethan mansion wing in Italianate style, which was devastated during the Civil War. Fine Corbet family monuments fill the adjacent church.

OPENING TIMES

Any reasonable daylight hours

VISIT US

Direction: In Moreton Corbet off B5063 (a turning off A49), 7 miles NE of Shrewsbury

Train: Yorton 4 miles

Bus: Arriva service 64 to Shawbury then ¾ mile walk

ACQ.1939 🐕 Ｐ ♿

Disabled access is limited.

MAP Page 342 (4C)
OS Map 126, 241: SJ561231

OLD OSWESTRY HILL FORT
SHROPSHIRE

Among the most hugely impressive Iron Age hillforts on the Welsh Borders, covering 40 acres, with formidable multiple ramparts.

Information panels tell you about the hillfort and its inhabitants.

OPENING TIMES

Any reasonable daylight hours

VISIT US

Direction: 1 mile N of Oswestry, off an unclassified road off A483

Train: Gobowen 2 miles

Bus: Arriva service 2, 2A, 53 to Gobowen Road or Arriva Oswestry town service 404 to Old Fort Way and then short walk

ACQ.1946 🐕 Ｐ

Sheep grazing on site.

MAP Page 342 (3B)
OS Map 126, 240/258: SJ295310

ST ANDREW'S CHURCH, WROXETER
SHROPSHIRE – SY5 6PH

St Andrew's is built on the site of Viriconium, the fourth largest town of Roman Britain, and evidence of its past can be found in and around the church. Parts of the building date from before the Domesday Book (1086) but the interior mostly dates from the 17th and 18th centuries and contains some wonderful monuments.

Owned and managed by The Churches Conservation Trust.

OPENING TIMES

Any reasonable daylight hours

VISIT US

Train: Shrewsbury 4 miles

Bus: Arriva Midlands bus route 96 Shrewsbury – Telford

Next to Wroxeter Roman City

MAP Page 342 (4C)
OS Map 126, 241: SJ564083

STOKESAY CASTLE
SEE FEATURE – PAGE 214

WENLOCK PRIORY SHROPSHIRE – TF13 6HS

WHITE LADIES PRIORY
SHROPSHIRE

The tranquil ruins of Wenlock Priory stand in a picturesque setting on the fringe of beautiful Much Wenlock. An Anglo-Saxon monastery was founded here in about 680 by King Merewalh of Mercia, whose abbess daughter Milburge was hailed as a saint. Her relics were miraculously re-discovered here in 1101, attracting both pilgrims and prosperity.

By then Wenlock had been re-founded by the Normans as a priory of Cluniac monks. The impressive remains of this medieval priory survive today, everywhere reflecting the Cluniac love of elaborate decoration. Parts of the great 13th-century church still stand high; and in the adjoining cloister garth is an unusual monks' washing fountain with 12th-century carvings. Once enclosed in an octagonal building, 16 monks could wash here at once before eating in the nearby refectory.

Perhaps the greatest glory of the priory is the extravagantly decorated chapter house of about 1140, its walls bedecked with interlocking blind arcading on multiple carved columns.

All this is enhanced by the topiary-filled cloister garden, and set against the backdrop of the complete infirmary wing,

converted into a mansion after the priory's dissolution and still a private residence.

Much Wenlock was the home of Dr William Penny Brookes, originator of the Wenlock Olympian Games first held here in 1850, a major inspiration for the modern International Olympics. July 2014 will see the 128th Wenlock Olympian Games contested in the town.

NON-MEMBERS

Adult	£4.20
Concession	£3.80
Child	£2.50

OPENING TIMES

1 Apr-30 Sep, daily	10am-6pm
1 Oct-2 Nov, daily	10am-5pm
3 Nov-15 Feb, Sat-Sun	10am-4pm
16-20 Feb, daily	10am-4pm
21 Feb-29 Mar, Sat-Sun	10am-4pm
24-26 Dec, 31 Dec-1 Jan	Closed

VISIT US

Direction: In Much Wenlock

Train: Telford Central 9 miles

Bus: Arriva service 88, 88A & 436

Tel: 01952 727466

ACQ.1964 🎧 📷 🐕 ❄ 🖥 🚹 P

📷 ♿ OVP

A non-refundable car parking charge of £1 applies.

MAP Page 342 (5C)
OS Map 127/138, 217/242: SJ625001

Ruins of the late 12th-century church of a small nunnery of 'white ladies' or Augustinian canonesses. Charles II came here in 1651 before seeking refuge at nearby Boscobel House (p.209).

Permissive path to White Ladies Priory from Boscobel House, where there is parking when the house is open. Approximately 20 minutes walk.

OPENING TIMES
Any reasonable daylight hours

VISIT US
Direction: Located 1 mile SW of Boscobel House off an unclassified road between A41 and A5; 8 miles NW of Wolverhampton

Train: Cosford 2½ miles

Bus: Coastal Liner 17 (Wed only); Arriva Midlands services 88/88A to Bishopswood then 1 mile walk

ACQ.1938 🐕

MAP Page 342 (4C)
OS Map 217, 242: SJ826076

WROXETER ROMAN CITY
SEE FEATURE – PAGE 216

STOKESAY CASTLE Shropshire – SY7 9AH

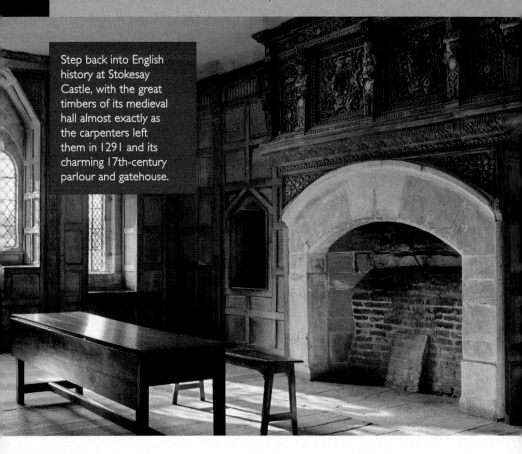

Step back into English history at Stokesay Castle, with the great timbers of its medieval hall almost exactly as the carpenters left them in 1291 and its charming 17th-century parlour and gatehouse.

VISIT US

Address: Stokesay Castle, Nr Craven Arms, Ludlow, Shropshire

Direction: 7 miles NW of Ludlow off A49

Train: Craven Arms 1 mile

Bus: Minsterley Motors (of Stiperstones) 435 to Stokesay turning on the A49 then ½ mile walk

Tel: 01588 672544

Local Tourist Information
Ludlow: 01584 875053

NON-MEMBERS

Adult	£6.40
Concession	£5.80
Child	£3.80
Family	£16.60

OPENING TIMES

1 Apr-30 Sep, daily	10am-6pm
1 Oct-2 Nov, daily	10am-5pm
3 Nov-15 Feb, Sat-Sun	10am-4pm
16-20 Feb, daily	10am-4pm
21 Feb-29 Mar, Sat-Sun	10am-4pm
24-26 Dec, 31 Dec-1 Jan	Closed

Last admission 30 mins before closing

 ACQ.1986

A non-refundable car parking charge of £1 applies.

Disabled access (call site for details).

Dogs allowed within the grounds on a lead but not allowed within the Castle.

Entrance to the courtyard is through a historic gate. Unsuitable for motorised scooters and unassisted wheelchair users.

Tearoom (seasonal): 1 Apr-2 Nov.

MAP Page 342 (5B)
OS Map 137/148, 203: SO436815

An audio tour will help you to imagine Stokesay as the centre of medieval life. Its grounds include cottage-style gardens, a tearoom open from April to October, and a gift shop.

Stokesay Castle is the finest and best preserved fortified medieval manor house in England. Set in peaceful countryside near the Welsh border, the castle, timber-framed gatehouse and parish church form an unforgettably picturesque group.

Lawrence of Ludlow, a wealthy local wool-merchant wishing to set up as a country gentleman, bought the property in 1281, when the long Anglo-Welsh wars were ending. So it was safe to raise here one of the first fortified manor houses in England, 'builded like a castle' for effect but lit by large domestic-style windows.

Extensive recent tree-ring dating confirms that Lawrence had completed virtually the whole of the still-surviving house by 1291, using the same team of carpenters throughout. More remarkably, the dating also revealed that it has scarcely been altered since.

Stokesay's magnificent open-hearthed great hall displays a fine timber roof, shuttered gable windows and a precipitous staircase, its treads cut from whole tree-trunks. It is flanked by the north tower, with an original medieval tiled floor and remains of a wall painting, and a 'solar' or private apartment block and the

tall south tower – the most castle-like part of the house, self-contained and reached by a defensible stairway.

The solar block contains one of the few post-medieval alterations to the house, a fine panelled chamber. Its dominating feature is a fireplace with a richly carved overmantel, still bearing clear traces of original painting in five colours. This was added in about 1641, at the same time as the truly delightful gatehouse: an outstanding and recently-conserved example of the Marches style of lavishly showy timber-framing, bedecked with charming carvings of Adam and Eve.

A few years later, in 1645, Stokesay experienced its only known military encounter, surrendering without fighting to a Parliamentarian force. So the house remained undamaged, and sensitive conservation by Victorian owners and English Heritage have left it the medieval jewel which survives today.

An audio tour helps you to imagine Stokesay as a centre of medieval life. Its attractions include beautiful cottage-style gardens, a moat, a tearoom open from April to October, and a gift shop.

WROXETER ROMAN CITY Shropshire – SY5 6PH

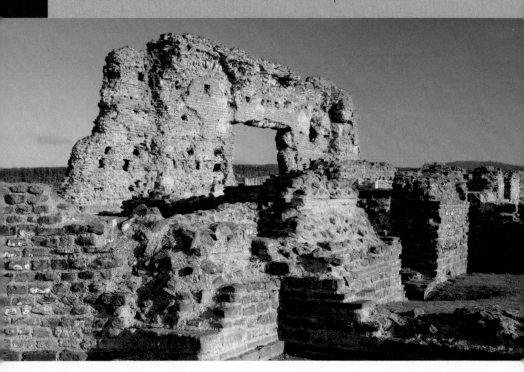

VISIT US

Direction: 5 miles SE of Shrewsbury, on a minor road signposted from the B4380

Train: Shrewsbury 5½ miles; Wellington Telford West 6 miles

Bus: Arriva 96 Telford – Shrewsbury (passes close to ⟨≢⟩ Telford Central)

Tel: 01743 761330

NON-MEMBERS

Adult	£5.40
Concession	£4.90
Child	£3.20
Family	£14.00

OPENING TIMES

1 Apr-2 Nov, daily	10am-5pm
3 Nov-29 Mar, Sat-Sun	10am-4pm
24-26 Dec, 31 Dec-1 Jan	Closed

Last admission 30 mins before closing

ACQ. 1947 🎧 🎌 🖼 🎭 🖥 🚶 🚻 🖼
P 🎏 📷 ⚠ OVP

MAP Page 342 (4B)
OS Map 126, 241: SJ565087

Now set among fields, Wroxeter (or 'Viriconium') was once the fourth largest city in Roman Britain, with up to 5000 citizens. It began as a legionary fortress and developed into a thriving civilian city, populated by retired soldiers and traders. Today the most impressive features are the remains of the 2nd-century municipal baths and the huge wall dividing them from the exercise hall, once in the heart of the city.

The audio tour reveals how Wroxeter worked in its heyday, and the fascinating site museum displays an amazing wealth of site finds, from military weapons and equipment to fashion accessories and medical instruments, illustrating the everyday life of the citizens. Vivid interpretation traces the rise, flourishing and eventual abandonment of the city.

An unusual and popular feature of the site is a recreation of a Roman town house, complete with dining-room, bedroom and bath-suite. Inspired by houses excavated here, it was built using traditional methods as interpreted by six modern building-trade workers, for the Channel 4 series 'Rome Wasn't Built in a Day'. It now also features replicas of Roman furniture.

An education room is available for schools.

STAFFORDSHIRE

CROXDEN ABBEY
STAFFORDSHIRE

The impressive remains of an abbey of Cistercian 'white monks', including towering fragments of its 13th-century church, infirmary and 14th-century abbot's lodging. Information panels and a display of decorative stonework tell the story of the abbey's spectacular architecture.

OPENING TIMES

1 Apr-2 Nov, daily	10am-6pm
3 Nov-29 Mar, daily	10am-4pm
24-26 Dec & 1 Jan	Closed

VISIT US

Direction: 5 miles NW of Uttoxeter off A522

Train: Uttoxeter 6 miles

Bus: Closest service is Phil Smith 185 to Hollington (Fri only). Otherwise First 32 to Fole or First 32A to Alton then 2½ miles walk

ACQ.1936

No climbing on the walls.

Limited parking.

MAP Page 342 (3D)
OS Map 128, 259: SK066397

WALL ROMAN SITE (LETOCETUM)
STAFFORDSHIRE
WS14 0AW

Wall was an important staging post on Watling Street, the Roman military road to North Wales. It provided overnight accommodation for travelling Roman officials and imperial messengers. The foundations of an inn and bathhouse can be seen, and many of the excavated finds are displayed in the on-site museum.

Managed by English Heritage on behalf of the National Trust, with thanks to the Friends of Letocetum.

OPENING TIMES

Site

1 Apr-2 Nov, daily	10am-5pm
3 Nov-29 Mar, daily	10am-4pm
24-26 Dec & 1 Jan	Closed

Museum

29-30 Mar, 19-21 Apr, 3-5 May, 28-29 Jun, 13, 20, 26-27 Jul, 3, 10, 17, 23-25, 30-31 Aug, 27-28 Sep, 25-26 Oct	11am-4pm

or dusk, whichever comes sooner

VISIT US

Direction: Off Eastbound A5 at Wall, near Lichfield

Train: Shenstone 1½ miles

Bus: Arriva Midland service 35B

ACQ.1949

MAP Page 342 (4D)
OS Map 139, 244: SK098066

WARWICKSHIRE

ALL SAINTS' CHURCH, BILLESLEY
WARWICKSHIRE
B49 6NF

© Sarah McCarthy

Tradition has it that William Shakespeare married Anne Hathaway here. His granddaughter's wedding is also said to have taken place in this church that dates back 1000 years. Some remains of the early church survive, in particular two spectacular 12th-century stone carvings.

Owned and managed by The Churches Conservation Trust.

OPENING TIMES
Any reasonable daylight hours

VISIT US

Train: Wilmcote 2½ miles and Stratford-upon-Avon 4 miles

Bus: Stagecoach Warwickshire service 26 Stratford-Redditch. Nearest official stop is Haselhor, but ask driver to drop you off near the Redhill intersection from whence it is c. ½ mile walk

30 mins to Kenilworth Castle and Elizabethan Garden

MAP Page 342 (6E)
OS Map 151, 205: SP148568

Don't forget to check opening times online before you visit.

www.english-heritage.org. uk/daysout/properties

KENILWORTH CASTLE AND ELIZABETHAN GARDEN
Warwickshire – CV8 1NG

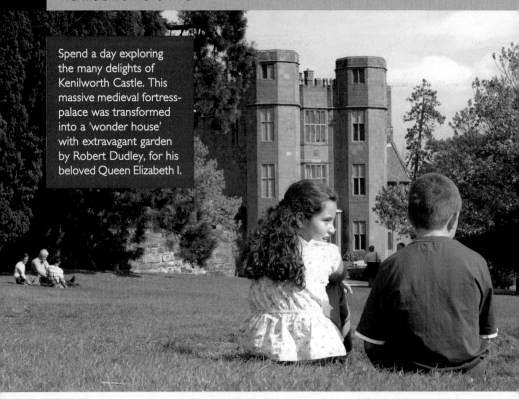

Spend a day exploring the many delights of Kenilworth Castle. This massive medieval fortress-palace was transformed into a 'wonder house' with extravagant garden by Robert Dudley, for his beloved Queen Elizabeth I.

VISIT US

Address: Kenilworth Castle, Castle Green, Off Castle Road, Kenilworth, Warwickshire

Direction: In Kenilworth off A46. Clearly signposted from the town centre, off B4103

Train: Warwick or Coventry 5 miles

Bus: Johnsons of Henley 539 passes the castle site; Travel West Midlands 11 & 11X; Stagecoach U12 all serve Kenilworth from surrounding area

Tel: 01926 852078

Local Tourist Information
Kenilworth: 0300 555 8171

NON-MEMBERS

Adult	£9.30
Concession	£8.40
Child	£5.60
Family	£24.20

Additional charges for members and non-members may apply on event days

OPENING TIMES

1 Apr-30 Sep, daily	10am-6pm
1 Oct-2 Nov, daily	10am-5pm
3 Nov-15 Feb, Sat-Sun	10am-4pm
16-20 Feb, daily	10am-4pm
21 Feb-29 Mar, Sat-Sun	10am-4pm
24-26 Dec, 31 Dec-1 Jan	Closed

Last admission 30 mins before closing

Access to Leicester's Gatehouse and/or the Stables Tearoom may be limited if there is a hospitality event booked, please call or check the website before you visit

Audio tours available (English, French, German and a children's version). Audio tours not available on Bank Holiday weekends or special event days.

Tearoom open as per site, finishing 30 minutes before site closes.

A car parking charge applies to ensure that EH members and paying visitors have priority. The charge will be refunded on admission, except on Bank Holiday weekends and at selected special events.

MAP Page 342 (5E)
OS Map 140, 221: SP278723

⊤ Available for corporate and private hire

▲ Licensed for civil wedding ceremonies

NEW FOR 2014

From summer 2014, for the first time in over 350 years, you can experience 'Queen's eye-views' of Kenilworth Castle from the upper levels of Leicester's Building.

The dramatic towering shell of this extravagant miniature palace has previously been viewable only from ground level. Now new viewing platforms and interpretation panels will allow visitors to see its interior walls at close range, and imagine it in its heyday. By safely ascending nearly 60 feet (18m) to the level of the Queen's apartments and 'dancing chamber', you can also enjoy once again the exclusive vistas over the castle and the surrounding countryside originally admired by Elizabeth and her courtiers.

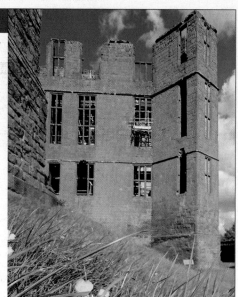

A vast medieval fortress which became an Elizabethan palace, Kenilworth Castle is one of Britain's largest and most impressive historic sites. Extensive developments here highlight Kenilworth's famous associations with Queen Elizabeth I and her favourite, Robert Dudley; most spectacularly the re-creation of the fabulous garden, which Dudley commissioned to astound visitors – especially Queen Elizabeth!

Spanning more than five centuries, Kenilworth's varied buildings and architectural styles reflect its long connection with successive English monarchs. Geoffrey de Clinton, Henry I's treasurer, began the massive Norman keep at the core of the fortress in the 1120s, and under Henry II Kenilworth became a royal castle. King John greatly strengthened it between 1210 and 1215, enlarging the surrounding watery 'mere' which effectively made it an island stronghold. Thus it could withstand an epic siege in 1266, when rebellious barons held out against Henry III's siege engines for six months, succumbing only to starvation. In the impressively-timbered

Tudor stables, which now house the castle's tearoom, trebuchet balls from the siege can be seen in the fascinating interactive display on the castle's history.

During the late 14th century John of Gaunt, Duke of Lancaster, rebuilt the splendid great hall and staterooms of Kenilworth's inner court, beginning the castle's transition into a palace and favourite residence of the Lancastrian and early Tudor kings. Here Henry V received the insulting French 'gift' of tennis-balls which sparked off the Agincourt campaign, and by Henry VIII's time the castle was already renowned for its 'many fair chambers'. The scene was set for Kenilworth's greatest period of fame.

This began when Queen Elizabeth's I favourite, Robert Dudley, Earl of Leicester, took possession of the castle in 1563. He then lavished a fortune on converting it into a great showpiece mansion, designed to receive the Queen and her court on their ceremonial 'progresses' around her realm. Striking evidence of Dudley's transformation

CONTINUED ▶

can still be seen everywhere at Kenilworth. Not content with remodelling its existing structures, he added the tall, mansion-sized 'Leicester's Building' specifically for the Queen's use: as well as an imposing new entrance to his quasi-royal palace, 'Leicester's Gatehouse'.

As part of a multi-million pound investment in Kenilworth Castle, Leicester's Gatehouse is displayed with the chambers on its lower floors re-created as they might have appeared when the gatehouse was last inhabited in the 1930s, while the top floor houses 'The Queen and the Castle: Robert Dudley's Kenilworth'. Featuring items both from museums and private collections, this exhibition tells the story of Elizabeth I's relationship with Dudley and her four visits to Kenilworth.

On the last and most famous of these visits, in July 1575, Elizabeth stayed here for 19 days – her longest sojourn in a courtier's house during any of her progresses. Dudley not only entertained her lavishly throughout with music, dancing, hunting and plays; he also created specially for her visit a fabulous garden, re-created by English Heritage following five years of intensive archaeological excavations, research and development. A bejewelled Renaissance aviary; magnificent carved arbours; a planting scheme abundant in colour, perfume and fruit and an 18-foot-high fountain carved from dazzling Carrara marble. These are just some of the glories of Robert Dudley's garden at Kenilworth Castle. In an age famous for its

extravagance, it was designed to score off rival aristocratic garden-creators, but principally to astound visitors, including Elizabeth I.

This garden, lost for centuries, has been brought back to life by a pioneering team of historians, archaeologists, plantsmen and plantswomen, designers, craftspeople and gardeners. It presents the most complete evocation of an Elizabethan garden anywhere in the world – a garden to seduce and beguile visitors today, just as it did in 1575.

Celebrating its fifth anniversary in 2014, such an outstandingly comprehensive re-creation of Elizabethan garden architecture, design, statuary and planting has never been attempted on this scale before. It has been made possible by important advances in garden archaeology and the survival of an extraordinary eye-witness description of the Kenilworth garden, written by Robert Langham in 1575.

Thus a garden that was once the 'glory of England' can once again be admired at this most romantic of castles. It opens a window on the period's most enduring love story – that of Elizabeth I and her favourite, Robert Dudley.

Though largely unscathed during the Civil War, Kenilworth was afterwards rendered indefensible and gradually fell into dilapidation. Made famous by Walter Scott's romantic novel, Kenilworth (1821), it came into state guardianship in 1938.

WEST MIDLANDS

HALESOWEN ABBEY
WEST MIDLANDS – B62 8RJ

Remains of an abbey founded by King John in the 13th century.

OPENING TIMES

Open to view from the public footpath only. Check English Heritage website for open days during 2014

VISIT US

Directions: Off A456, ½ mile W of J3, M5

Train: Old Hill 2½ miles

Bus: Diamond services 002; Central Buses 007; National Express West Midlands services 9 & 241 (then ½ mile walk)

ACQ.1976

MAP Page 342 (5D)
OS Map 139, 219: SO975828

J. W. EVANS SILVER FACTORY
BIRMINGHAM – B1 3EA

Established in 1881, J. W. Evans is one of the most complete surviving historic factories in Birmingham's Jewellery Quarter. Behind the frontage of four terraced houses, the workshops retain their original drop stamps and fly presses. They are packed with thousands of dies for the manufacture of silverware, as well as the whole of the working equipment, stock and records of the business. English Heritage stepped in to rescue the factory in 2008. The site is now open for pre-booked guided tours only.

J. W. EVANS SILVER FACTORY

OPENING TIMES

Pre-booked tours only (charge applies). Max 10 persons per tour

| 7, 12, 23 Apr |
| 10, 17, 21 May |
| 4, 14, 25 Jun |
| 5, 16, 26 Jul |
| 2 Aug |
| 6, 17, 27 Sep |
| 8, 15, 25 Oct |

VISIT US

Direction: 54-57 Albion Street, ½ mile from City Centre

Train: New Street ½ mile

Bus: From surrounding areas

Tel: 0870 333 1181

ACQ.2008

MAP Page 342 (5D)
OS Map 139, 220: SP062870

WORCESTERSHIRE

CHURCH OF ST MARY MAGDALENE, CROOME D'ABITOT
WORCESTERSHIRE
WR8 9DW

© CCT

A masterpiece of architectural fantasy. The original church at Croome was demolished, and replaced by this 'Georgian Gothic' church in Croome Park. Built by some of the finest craftsmen in England, every

CHURCH OF ST MARY MAGDALENE, CROOME D'ABITOT

detail has been considered, from pretty plaster mouldings to handsome carved pews and elegant Gothic windows.

Owned and managed by The Churches Conservation Trust.

OPENING TIMES

Open when Croome Park is open. (see National Trust website)

VISIT US

Train: Pershore 7 miles

Bus: Astons Summer Sunday service 381 serves Croome Park. Otherwise First service 362 Worcester-Upton On Severn serves the nearby village of Kinnersley (approx. 2 miles walk)

MAP Page 342 (6D)
OS Map 150, 190: SO886450

LEIGH COURT BARN
WORCESTERSHIRE

An outstanding display of medieval carpentry, this huge timber-framed barn is the largest cruck-framed structure in Britain. Built in 1344, it is 46 metres (150 feet) long.

OPENING TIMES

1 Apr-2 Nov, Thu-Sun	10am-5pm
3 Nov-29 Mar, Thu-Sun	10am-4pm
24-26 Dec & 1 Jan	Closed

VISIT US

Direction: 5 miles W of Worcester on an unclassified road off A4103

Train: Worcester Foregate Street 5 miles

Bus: Astons service 417, LMS Travel 423 & 425 (Fri only) to within 1 mile

ACQ.1990

MAP Page 342 (6C)
OS Map 150, 204: SO783535

WITLEY COURT AND GARDENS
Worcestershire – WR6 6JT

A hundred years ago, Witley Court was one of England's great country houses, hosting many extravagant parties. Today it is a spectacular ruin, the result of a disastrous fire in 1937.

VISIT US

Address: Witley Court, Worcester Road, Great Witley, Worcestershire

Direction: 10 miles NW of Worcester on A443

Train: Droitwich Spa 8½ miles

Bus: Yarranton service 758 Worcester – Tenbury Wells (passes close Worcester Foregate Street ≋); Worcestershire Fleet transport service 359 (Fri only); R&B service 760 (Thu only)

Tel: 01299 896636

Local Tourist Information
Worcester: 01905 726311

NON-MEMBERS

Adult	£7.10
Concession	£6.40
Child	£4.30
Family	£18.50

OPENING TIMES

1 Apr-30 Sep, daily	10am-6pm
1 Oct-2 Nov, daily	10am-5pm
3 Nov-15 Feb, Sat-Sun	10am-4pm
16-20 Feb, daily	10am-4pm
21 Feb-29 Mar, Sat-Sun	10am-4pm
24-26 Dec, 31 Dec-1 Jan	Closed

Last entry 1 hour before site closes

Disabled access (exterior and grounds only). A terrain guide is available on the website.

Tearoom (seasonal): 1 Apr-2 Nov (not managed by EH).

MAP Page 342 (6C)
OS Map 138/150, 204: SO769649

The restored Perseus and Andromeda fountain will be firing between Apr and Oct. (Apr-Sep weekdays: 11am, 12pm, 2pm, 3pm, 4pm & 5pm and weekends on the hour every hour from 11am-5pm. Oct weekdays: 11am, 12pm, 2pm, 3pm & 4pm and weekends on the hour every hour from 11am-4pm).

NB. Due to conservation maintenance work during 2014, the fountain may not be in operation during the times stated.

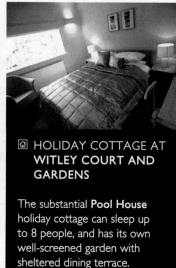

⌂ HOLIDAY COTTAGE AT
**WITLEY COURT AND
GARDENS**

The substantial **Pool House**
holiday cottage can sleep up
to 8 people, and has its own
well-screened garden with
sheltered dining terrace.

The vast remains of the palatial 19th-century mansion are surrounded by magnificent landscaped gardens, with huge stone fountains. The largest, representing Perseus and Andromeda – now restored – was described in its day as making the 'noise of an express train' when fired.

Witley's gardens are the work of the leading landscape designer of the time, William Andrews Nesfield. He started work in 1854, creating the South Parterre with its great Perseus and Andromeda fountain and elegantly designed plantings and parterres. The East Parterre garden, with its Flora Fountain, was designed in the Parterre de Broderie style, resembling embroidery.

Following the disastrous fire in 1937 the Witley Estate fell into long decline. English Heritage has now restored the south garden and the East Parterre garden. The Woodland Walks in the North Park pass many different species of tree and shrub from all over the world. Discover some of Witley's wildlife with a stroll around the lakeside walk.

Witley Court also has a new Wilderness Play Area for children of all ages, with an organic twist, close to the visitor centre in the North Park. With a beautiful woodland setting, and lots of exciting activities for different age groups (from two years upwards), this is the kind of place that children dream about. The centrepiece is a tree house, reached by a wobbly bridge and shaped like a large seed pod cracked open.

A section for younger children includes musical elements in the style of leaves, hazelnuts and catkins, as well as a 'nest-like' basket swing and wooden animal rides. For the more adventurous, there is a play area with a scramble net, slide and rope walks. However many visits they make, children will have a different experience every time they come.

Close to Witley Court is Great Witley Church (not managed by English Heritage), with its amazing Italianate Baroque interior. There is a tearoom by the church.

DISCOUNTED ATTRACTIONS:

Use your membership to get exclusive discounts at these independent attractions in the West Midlands. Please remember to show your card as proof of membership.

COMPTON VERNEY
Warwickshire CV35 9HZ
Visitors of all ages are warmly welcomed to this award-winning art gallery. Explore art from around the world and relax and play in 'Capability' Brown landscaped parkland.
www.comptonverney.org.uk
Tel. 01926 645500

EASTNOR CASTLE
Herefordshire HR8 1RL
Eastnor is a dramatic, fairytale castle situated in the foothills of the Malvern Hills, within an Area of Outstanding Natural Beauty. Please see website for seasonal opening.
www.eastnorcastle.com
Tel. 01531 633160

HAWKSTONE PARK FOLLIES
Shropshire SY4 5UY
A great day out for all the family. A powerful and timeless landscape, filled with eccentric follies.
www.hawkstone.co.uk
Tel. 01948 841700

HERITAGE MOTOR CENTRE
Warwickshire CV35 0BJ
The Centre is home to the world's largest collection of historic British cars. Check website for activities and special events.
www.heritage-motor-centre.co.uk
Tel. 01926 641188

IRONBRIDGE GORGE MUSEUMS – Ironbridge
Shropshire TF8 7DQ
Explore the ten Ironbridge Gorge Museums in this World Heritage Site with a great value Annual Passport Ticket.
www.ironbridge.org.uk
Tel. 01952 433424

ROYAL SHAKESPEARE COMPANY
Warwickshire CV37 6BB
Take a trip up the Royal Shakespeare Theatre Tower to experience an alternative view across Stratford-upon-Avon and beyond.
www.rsc.org.uk
Tel. 0844 800 1110

WEST MIDLANDS

Discount applies to:

KEY ⊞ MEMBERS | OVP OVP HOLDERS | ᶠᵗᶠ? NO. OF MEMBER'S CHILDREN

Terms and conditions may apply, so make sure you check the individual pages on our website or call the individual property for more details.

2 for 1 ENTRY 3-HOUSE PASS

⊞

SHAKESPEARE'S BIRTHPLACE
Warwickshire CV37 6QW
Explore the town houses of Shakespeare's Birthplace, Hall's Croft and Nash's House & New Place. Discover the fascinating story of Shakespeare's life.
www.shakespeare.org.uk
Tel. 01789 204016

2 for 1 ENTRY 5-HOUSE PASS

⊞

SHAKESPEARE'S HOUSES AND GARDENS
Warwickshire CV37 6QW
Visit all five properties: Shakespeare's Birthplace, Anne Hathaway's Cottage, Mary Arden's Farm, Hall's Croft and Nash's House & New Place.
www.shakespeare.org.uk
Tel. 01789 204016

15% DISCOUNT ON ENTRY

⊞ OVP

STONELEIGH ABBEY
Warwickshire CV8 2LF
A source of inspiration to Jane Austen, Stoneleigh Abbey covers 800 years of history and is situated in beautiful parkland. Viewed by guided tours.

www.stoneleighabbey.org
Tel. 01926 858535

50% DISCOUNT ON ENTRY

⊞ ᶠᵗᶠ 2

WARWICK CASTLE
Warwickshire CV34 4QU
Immerse yourself in a thousand years of history, come rain or shine. See lavishly decorated state rooms, walk the towers and ramparts, or explore the 60 acres of glorious gardens.
www.warwick-castle.com
Tel. 0871 265 2000

25% DISCOUNT ON ENTRY

⊞ ᶠᵗᶠ 4

THE WEDGWOOD MUSEUM
Staffordshire ST12 9ER
The story of Josiah Wedgwood, the Company he founded and its craftsmanship throughout Wedgwood's 250 year heritage.

www.wedgwoodmuseum.org.uk
Tel. 01782 371919

GIVE THE GIFT OF MEMBERSHIP
Give friends and family the opportunity to enjoy these fantastic discounts too!

- Free entry to over 400 historic properties
- Kids go free (up to six per adult in a family group)
- Free or discounted entry to hundreds of events
- Free handbook worth £10.95
- Exclusive Members' Magazine

See page 355 for full details.

YORKSHIRE
AND THE
HUMBER

Rievaulx Abbey

Keep up to date with events, news and offers www.english-heritage.org.uk/newsletter

Whitby Abbey

17
23
18 Richmond
10
15
North Yorkshire
Northallerton
26
Whitby
27
14
19 11
8
16
Scarborough
20
13
22 Ripon
7
12
25
Settle
1
Bridlington
Harrogate
Skipton
21
28 York
9
3
Hornsea
East Riding
West Yorkshire
Beverley
Bradford
Leeds
24
Selby
Halifax
2
Goole
Kingston upon Hull
5
Huddersfield
North Lincolnshire
6
Scunthorpe
Grimsby
31
29
Barnsley
South Yorkshire
30
Doncaster
4
North East Lincolnshire
Rotherham
32
Sheffield

Details of local public transport information in England are available from Traveline **www.traveline.org.uk** or call 0871 200 2233.

HIGHLIGHTS FOR 2014/15 IN **YORKSHIRE & THE HUMBER**

Brodsworth Hall & Gardens: a mansion charmingly frozen in time, Brodsworth offers a First World War exhibition and events this year.

Conisbrough Castle: this well-preserved and strikingly different medieval castle re-opens in 2014 with exciting new state-of-the-art interpretation.

Middleham Castle: start our new Richard III Trail at his favourite home in the Yorkshire Dales.

PROPERTIES

EAST RIDING OF YORKSHIRE
1 Burton Agnes Manor House
2 Howden Minster
3 Skipsea Castle

NORTH LINCOLNSHIRE
4 Gainsthorpe Medieval Village
5 St Peter's Church, Barton-upon-Humber
6 Thornton Abbey and Gatehouse

NORTH YORKSHIRE
7 Aldborough Roman Site
8 Byland Abbey

9 Clifford's Tower
10 Easby Abbey
11 Helmsley Castle
12 Kirkham Priory
13 Marmion Tower
14 Middleham Castle
15 Mount Grace Priory
16 Pickering Castle
17 Piercebridge Roman Bridge
18 Richmond Castle
19 Rievaulx Abbey
20 Scarborough Castle
21 Spofforth Castle
22 St Mary's Church, Studley Royal

23 Stanwick Iron Age Fortifications
24 Steeton Hall Gateway
25 Wharram Percy Deserted Medieval Village
26 Wheeldale Roman Road
27 Whitby Abbey
28 York Cold War Bunker

SOUTH YORKSHIRE
29 Brodsworth Hall and Gardens
30 Conisbrough Castle
31 Monk Bretton Priory
32 Roche Abbey

Remember to check opening times before you visit any of our properties
www.english-heritage.org.uk/daysout

EAST RIDING OF YORKSHIRE

BURTON AGNES MANOR HOUSE
EAST RIDING OF YORKSHIRE

A medieval manor house interior, with a rare and well-preserved Norman undercroft and a 15th-century roof, all encased in brick during the 17th and 18th centuries.

OPENING TIMES

1 Apr–31 Oct, daily	11am–5pm
1 Nov–29 Mar	Closed

The nearby Burton Agnes Hall and Gardens are privately owned and are not managed by English Heritage

VISIT US

Direction: In Burton Agnes village, 5 miles SW of Bridlington on A166

Train: Nafferton 5 miles

Bus: East Yorkshire service 45, 46 & 121

ACQ.1948 🐕

Parking (in Hall and Gardens car park, subject to charge).

MAP Page 345 (3J)
OS Map 101, 295: TA102632

HOWDEN MINSTER
EAST RIDING OF YORKSHIRE

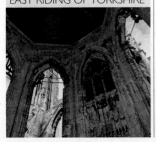

HOWDEN MINSTER

The ruins of an elaborately decorated 14th-century chancel and chapter house (viewable only from the outside), attached to the working 'minster' parish church of Howden.

OPENING TIMES

Any reasonable daylight hours

24–26 Dec & 1 Jan	Closed

VISIT US

Direction: In Howden; 23 miles W of Kingston Upon Hull, 25 miles SE of York, near the junction of A63 and A614

Train: Howden 1½ miles

Bus: Arriva Yorkshire service 4; East Yorkshire services X55, X56, 155 (Sun),160, 162 (Wed & Sat only), 358 (Tue)

ACQ.1971 🐕 P

Parking (on-street parking nearby – pay and display).

MAP Page 345 (4H)
OS Map 105/106, 291: SE748283

SKIPSEA CASTLE
EAST RIDING OF YORKSHIRE

The impressive earthwork remains of a big Norman motte and bailey castle, dating from the 1070s and among the first built in Yorkshire.

OPENING TIMES

Any reasonable daylight hours

VISIT US

Direction: Located 8 miles S of Bridlington; W of Skipsea village

Train: Bridlington 9 miles

Bus: Phoenix Buses service 136 pass within ⅓ mile; East Yorkshire services 130 & X30 serve Skipsea village

ACQ.1911 🐕

Dogs on leads (restricted areas only).

Waterproof footwear recommended.

MAP Page 345 (3J)
OS Map 107, 295: TA162551

NORTH LINCOLNSHIRE

GAINSTHORPE MEDIEVAL VILLAGE
NORTH LINCOLNSHIRE

A deserted medieval village, one of the best-preserved examples in England, clearly visible as a complex of grassy humps and bumps. According to legend demolished as a den of thieves, the real reason for its abandonment remains uncertain.

OPENING TIMES

Any reasonable daylight hours

VISIT US

Direction: Located on minor road W of A15 – towards Cleatham; S of Hibaldstow; 5 miles SW of Brigg

Train: Kirton Lindsey 3 miles

Bus: Hornsby Travel service 94

ACQ.1974 🐕

Access via grazing field. Farm livestock likely to be present.

MAP Page 345 (5J)
OS Map 112, 281: SE954011

ST PETER'S CHURCH, BARTON-UPON-HUMBER
SEE FEATURE – PAGE 232

VISIT US

Direction: 18 miles NE of Scunthorpe, on a road N of A160; 7 miles SE of the Humber Bridge, on a road E of A1077

Train: Thornton Abbey ¼ mile

Bus: Stagecoach in Lincolnshire services 260, 360 pass the site

Tel: 01469 541445

NON-MEMBERS

Adult	£4.60
Concession	£4.10
Child	£2.80

OPENING TIMES

1 Apr-30 Jun, Wed-Sun & Bank Hols	10am-5pm
1 Jul-31 Aug, daily	10am-5pm
1 Sep-31 Oct, Sat-Sun	10am-5pm
1 Nov-29 Mar, Sat-Sun	10am-4pm
24-26 Dec, 31 Dec-1 Jan	Closed

Disabled access (except gatehouse interior and part of chapter ruins).

Dogs on leads (restricted areas only).

The enormous and ornate fortified gatehouse of Thornton Abbey is the largest and among the finest of all English monastic gatehouses. An early example of brick building in England, it proclaimed the wool trade-based prosperity of one of the wealthiest English Augustinian monasteries, for centuries a focus of spiritual and economic influence. Begun in the 1380s, the gatehouse stands some 21 metres (69 feet) high. It may have protected the abbey's treasures, as well as providing spacious lodgings for the abbot and his guests.

Within the grounds stand the ruins of the monastic buildings, notably the elegantly decorated octagonal chapter house of 1282-1308. These buildings were plundered for stone to build a 'most stately' Jacobean manor house which, mysteriously, 'fell quite down to the bare ground without any visible cause' (Abraham de la Pryme). Evidence of its formal gardens has recently been discovered.

An oak staircase gives visitors access to the restored gatehouse's atmospheric interior. An exhibition with children's activities offers an insight into the abbey's history, including its role as the meeting place for huge Victorian Temperance rallies.

St Peter's Church, Barton-upon-Humber (see p.232) is nearby.

MAP Page 345 (5J)
OS Map 113, 284: TA118189

NEW FOR 2014

Never before seen objects on display, including the Seal of Thornton Abbey College. Extremely rare and with a wonderful survival story.

ST PETER'S CHURCH, BARTON-UPON-HUMBER
NORTH LINCOLNSHIRE
DN18 5EX

This famous Anglo-Saxon and medieval church is an archaeological as well as an architectural treasure, and one of Britain's largest resources for historic bone analysis. The analysis of over 2800 burials excavated here has brought remarkable insight into medieval disease, diet and burial practice, and informed modern medical understanding.

The *Buried Lives* exhibition investigates the late 11th-century origins of the church, tracking its fortunes and those of its people through 1000 years. Thornton Abbey and Gatehouse (see p.231) is nearby.

NON-MEMBERS

Adult	£3.80
Concession	£3.40
Child	£2.30

OPENING TIMES

1 Apr-30 Sep, Sat-Sun	10am-3pm
1 Oct-29 Mar	Closed

VISIT US

Direction: In Barton-upon-Humber

Train: Barton-upon-Humber ½ mile

Bus: Stagecoach in Lincolnshire services 260, 350, 360, 450 and Humber Flyer; Stagecoach/East Yorkshire Humber Fast Cat service 350 also passes close by

Tel: 01469 541445

ACQ.1923 | E ♿ ♨ ♿ ☂ ♿ ☐ ☐
♿ OVP

MAP Page 345 (5J)
OS Map 107, 112, 281: TA035219

NORTH YORKSHIRE

ALDBOROUGH ROMAN SITE
N. YORKSHIRE – YO51 9ES

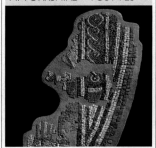

Among the northernmost urban centres in the Roman Empire, Aldborough was the 'capital' of the Romanised Brigantes, the largest tribe in Britain. One corner of the defences is laid out amid a Victorian arboretum, and two mosaic pavements can be viewed in their original positions. The site museum has an outstanding collection of Roman finds.

NON-MEMBERS

Adult	£3.60
Concession	£3.20
Child	£2.20

OPENING TIMES

1 Apr-30 Sep, Sat-Sun & Bank Hols	10am-6pm
1 Oct-29 Mar	Closed

VISIT US

Direction: Located in Aldborough, ¾ mile SE of Boroughbridge on a minor road off B6265; within 1 mile of junction of A1 and A6055

Train: Cattal 7½ miles

Bus: From York: 142 & 143 (Sat), 812 (Sun & Bank Hols, 5 May-20 Oct). From Harrogate: 57 & 57A

Tel: 01423 322768

ACQ.1952 | ♨ ♿ ♿ ☐ ☂ ♿ ☐
☐ ☐ OVP

Dogs on leads (restricted areas only).

MAP Page 345 (3G)
OS Map 299, 99: SE405662

BYLAND ABBEY
SEE FEATURE OPPOSITE

CHURCH OF CHRIST THE CONSOLER, SKELTON-CUM-NEWBY
N. YORKSHIRE – HG4 5AE

© CCT

A grieving mother built this impressive church in the grounds of Newby Hall as a memorial for her murdered son. The interior is wonderfully rich, with pattern and colour everywhere, and a little carved stone dog provides a sweetly domestic touch amid the magnificent splendour. The same patroness and architect built St Mary's, Studley Royal (see p.241)

Owned and managed by The Churches Conservation Trust.

OPENING TIMES
Open daily during daylight hours

VISIT US

Train: Knaresborough 6½ miles

Bus: Eddie Brown/Harrogate Coach Travel services 142 & 143

15 mins from Aldborough Roman Site, 40 mins from Rievaulx Abbey

MAP Page 345 (3G)
OS Map 99, 299: SE360679

Don't forget to check opening times online before you visit.
www.english-heritage.org.uk/daysout/properties

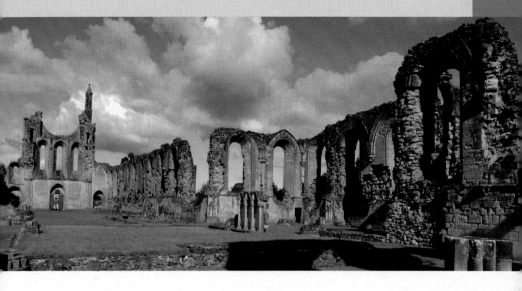

VISIT US

Direction: 2 miles S of A170, between Thirsk and Helmsley; near Coxwold village

Train: Thirsk 10 miles

Bus: Hutchinsons 12 (Sun only); Stephensons 31/31X

Tel: 01347 868614

Local Tourist Information 01751 473791

NON-MEMBERS

Adult	£4.60
Concession	£4.10
Child	£2.80

OPENING TIMES

1 Apr-30 Jun, Wed-Sun & Bank Hols	10am-6pm
1 Jul-31 Aug, daily	10am-6pm
1-30 Sep, Wed-Sun	10am-6pm
1 Oct-2 Nov, Wed-Sun	10am-5pm
3 Nov-29 Mar, Sat-Sun	10am-4pm
24-26 Dec, 31 Dec-1 Jan	Closed

ACQ.1921 🐾 🚃 ♿ 📷 📠 ♿
⚠ OVP

Parking (adjacent to Abbey Inn).

Toilets at Abbey Inn.

Byland was one of the great Yorkshire Cistercian abbeys, housing at its zenith well over 200 monks and lay brothers. Much of its huge cathedral-sized church survives, including the whole north side and the greater part of the 13th-century west front. The mixture of rounded Romanesque and pointed Gothic arches shows how architectural styles changed, and reveals that Byland was one of the earliest Gothic buildings in the north. Its great circular rose window, now surviving only in part, was probably the model for the rose window of York Minster.

Archaeological research by English Heritage is beginning to throw light on the abbey's wider landscape setting, revealing how the monks tamed a very boggy and inhospitable site when building work started in the mid-12th century. The compact museum is full of archaeological site finds, intermingled with colourful interpretation panels giving an insight into monastic life.

Rievaulx Abbey and Helmsley Castle are within reasonable travelling distance.

MAP Page 345 (2G)
OS Map 100, OL26/299: SE549789

THE ABBEY INN

Overlooking Byland Abbey, The Abbey Inn offers a tearoom, bed and breakfast and venue hire for special events. Serving drinks, lunches and cakes using locally sourced ingredients, the tearoom opens 1 Apr-2 Nov. Venue hire and bed and breakfast offered year-round. Owned and managed by English Heritage. www.bylandabbeyinn.co.uk to confirm opening times.

CHURCH OF ST JOHN THE BAPTIST, STANWICK
N. YORKSHIRE – DL11 7RT

© CCT

Surrounded by the high ramparts and impressive earthworks of Stanwick Camp, an important settlement in pre-Roman Britain, this Early English church is in an area of great natural beauty. St John's has the best collection of Anglo-Saxon grave markers in North Yorkshire. A 9th-century cross-shaft found in the churchyard and carved stones set into the walls suggest an even earlier building than Early English occupied this site.

Owned and managed by The Churches Conservation Trust.

OPENING TIMES
Open daily during daylight hours

VISIT US
Train: Darlington 7 miles

1 mile Stanwick Iron Age Fortification

MAP Page 345 (1F)
OS Map 92, 304: NZ185120

CLIFFORD'S TOWER, YORK
SEE FEATURE OPPOSITE

EASBY ABBEY
N. YORKSHIRE

The impressive ruins of an abbey of Premonstratensian 'white canons', most notable for the lavishly-appointed refectory of c.1300 and extensive monastic buildings. Within the precinct is the still-active parish church, displaying outstanding 13th-century wall-paintings. In a beautiful setting by the River Swale, Easby can also be reached in dry weather via a pleasant walk from Richmond Castle (p.242).

A free audio tour of the abbey can be downloaded from our website.

OPENING TIMES

1 Apr-30 Sep, daily	10am-6pm
1-31 Oct, daily	10am-5pm
1 Nov-29 Mar, daily	10am-4pm
24-26 Dec & 1 Jan	Closed

VISIT US
Direction: 1 mile SE of Richmond, off B6271

Bus: Dales & District X34, 55; Esk Valley 27 (Wed only)

ACQ.1930 Guidebook (from Richmond Castle).

MAP Page 345 (2F)
OS Map 92, 304: NZ185003

HELMSLEY CASTLE
SEE FEATURE – PAGE 236

HOLY TRINITY CHURCH, WENSLEY
N. YORKSHIRE – DL8 4HX

© Graham Moore

Built on 8th-century Saxon foundations, this church stands on the bank of the River Ure in picturesque Wensleydale. Inside, there are interesting medieval wall paintings and a fine Flemish brass, and visitors can sit and marvel at the sumptuous richness of the local landowners' family pew, said to have come from Easby Abbey.

Owned and managed by The Churches Conservation Trust.

OPENING TIMES
Open daily during daylight hours

VISIT US
Train: Northallerton 17 miles

Bus: Dales & District service 156 serves Wensley

10 mins from Middleham Castle

MAP Page 345 (2F)
OS Map 99, OL30: SE092895

For information on events taking place at **Clifford's Tower** check out www.english-heritage.org.uk/daysout/events

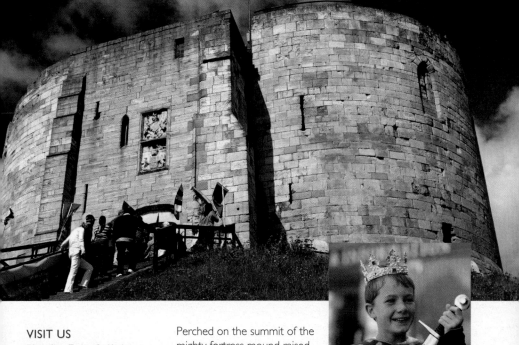

VISIT US

Direction: Tower St, York

Train: York 1 mile

Bus: From surrounding areas

Tel: 01904 646940

Local Tourist Information
York: 01904 550099

NON-MEMBERS

Adult	£4.30
Concession	£3.90
Child	£2.60
Family	£11.20

OPENING TIMES

1 Apr-30 Sep, daily	10am-6pm*
1 Oct-2 Nov, daily	10am-5pm
3 Nov-29 Mar, daily	10am-4pm
24-26 Dec & 1 Jan	Closed

*reduced opening hours on 6 July due to Tour De France Grand Depart, please check website for details

⚠ OVP

Parking (local charge).

Access (via steep steps).

MAP Page 345 (3G)
OS Map 105, 290: SE605515

Perched on the summit of the mighty fortress mound raised by William the Conqueror in 1068, Clifford's Tower was the keep and chief strongpoint of York Castle, the greatest royal stronghold in medieval northern England. Built during the 1250s for Henry III, its four-lobed shape – giving it the old local nickname 'the Minced Pie' – is unique in England. Like the city it once overawed, the tower has a rich history. A timber predecessor was burnt when York's Jews committed mass suicide there to avoid massacre by a mob in 1190. In 1322 Lord Roger de Clifford, a baronial rebel against Edward II, was hung in chains from its walls, allegedly giving the tower its name. Following plots to sell off its stonework by a crooked Elizabethan custodian, the tower was used as a Civil War gun-platform.

Today it remains the principal surviving remnant of the medieval castle, still commanding amazing 360 degree panoramas from its lofty rampart walk. There are unrivalled views of the Minster; the towers and spires of York's medieval and later churches; and the fine Georgian buildings in the old castle bailey. In the distance the Yorkshire Wolds and – on a clear day – even the North York Moors can be seen.

Family events bring the history of the tower to life during the summer holidays

Clifford's Tower is part of the Richard III Trail (see Middleham Castle – p.239).

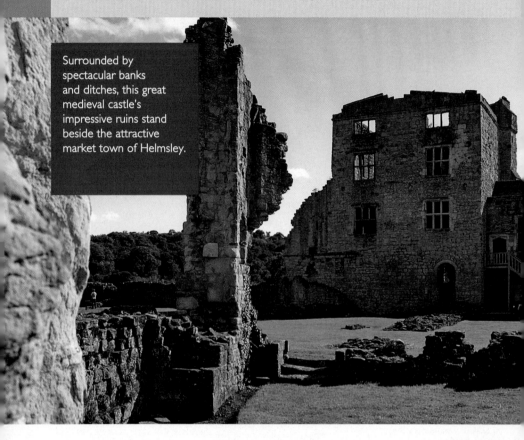

Surrounded by spectacular banks and ditches, this great medieval castle's impressive ruins stand beside the attractive market town of Helmsley.

VISIT US

Address: Helmsley Castle, Castlegate, Helmsley, North Yorkshire YO62 5AB

Direction: Near the town centre

Bus: Stephenson's 29, 31, 31X, 194, 195; Scarborough & District 128

Tel: 01439 770442

NON-MEMBERS

Adult	£5.20
Concession	£4.70
Child	£3.10
Family	£13.50

OPENING TIMES

1 Apr-30 Sep, daily	10am-6pm
1 Oct-2 Nov, daily	10am-5pm
3 Nov-15 Feb, Sat-Sun	10am-4pm
16-20 Feb, daily	10am-4pm
21 Feb-29 Mar, Sat-Sun	10am-4pm
24-26 Dec, 31 Dec-1 Jan	Closed

Last admission is 30 mins before closing

Helmsley Archaeology store tours
23 Apr, 21 May, 25 Jun,
23 Jul, 24 Sep, 15 Oct   11am & 2pm
Booking essential on 01439 770442.
Tours are free to members and non-members and are led by the Collections Curators. Please note: Archaeological Store not located on site (Riccal Drive)

Audio tours.

Parking (large car park adjacent to castle; charge payable).

Toilets (in car park and town centre).

MAP Page 345 (2G)
OS Map 100, OL26: SE611836

Rievaulx and Byland Abbeys are both nearby. Rievaulx can be reached on foot via the Cleveland Way National Trail. Approx. 1½ hours (3½ miles/5.6 km) each way. Strong footwear is required.

Sculptures by Malcolm Brocklesby.

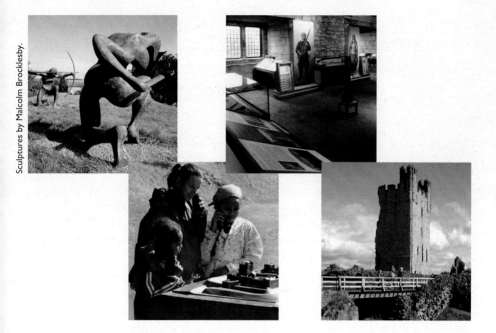

The fortress was probably begun after 1120 by Walter Espec – 'Walter the Woodpecker'. Renowned for piety as well as soldiering, this Norman baron of 'gigantic stature' also founded nearby Rievaulx Abbey and Kirkham Priory, both English Heritage properties.

Most of Helmsley's surviving stonework defences were raised during the late 12th and 13th centuries by the crusader Robert de Roos and his descendants. They include a pair of immensely strong 'barbican' entrances and the high, keep-like east tower, unusually D-shaped in plan, which still dominates the town.

But Helmsley is not only a medieval fortress. During the Elizabethan period the Manners family remodelled the castle's chamber block into a luxurious mansion, whose fine plasterwork and panelling still partly survive. The castle's first and last military trial came during the Civil War. Held for King Charles, it endured a three-month siege before being starved into submission in November 1644 by

Parliamentarians under Sir Thomas Fairfax, who was seriously wounded in the fighting. Fairfax then dismantled the defences but spared the mansion, subsequently the home of his daughter and her husband, the profligate Duke of Buckingham.

Demoted to a romantic backdrop when later owners moved to nearby Duncombe Park, Helmsley Castle has been revitalised by English Heritage, making it more accessible to a wide range of visitors. This includes a visitor centre building with shop and information point, an audio tour and an imaginative hands-on exhibition in the mansion range. Displaying a fascinating array of finds from Civil War cannon balls to early tableware, this exhibition explores the social and domestic, as well as the military, aspects of the fortress. Facilities for disabled visitors include full ground-level ramping, a virtual tour of less accessible areas, and a tactile model with braille text. Enhanced learning resources include family-friendly books and activities.

HOLY TRINITY CHURCH, YORK
N. YORKSHIRE– YO1 7LF

© Graham White

Holy Trinity has the air of a hidden treasure, standing in a secluded churchyard behind York's busiest shopping street. On sunny days, gems of coloured light are scattered on the walls. The box pews and medieval stained glass are exceptionally fine, and monuments paint a picture of city life.

Owned and managed by The Churches Conservation Trust.

OPENING TIMES

Tue-Sat	10am-4pm
Sun-Mon	12pm-4pm

VISIT US

Train: York ½ mile

Bus: Served by many operators

10 min walk from Clifford's Tower

MAP Page 345 (3G)
OS Map 105, 290: SE605522

KIRKHAM PRIORY
N. YORKSHIRE – YO60 7JS

The riverside ruins of an Augustinian priory, picturesquely set in the beautiful Derwent valley. Features include a gatehouse bedecked with heraldry, including that of the De Roos family, Barons of Helmsley Castle; handsome monastic washbasins; and a small display of monastic artefacts.

NON-MEMBERS

Adult	£3.60
Concession	£3.20
Child	£2.20

OPENING TIMES

1 Apr-31 Jul, Wed-Sun	10am-6pm
1-31 Aug, daily	10am-6pm
1-30 Sep, Wed-Sun	10am-6pm
1 Oct-29 Mar	Closed

VISIT US

Direction: 5 miles SW of Malton, on a minor road off A64

KIRKHAM PRIORY

Train: Malton 6 miles

Bus: Ryecat 184 & 185 to Kirkham Priory village (Tue, Fri, Sat); otherwise Yorkshire Coastliner X40, 840, 843 & 845 (pass York and ⊕ Malton) to Whitwell On The Hill then ¾ mile walk

Tel: 01653 618768

Local Tourist Information
01653 600048

MAP Page 345 (3H)
OS Map 100, 300: SE736658

MARMION TOWER
N. YORKSHIRE

The fine 15th-century gatehouse of a vanished riverside manor house, with a beautiful oriel window. The monuments of the manor's Marmion family owners grace the adjacent church.

OPENING TIMES

1 Apr-30 Sep, daily	10am-6pm
1-31 Oct, daily	10am-5pm
1 Nov-29 Mar, daily	10am-4pm
24-26 Dec & 1 Jan	Closed

VISIT US

Direction: On A6108 in West Tanfield

Train: Thirsk 10 miles

Bus: Dales & District service 159

ACQ.1976

MAP Page 345 (3F)
OS Map 99, 298: SE268787

GIVE THE GIFT OF MEMBERSHIP
...which lasts a whole year and is the perfect gift idea for family and friends. Call us now on **0870 333 1181** or visit **www.english-heritage.org.uk/gift** – see page 355 for full details.

THE RICHARD III TRAIL

Richard III represented one great dynasty with roots in the north – the House of York. He married into another – the Nevilles of Middleham Castle. Their castles still stand to bear witness to their dramatic history.

At any of the six castles listed below, now cared for by English Heritage, you can collect a trail handout. This acts as a holder for six postcards, one available at each of the castles. Each card represents a member of Richard's family and a piece of his story. Collect and combine all the cards to make a poster of Richard III. Barnard Castle; Carlisle Castle; Clifford's Tower, York; Conisbrough Castle; Middleham Castle; Richmond Castle.

VISIT US

Direction: Located at Middleham; 2 miles S of Leyburn on A6108

Train: Leyburn (Wensleydale Railway) 2 miles

Bus: Dales & District 159

Tel: 01969 623899

Local Tourist Information
Leyburn: 01969 623069

NON-MEMBERS

Adult	£4.60
Concession	£4.10
Child	£2.80

OPENING TIMES

1 Apr-30 Sep, daily	10am-6pm
1 Oct-2 Nov, daily	10am-5pm
3 Nov-29 Mar, Sat-Sun	10am-4pm
24-26 Dec, 31 Dec-1 Jan	Closed

ACQ.1926 ⚤ E ⚒ ▢ ⩰ ◌ ♿
⚠ OVP

Disabled access (except keep).

MAP Page 345 (2F)
OS Map 99, OL30: SE127876

Set in a delightful little Wensleydale market town, Middleham Castle was traditionally the favourite home of Richard III, and was certainly his northern power-base.

The core of the castle is the mighty keep, three storeys high and with twelve-foot thick walls, probably built during the 1170s by Robert fitz Randolph. Around this keep the mighty Neville family, Earls of Westmorland and of Warwick, progressively constructed three ranges of luxurious chambers and lodgings, turning the castle into a fortified palace – 'the Windsor of the North' – by the mid 15th century. Though roofless, many of these buildings survive, including a multi-storey latrine tower and a horse-mill, making Middleham a fascinating castle to explore.

Richard III probably spent part of his youth here, in the guardianship of Richard Neville, known as 'Warwick the Kingmaker': the Kingmaker also twice received Edward IV here during the Wars of the Roses, once as an honoured guest and once as a prisoner. After Warwick's death in battle, Richard married his daughter Anne, and took over the castle. Here Richard's son Edward of Middleham was born, and here he died in 1484, aged no more than ten.

There are wonderful views over Wensleydale from the viewing platform on the keep. An exhibition about notable personalities from the castle's past includes a replica of the beautiful Middleham Jewel, a 15th-century pendant decorated with a large sapphire found near the castle. Family-friendly books and activities.

⌂ HOLIDAY COTTAGE AT **MOUNT GRACE PRIORY**

Prior's Lodge sleeps four, with views over the mansion's garden in one direction, the monastic ruins in the other.

VISIT US

Direction: 12 miles N of Thirsk; and 6 miles NE of Northallerton, near A19. Warning: take care when turning off the fast dual carriageway. Look out for brown EH direction signs placed approx. ½ mile before the turning

Train: Northallerton 6 miles

Bus: Abbott services 80, 89 alight Priory Road End, then ½ mile walk

Tel: 01609 883494

Local Tourist Information
Thirsk: 01845 522755

NON-MEMBERS

Adult	£5.60
Concession	£5.00
Child	£3.40
Family	£14.60

National Trust members admitted free, except on event days

OPENING TIMES

1 Apr-30 Sep, daily	10am-6pm
1 Oct-2 Nov, daily	10am-5pm
3 Nov-29 Mar, Sat-Sun	10am-4pm
24-26 Dec, 31 Dec-1 Jan	Closed

During the winter, the attics may close early due to low light levels

ACQ.1955

New guidebook.

Picturesquely set beneath a wooded slope of the Cleveland Hills, Mount Grace Priory is among the most unusual and important of English Heritage's monastic sites, with the bonus of an 'Arts and Crafts' mansion to admire.

Much the best-preserved Carthusian priory in England, Mount Grace differs radically from conventional monasteries. For instead of living together like other monks, Carthusians ('Christ's Poor Men') were communities of hermits. Founded by St Bruno at the Grand Chartreuse in France, the order was revered for piety, humility and intense spirituality. Thomas Holland, Duke of Surrey, founded this last of the great Yorkshire monasteries in 1398.

The furnished reconstruction of one of the monk's cells ranged round the immense great cloister reflects the Carthusian ideal of solitude. The cottage-like building has its own little private cloister, walled garden and outside toilet. The occupant lived in strict isolation, not even seeing the lay brother who passed his frugal meatless meals through an L-shaped serving hatch.

All this is approached through a mansion adapted in 1654 from the priory's guest range, and much extended in 1901 by Sir Lowthian Bell, wealthy patron of the Arts and Crafts movement. Several of its rooms have been refurbished in this style, using William Morris wallpapers, and its attics have recently been opened to the public for the first time. It also displays a fascinating introductory exhibition and some notable site artefacts.

Owned by the National Trust, maintained and managed by English Heritage.

MAP Page 345 (2G)
OS Map 99, OL26: SE449985

⏐ Available for corporate and private hire

PICKERING CASTLE
N. YORKSHIRE – YO18 7AX

A fine early Norman castle set in an attractive moors-edge market town, with spectacular views from the motte-top. Pickering is a classic and well-preserved example of an early earthwork castle refortified in stone during the 13th and 14th centuries. There is an exhibition in the chapel.

NON-MEMBERS

Adult	£4.20
Concession	£3.80
Child	£2.50
Family	£10.90

OPENING TIMES

1 Apr-30 Sep, daily	10am-6pm
1 Oct-2 Nov, daily	10am-5pm
3 Nov-29 Mar	Closed

VISIT US

Direction: In Pickering; 15 miles SW of Scarborough

Train: Malton (9 miles) or Pickering (North Yorkshire Moors Rly) ¼ mile

Bus: Scarborough & District 128; Ryecate 175; Yorkshire Coastliner 840 & X40 (Sun), Summer Sundays and Bank Hols Moorsbus M3, M5, M6, M8 & M14. Also Coastal & Country 90 (Wed); Hutchinsons 170 & 171; Stephensons 173, 174 (Mon & Fri) & 175 (Mon & Fri)

Tel: 01751 474989

Local Tourist Information
Pickering: 01751 473791

PICKERING CASTLE

ACQ.1926 🏛 🚌 E 🖐 🏠 🚶 🧍 P
🎫 🏠 ♿ ⚠ OVP
Disabled access (except motte).

MAP Page 345 (2H)
OS Map 100, OL27: SE799845

PIERCEBRIDGE ROMAN BRIDGE
N. YORKSHIRE

Stonework foundations of a bridge, now marooned in a field, which once led to Piercebridge Roman Fort.

OPENING TIMES

Any reasonable daylight hours

VISIT US

Direction: At Piercebridge; 4 miles W of Darlington, on B6275

Train: Darlington 5 miles

Bus: Arriva 75, 76

ACQ.1975 🏛 ⚠

Parking available at nearby George Hotel. May infrequently be restricted when hosting large functions. Not managed by English Heritage.

MAP Page 345 (1F)
OS Map 93, 304: NZ214155

RICHMOND CASTLE
SEE FEATURE – PAGE 242

RIEVAULX ABBEY
SEE FEATURE – PAGE 244

SCARBOROUGH CASTLE
SEE FEATURE – PAGE 246

ST MARY'S CHURCH, STUDLEY ROYAL
N. YORKSHIRE – HG4 3DY

This magnificent High Victorian Anglican church was designed in the 1870s by the flamboyant architect William Burges, and has been called his 'ecclesiastical masterpiece'. The extravagantly decorated interior displays coloured marble, stained glass, a splendid organ and painted and gilded figures in all their original glory.

Owned by English Heritage and managed by the National Trust as part of the Fountains Abbey and Studley Royal Estate (see p.256).

OPENING TIMES

1 Apr-30 Sep, daily	12pm-4pm
1 Oct-29 Mar	Closed

VISIT US

Direction: Located 2½ miles W of Ripon, off B6265; in the grounds of the Studley Royal Estate

Bus: Dales & District 139 (operated by The Little Red Bus on Sun & Bank Hols)

Tel: 01765 608888

ACQ.1975 🏛 P ♿

Parking (at visitor centre or Studley Royal).

MAP Page 345 (3F)
OS Map 99, 298/299: SE275693

VISIT US

Direction: In Richmond just off the market place

Bus: Arriva 26A, X26, X27, 59 & X59; Dales & District 29, 30, 31, 31A, 31B, 31C, 32, 32A, X34, 34A, 54, X54, 55, 73, 159; Hodgsons Coaches 79, 79A (Thu) & 79X

Tel: 01748 822493

NON-MEMBERS

Adult	£4.90
Concession	£4.40
Child	£2.90

OPENING TIMES

1 Apr-30 Sep, daily	10am-6pm
1 Oct-2 Nov, daily	10am-5pm
3 Nov-15 Feb, Sat-Sun	10am-4pm
16-20 Feb, daily	10am-4pm
21 Feb-29 Mar, Sat-Sun	10am-4pm
24-26 Dec, 31 Dec-1 Jan	Closed

Parking (2 hours free in market place – not managed by English Heritage).

Disabled parking available at site on request, or in market place.

MAP Page 345 (2F)
OS Map 92, 304: NZ172007

Richmond Castle is impressively sited on a rocky promontory above the River Swale, overlooking a picturesque market town in beautiful Swaledale. Among the oldest Norman stone fortresses in Britain, it was begun in about 1070 by William the Conqueror's Breton supporter Alan the Red. The towering keep, added about a century later during the reign of Henry II, stands over 100 feet (30m) high, with walls up to 11 feet (3.35m) thick. It is remarkably complete within, and visitors can climb to the top for panoramic views over the castle's great courtyard, the marketplace of Richmond and the Yorkshire Dales.

According to legend, King Arthur and his knights lie sleeping in a cavern beneath the keep, and the drumbeats of a drummer-boy lost in a secret passage can still be heard.

A fascinating exhibition traces the building of the castle, its relationship with the town, and the shocking story of the 'Richmond Sixteen'. These 'Conscientious Objectors' were imprisoned here for refusing to fight in the First World War, before being taken to France and sentenced to death for refusing to obey military orders. A touch-screen display lets visitors view the poignant inscriptions they left on their cell walls. Family-friendly books and activities.

Richmond Castle is part of the Richard III Trail (see Middleham Castle, p.239).

SPOFFORTH CASTLE
N. YORKSHIRE

The ruined hall and chamber of a fortified manor house of the powerful Percy family, begun in the 13th and rebuilt in the 15th century. Its undercroft is cut into a rocky outcrop.

Managed by Spofforth-with-Stockeld Parish Council.

OPENING TIMES
1 Apr-30 Sep, daily	10am-6pm
1 Oct-29 Mar, daily (managed by a keykeeper)	10am-4pm
24-26 Dec & 1 Jan	Closed

VISIT US
Direction: 3½ miles SE of Harrogate; off A661 at Spofforth

Train: Pannal 4 miles

Bus: Transdev Harrogate & District services 770 & 771; Harrogate Coach Travel X70

ACQ.1924

Dogs on leads (restricted areas only).

MAP Page 345 (4G)
OS Map 104, 289: SE360511

STANWICK IRON AGE FORTIFICATIONS
N. YORKSHIRE

A section of the ramparts of the huge Iron Age trading and power-centre of the Brigantes, the most important tribe in pre-Roman northern Britain. This is a short reconstructed portion of a much larger circuit of defences, once some 4 miles (6½ kilometres) long and enclosing an area of 766 acres (310 hectares). Following Roman conquest, the Brigantian centre moved to Aldborough Roman Site (see p.232).

OPENING TIMES
Any reasonable daylight hours

VISIT US
Direction: Located on a minor road off A6274, at Forcett Village

Train: Darlington 10 miles

Bus: Dales & District service 29; Hodgsons 79A (Thu)

ACQ.1953

Dogs on leads (restricted areas only).

MAP Page 345 (1F)
OS Map 92, 304: NZ179124

STEETON HALL GATEWAY
N. YORKSHIRE – LS25 5PD

A fine example of a small, well-preserved manorial gatehouse dating from the 14th century.

OPENING TIMES
1 Apr-29 Mar, daily (exterior only)	10am-5pm
24-26 Dec & 1 Jan	Closed

VISIT US
Direction: Located 4 miles NE of Castleford, on a minor road off A162 at South Milford

Train: South Milford 1 mile

Bus: Arriva Yorkshire services 492 & 493; Utopia Coaches 404 (Sun), 424 & 491

ACQ.1948

Dogs on leads (restricted areas only).

MAP Page 345 (4G)
OS Map 105, 290: SE484314

ST PETER'S CHURCH, WINTRINGHAM
N. YORKSHIRE
YO17 8HU

© Cameron Newham

This beautiful and peaceful church, with an elegant spire, has Norman origins and is full of interesting furnishings including Jacobean bench pews, medieval carvings and stained glass. If you look carefully, you might even find some mythical beasts and ancient sword markings!

Owned and managed by The Churches Conservation Trust.

OPENING TIMES
Open daily during daylight hours

VISIT US
Train: Malton 6 miles

Bus: Yorkshire Coastliner service 187 or 843 to Scampston, Wintringham Lane End and then walk (approx. 2 mile)

20 mins from Wharram Percy Deserted Medieval Village, 35 mins from Scarborough Castle

MAP Page 345 (3H)
OS Map 101, 300: SE887731

For information on events in Yorkshire, visit **www.english-heritage.org.uk/events**

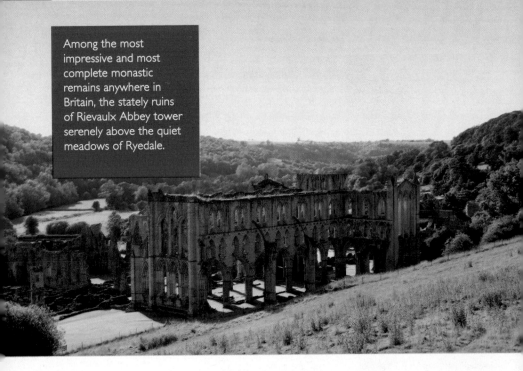

Among the most impressive and most complete monastic remains anywhere in Britain, the stately ruins of Rievaulx Abbey tower serenely above the quiet meadows of Ryedale.

VISIT US

Address: Rievaulx Abbey, Rievaulx, Nr Helmsley, North Yorkshire

Direction: In Rievaulx; 2¼ miles N of Helmsley, on minor road off B1257

Bus: Nearest location is Helmsley (approx. 2 mile walk) served by Stephenson's 29, 31, 31X, 194, 195; Scarborough & District 128

Tel: 01439 798228

Local Tourist Information
Helmsley: 01751 473791

NON-MEMBERS

Adult	£6.20
Concession	£5.60
Child	£3.70

OPENING TIMES

1 Apr-30 Sep, daily	10am-6pm
1 Oct-2 Nov, daily	10am-5pm
3 Nov-15 Feb, Sat-Sun	10am-4pm
16-20 Feb, daily	10am-4pm
21 Feb-29 Mar, Sat-Sun	10am-4pm
24-26 Dec, 31 Dec-1 Jan	Closed

Audio tours (also available for the visually impaired, those with learning difficulties and in French and German).

Parking: Limited pay and display parking, refundable to EH members and paying visitors on purchase of admission ticket.

Tearoom closes 30 minutes before the Abbey.

MAP Page 345 (2G)
OS Map 100, OL26: SE577850

Enjoy afternoon tea made from local produce in the cosy on-site café.

HOLIDAY COTTAGE AT **RIEVAULX ABBEY**

Set in a beautiful valley, Rievaulx is among the most tranquil and atmospheric of all the ruined abbeys of the North. Nestled into its breathtaking surroundings is a stunning detached holiday cottage, which comfortably sleeps four people.

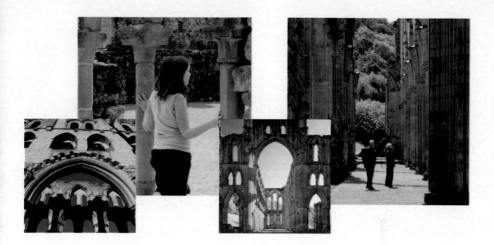

'Everywhere peace, everywhere serenity, and a marvellous freedom from the tumult of the world.' Written over eight centuries ago by the monastery's third abbot, St Aelred, these words still describe Rievaulx today.

Words are not the only link to Rievaulx's medieval monks. Over the past few years, the site has become something of an archaeological treasure, with unexpected discoveries shedding new light on the lives of the monks and the extensive renewal and rebuilding of their abbey church in the Early English Gothic style. Archaeologists continue to study the landscape around Rievaulx, revealing the remarkable extent of the abbey's influence and industry. Their discoveries are showcased within the on-site museum.

The abbey was established by St Bernard of Clairvaux, as part of the missionary effort to reform Christianity in western Europe. Twelve Clairvaux monks came to Rievaulx in 1132. From these modest beginnings grew one of the wealthiest monasteries of medieval England and the first northern Cistercian monastery. Rievaulx also enjoyed the protection of Walter Espec of nearby Helmsley Castle, who provided much of the abbey's land.

A steady flow of monks came to Rievaulx, attracted by the prestige of Abbot Aelred, author and preacher, who was regarded then and later as a wise and saintly man. Following his death in 1167, the monks of Rievaulx sought canonisation for their former leader, and in the 1220s they rebuilt the east part of their church in a much more elaborate style to house his tomb. Most of this 13th-century 'presbytery' still stands to virtually its full impressive height, a reminder of Rievaulx's original splendour.

Rievaulx was still a vibrant community when Henry VIII dissolved it in 1538. Its new owner, Thomas Manners, first Earl of Rutland, swiftly instigated the systematic destruction of the buildings, yet the substantial remains constitute one of the most eloquent of all monastic sites, free 'from the tumult of the world'. Schoolchildren from the local area have helped to create a Sensory Garden full of scented and flavoured herbs, amid tile motifs based on medieval designs.

Don't miss the indoor exhibition, *The Work of God and Man*, which explores the agricultural, industrial, spiritual and commercial aspects of Rievaulx's history, employing a variety of lively and interactive displays. A display also traces the rediscovery of Rievaulx Abbey and its archaeology and conservation. There are family-friendly events, books and activities during school holidays.

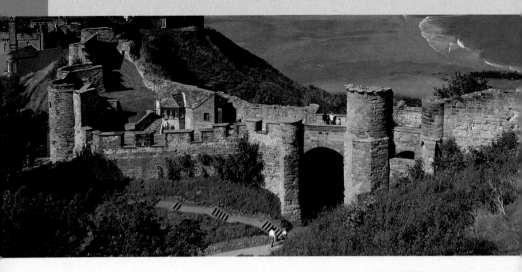

VISIT US

Direction: Castle Road, E of the town centre

Train: Scarborough 1 mile

Bus: From surrounding areas

Tel: 01723 372451

Local Tourist Information
Scarborough: 01723 383636

NON-MEMBERS

Adult	£5.00
Concession	£4.50
Child	£3.00
Family	£13.00

OPENING TIMES

1 Apr-30 Sep, daily	10am-6pm
1 Oct-2 Nov, daily	10am-5pm
3 Nov-15 Feb, Sat-Sun	10am-4pm
16-22 Feb, daily	10am-4pm
23 Feb-29 Mar, Sat-Sun	10am-4pm
24-26 Dec, 31 Dec-1 Jan	Closed

Please note: tearoom closes 30 mins before castle

Parking (pre-booked parking only for disabled visitors, otherwise located in town centre).

MAP Page 345 (2J)
OS Map 101, 301: TA050892

Scarborough Castle defends a prominent headland between two bays, with sheer drops to the sea and only a narrow landward approach. Specially constructed viewing platforms on the battlements offer panoramic views. Long before the castle was built, this natural fortress was favoured by prehistoric settlers, and later housed a defended Roman signal station.

Henry II's towering 12th-century keep, dominating the approach, is the centrepiece of fortifications developed over later centuries in response to repeated sieges – notably by rebel barons in 1312 and twice during the Civil War. Though again strengthened with barracks and gun-batteries against Jacobite threats in 1745, the castle failed to defend the harbour against the American sea-raider John Paul Jones in 1779, and was itself damaged by German naval bombardment in 1914. During the Second World War it played the more covert role of hosting a secret listening post.

The site's 3000 year history is explored in the restored Master Gunner's House, accompanied by artefacts from each period of Scarborough's past. Less mobile visitors can enjoy a ground-floor, touch-screen virtual tour of the displays, as well as virtual views reproducing those from the raised platforms.

Timelined graphic panels around the castle focus on characters from the past and there are free activity sheets, an audio tour, and an investigative story box to help younger visitors visualise and understand the history of the castle.

Complete your day out with afternoon tea made from local produce in the cosy on-site café.

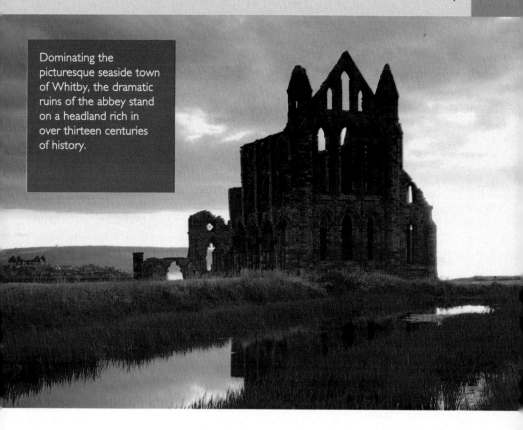

Dominating the picturesque seaside town of Whitby, the dramatic ruins of the abbey stand on a headland rich in over thirteen centuries of history.

VISIT US

Address: Whitby Abbey, Abbey Lane, Whitby, North Yorkshire

Direction: On cliff top, E of Whitby

Train: Whitby ½ mile

Bus: Esk Valley service 97 & 97A actually serve Whitby Abbey; The Whitby Town Tour is also operated by Coastal & Country and serves the Abbey. The town is served by Arriva, Coastal & Country, Esk Valley and Yorkshire Coastliner

Tel: 01947 603568

Local Tourist Information
01723 383636

NON-MEMBERS

Adult	£6.60
Concession	£5.90
Child	£4.00
Family	£17.20

OPENING TIMES

1 Apr-30 Sep, daily	10am-6pm
1 Oct-2 Nov, daily	10am-5pm
3 Nov-15 Feb, Sat-Sun	10am-4pm
16-20 Feb, daily	10am-4pm
21 Feb-29 Mar, Sat-Sun	10am-4pm
24-26 Dec, 31 Dec-1 Jan	Closed

ACQ.1920

Disabled access (south entrance parking, charged).

Dogs welcome on leads.

Parking not managed by English Heritage (charge payable).

Toilets situated in the car park are not operated by English Heritage.

Tearoom not managed by English Heritage.

MAP Page 345 (1J)
OS Map 94, OL27: NZ903112

The first monastery here was founded in AD 657 by King Oswy of Northumbria. An Anglo-Saxon style 'double monastery' for men and women, its first head was the formidable royal princess Abbess Hild; here Caedmon the cowherd was miraculously transformed into an inspired poet; here the future of the English church was decided in 664; and here the relics of Northumbrian kings and saints were enshrined.

Though many excavated finds from it are displayed in the visitor centre, nothing survives

CONTINUED ▶

above ground of the Anglo-Saxon monastery. The imposing ruins belong to the church of the Benedictine abbey refounded on its site in 1090 by the Normans. From 1220 onwards, the abbey church was completely rebuilt in the Early English style. The pinnacled east end and north transept still stand high, richly carved with characteristic 'dog's tooth' embellishment. Time, war and nature have left their marks. Parts of the church collapsed during storms, its west front was hit by German naval shelling in 1914 and centuries of wind and rain have added their own etched and pitted decoration. These supremely romantic ruins enjoy panoramic views, and literary renown as the backdrop to Bram Stoker's *Dracula*, the Victorian novel which has made Whitby the 'Goth' capital of Britain. More recently the site has inspired *Shadowmancer* and other best-selling children's novels by ex-vicar and ex-policeman GP Taylor.

The ruins share the headland with the Cholmley family mansion, begun after Henry VIII's suppression of the abbey. Its impressive Classical façade of 1672 is fronted by a restoration of the 'hard garden' courtyard rediscovered during English Heritage excavations. The courtyard's centrepiece is a specially-commissioned bronze copy of the famous 'Borghese Gladiator' statue. The Roman marble original of this spectacular life-sized statue, now in the Paris Louvre, dates from the 1st century BC: it was found in 1611 in Italy and bronze casts were made for King Charles I. Copies graced many great English

houses and gardens including the Cholmleys' Whitby mansion, recalling the family's Civil War support for the Royalist cause.

The mansion now houses the highly imaginative and award-winning visitor centre. Displaying fascinating finds from the Anglo-Saxon, medieval and Cholmley periods, this is packed with digital displays and entertaining interactives: touch-screens allow visitors to question Whitby personalities, from Abbess Hild via a medieval monk to Bram Stoker.

Please note: from the Whitby harbour area, the abbey can only be directly reached on foot via the 199 'abbey steps'. Alternatively, a well-signposted road leads from the town outskirts to the cliff-top abbey.

The mansion now houses the highly imaginative and award-winning visitor centre, displaying fascinating finds from the Anglo-Saxon, medieval and Cholmley periods.

ST STEPHEN'S CHURCH, FYLINGDALES
N. YORKSHIRE
YO22 4PN

© CCT

St Stephen's, a fisherman's church, stands majestically on the hillside overlooking the sea. Resonating with a resilient North Sea fishing community there are memorials to the shipwrecked in both the church and churchyard. Outside, windswept gravestones huddle tightly round the church walls.

Owned and managed by The Churches Conservation Trust.

OPENING TIMES
Keyholder nearby

VISIT US
Train: Whitby 5 miles

Bus: Arriva Bus 93 runs a regular service from Middlesbrough bus station to Scarborough rail station going past the church

10 mins from Whitby Abbey

MAP Page 345 (2J)
OS Map 94, OL27: NZ942059

WHARRAM PERCY DESERTED MEDIEVAL VILLAGE
N. YORKSHIRE

The most famous and intensively studied of Britain's 3000 or so deserted medieval villages, Wharram Percy occupies a remote but attractive site in a

beautiful Wolds valley. Above the substantial ruins of the church, and a millpond, the outlines of many lost houses are traceable on a grassy plateau. First settled in prehistoric times, Wharram flourished as a village between the 12th and 14th centuries, before final abandonment in about 1500. Graphic interpretation panels tell its story and recreate the original appearance of the buildings.

A free downloadable audio tour is available on our website.

OPENING TIMES
Any reasonable daylight hours

VISIT US
Direction: 6 miles SE of Malton, on minor road from B1248; ½ mile S of Wharram-le-Street. Park in car park, then ¾ mile walk via uneven track, steep in places. Site also accessible on foot via Wolds Way ramblers' path. Sturdy and waterproof footwear required. Parts of site slope steeply, and farm livestock likely to be present on site and access path

Train: Malton 8 miles

Bus: Stephenson's 190 to Wharram-Le-Street then 1 mile walk

ACQ.1972

Please note: site is hazardous in snowy conditions.

MAP Page 345 (3H)
OS Map 100, 300: SE859644

WHEELDALE ROMAN ROAD
N. YORKSHIRE

A mile-long stretch of enigmatic ancient road – probably Roman but possibly later or earlier – still with its hard core and drainage ditches. Amid wild and beautiful moorland.

WHEELDALE ROMAN ROAD

OPENING TIMES
Any reasonable daylight hours

VISIT US
Direction: S of Goathland; W of A169; 7 miles S of Whitby

Train: Goathland (North Yorkshire Moors Rly) (4 miles) or Newtondale Halt (then 3 mile forest walk)

Bus: Yorkshire Coastliner service 840 to Goathland then 4 miles walk. Alternatively alight at Ellerbeck bridge and walk 2½ miles over Howl Moor

Local Tourist Information
Pickering: 01751 473791

ACQ.1912

MAP Page 345 (2H)
OS Map 94/100, OL27: SE806977

WHITBY ABBEY
SEE FEATURE – PAGE 247

YORK COLD WAR BUNKER
N. YORKSHIRE YO24 4HT

English Heritage's most modern, most unusual and perhaps most spine-chilling site, 'No. 20 Group Royal Observer Corps HQ' is the semi-subterranean bunker which would have monitored nuclear explosions and fallout in the Yorkshire region. In service between 1961 and 1991, the Bunker's control rooms display 'colour-

YORK COLD WAR BUNKER

psychology décor' together with original monitoring and communications equipment. Sealed away from the outside world, decontamination rooms and air filters would have protected 60 people from the effects of nuclear war. A guided tour, enhanced by a striking 10-minute film (PG rated) and interpretation, tells the story of the Cold War's 'Mutually Assured Destruction'.

NON-MEMBERS

Adult	£6.60
Concession	£5.90
Child	£4.00

OPENING TIMES

1 Apr-2 Nov, Fri-Sun	10am-6pm
3 Nov-29 Mar, Sun	10am-4pm
24-26 Dec, 31 Dec-1 Jan	Closed

By tour only. Tours last approx. 1 hour. No need to book. Last tour 1 hour before closing

Weekdays: Admission for schools and groups only. Booking 14 days in advance, minimum fee applies

VISIT US

Direction: Monument Close, off Acomb Road, near the Carlton Tavern, approx. 2 miles from York city centre

Train: York 1½ miles

Bus: First in York service 1; Arriva 412; Eddie Brown service 142 & 413

Tel: 01904 646940 (Clifford's Tower)

Local Tourist Information
York: 01904 550099

Free parking.

MAP Page 345 (3G)
OS Map 105, 290: SE580515

SOUTH YORKSHIRE

BRODSWORTH HALL AND GARDENS
SEE FEATURE OPPOSITE

CONISBROUGH CASTLE
SEE FEATURE – PAGE 254

HOLY TRINITY CHURCH, WENTWORTH
S. YORKSHIRE – S62 7TX

© CCT

Rooted in village history, this atmospheric, partly ruined building started life as a church but was converted to a mausoleum in 1877. Today, only the chancel and north chapel remain intact. Brass and stone memorials and effigies trace the fascinating history of the powerful Wentworth family.

Owned and managed by The Churches Conservation Trust.

OPENING TIMES
Any reasonable daylight hours

VISIT US
Train: Elsecar 1½ miles

Bus: TM Travel service 227 serve the village

20 mins from Conisbrough Castle

MAP Page 345 (5G)
OS Map 110/111, 278: SK384983

MONK BRETTON PRIORY
S. YORKSHIRE

The substantial ruins of a Cluniac monastery, later absorbed into the Benedictine order, with an unusually well-marked ground plan, almost complete west range and 15th-century gatehouse.

NON-MEMBERS
Charge may apply on event days

OPENING TIMES

1 Apr-29 Mar, daily	10am-3pm
(managed by a keykeeper)	
24-26 Dec & 1 Jan	Closed

VISIT US

Direction: Located 1 mile E of Barnsley town centre, off A633

Train: Barnsley 2½ miles

Bus: Stagecoach services 26, 26A, 28, 29, 29A, 30, 30A, 32 & X28; Tates 34A; Redline 32A, 37, 37A, 38 & 46 all to Cundy Cross from whence it is a short walk

ACQ.1932

MAP Page 345 (5G)
OS Map 110/111, 278: SE373065

Glossily-presented 'Downton Abbey' is fictional: but well-worn Brodsworth Hall is real. Nowhere else in England can visitors experience so vividly a lived-in mansion grown graciously old with time and use.

VISIT US

Address: Brodsworth Hall and Gardens, Brodsworth, Doncaster, South Yorkshire

Direction: In Brodsworth, 5 miles NW of Doncaster off A635 Barnsley Road; from junction 37 of A1(M)

Train: South Elmsall 4 miles; Moorthorpe 4½ miles; Doncaster 5½ miles; Adwick Le Street 3 miles

Bus: Tates Travel service 203

Tel: 01302 722598

Local Tourist Information
Doncaster: 01302 734309

NON-MEMBERS

House and gardens
Adult	£9.70
Concession	£8.70
Child	£5.80

Winter (3 Nov-29 Mar)
Adult	£6.10
Concession	£5.50
Child	£3.70

OPENING TIMES

House (Guided tours at 11am and 12 noon, free flow from 1pm)
1 Apr-2 Nov, daily	11am-5pm
3 Nov-29 Mar	Closed

Gardens
1 Apr-30 Sep, daily	10am-6pm
1 Oct-2 Nov, daily	10am-5pm
3 Nov-29 Mar, Sat-Sun	10am-4pm
24-26 Dec, 31 Dec-1 Jan	Closed

Servants' wing and tearooms
1 Apr-2 Nov, daily	10am-5.30pm
3 Nov-29 Mar, Sat-Sun	10am-4pm
24-26 Dec, 31 Dec-1 Jan	Closed

Last admission is 30 mins before closing

Mobility around the site
Prams and back carriers for babies are not allowed in the hall, small padded pushchairs and slings are available instead. For visitors with mobility needs or young children, an electric buggy operates a shuttle service from the car park. Benches throughout the gardens, although steps and steep slopes limit access to some areas. The hall has ramps and seats, and a lift to the first floor

MAP Page 345 (5G)
OS Map 111, 279: SE506070

Brodsworth Hall is unique. This is no glossily restored showpiece, frozen in manicured grandeur. 'Conserved as found', it is a mansion which grew comfortably old over the years, a country house

CONTINUED ▶

To mark the centenary of the First World War, an exhibition and a series of events will tell the story of those who lived and worked at Brodsworth Hall during the Great War. *Duty Calls: the Country House in Time of War* has been generously supported by the Heritage Lottery Fund.

as it really was: still reflecting its original opulence, but well-worn, gently conserved – and full of surprises.

Built in the 1860s by the fabulously wealthy Charles Thellusson, Brodsworth Hall was occupied by his family for over 120 years. The 'grand rooms' on the ground floor recall the house's Victorian heyday, but elsewhere Brodsworth's gentle decline during the 20th century is much more apparent. The last resident, the indomitable Sylvia Grant-Dalton, fought a losing battle against subsidence and leaking roofs in her latter years. Following her death in 1988, English Heritage took the bold decision to conserve the interiors as they were found, rather than restoring them.

Thus the house appears as she used it, making do and mending with dwindling funds and ever fewer servants. The Library's original wallpaper and carpets are faded, and Charles Thellusson's woodworking room is crowded with delightful clutter. Some bedrooms fell out of use, along with the spartan rooms of the redundant servants' wing. Others were partially modernised over the years, and include objects from the 1900s to the 1980s which may be startlingly familiar to many visitors.

Downstairs, the cavernous Victorian kitchen with its stupendous cooking range was deserted for a cosier 'Aga kitchen' and scullery. These remain as they were at the end of Brodsworth's active life, with their Tupperware, Formica and Fanny Craddock cookbooks. Beside the Aga rests the once-grand but battered and mended armchair of the house's last cook-housekeeper.

In contrast to the house, the extensive gardens have been wonderfully restored to their original horticultural splendour as 'a collection of grand gardens in miniature'.

Here are our suggestions for enjoying the best of the garden collections:

SPRING

Snowdrops, Bluebells and Daffodils put on a fantastic show.

SUMMER

The Rose Garden with its hundred varieties. Two contrasting herbaceous borders. The fern dell with its architectural foliage. On summer Sunday afternoons, the best of Yorkshire's brass bands play in the gardens.

AUTUMN

Brilliant autumn colours in the acer dell and clipped evergreen foliage in the formal gardens.

WINTER

The collection of Victorian hollies.

For garden lovers

In contrast to the house, the extensive gardens have been wonderfully restored to their original splendour as 'a collection of grand gardens in miniature', with vistas last enjoyed before the First World War.

The flower garden displays a fine selection of period bedding plants, while romantic views from the restored summerhouse take in both the formal gardens and the pleasure grounds. Stroll through the statue walks, the fern dell grotto and the beautiful wild rose dell.

A family-friendly property

Brodsworth Hall and Gardens are outstandingly user-friendly for visitors of all ages. For children, there is a playroom, a hands-on resources room, and an outdoor play area featuring a real ex-naval training boat. The friendly volunteer room stewards are another unique Brodsworth attraction: many knew the property before English Heritage acquired it.

VISIT US

Direction: Located NE of Conisbrough town centre off A630; 4½ miles SW of Doncaster

Train: Conisbrough ½ mile or Rotherham 6 miles

Bus: Stagecoach services 220, 221 & 222; First X78

Tel: 01709 863329

NON-MEMBERS

Adult	£4.70
Concession	£4.20
Child	£2.80
Family	£12.20

OPENING TIMES

May-30 Sep, daily	10am-6pm
1 Oct-2 Nov, daily	10am-5pm
3 Nov-29 Mar, Sat-Sun	10am-4pm
24-26 Dec, 31 Dec-1 Jan	Closed

New guidebook.

Dogs on leads (in grounds only).

Parking (visitors with disabilities may be dropped off at the visitor centre).

Access (limited to some areas).

MAP Page 345 (5G)
OS Map 111, 279: SK515989

NEW FOR 2014

Dramatically re-presented in 2014 after a major HLF-funded project, the keep of Conisbrough Castle is unique. Beautifully constructed in high-quality magnesian limestone, it is a tall cylinder ringed with semi-hexagonal turret buttresses, ingeniously adapted at battlement level to house water-cisterns, an oven and even a tiny private chapel. Nothing like it had ever before been seen in England – where until now keeps had usually been rectangular – and its design was never repeated. Soon afterwards, it was reinforced by curtain walls with semi-circular turrets, another very advanced feature.

Probably built before the 1180s, this piece of medieval one-upmanship was the work of Hamelin Plantagenet, illegitimate half-brother of King Henry II. Having achieved wealth and status by marrying Conisbrough's heiress, the 'Woman of Power' Lady Isabel, he was determined to make his mark among older-established barons.

Now English Heritage is giving his latest thing in 12th-century castle design the latest thing in 21st-century presentations. The keep's three floors will be inhabited by wall-projected larger than life characters who talk to visitors: a range of audio-visuals; film; models; recreated furnishings; original site-finds and display panels in 'graphic novel' style tell the story of Hamelin and Isabel, and reveal how medieval castles worked. There will also be a virtual tour for those unable to ascend the keep.

Conisbrough Castle is part of the Richard III Trail (see Middleham Castle, p.239).

ROCHE ABBEY
S. YORKSHIRE – S66 8NW

Beautifully set in a valley landscaped by 'Capability' Brown in the 18th century, the most striking feature of this Cistercian abbey is the eastern end of its church, built in the new Gothic style in c. 1170. It has one of the most complete ground plans of any English Cistercian monastery, laid out as excavated foundations. Not far from Conisbrough Castle.

NON-MEMBERS

Adult	£3.60
Concession	£3.20
Child	£2.20

OPENING TIMES

1 Apr-2 Nov, Wed-Sun	10am-5pm
3 Nov-29 Mar	Closed

VISIT US

Direction: 1½ miles S of Maltby, off A634

Train: Conisbrough 7 miles

Bus: First services 1 to Maltby Muglet Lane then 1½ miles walk. Alternatively TM Travel service 20 to Firbeck Village (then a 2 mile walk)

Tel: 01709 812739

ACQ.1921 🌳 🏛 🖼 🧍 ♿ 🅿 📷
♿ OVP ⚠

MAP Page 345 (6G)
OS Map 111/120, 279: SK544898

WEST YORKSHIRE

ALL SAINTS' CHURCH, HAREWOOD
W. YORKSHIRE – LS17 9LG

© CCT

All Saints', standing in the grounds of Harewood House, is remarkable for six pairs of alabaster effigies – virtually without rival in England – commemorating the owners of Harewood. They provide a fascinating insight into the armour, robes, jewellery and headdresses of the 15th century.

Owned and managed by The Churches Conservation Trust.

OPENING TIMES

Apr-Oct, daily	10am-6pm

Other times call Harewood House Trust Office on 0113 218 1010 in advance of your visit

VISIT US

Train: Weeton 3 miles

Bus: Harrogate & District service 36 passes the entrance to Harewood Park

20 mins from Spofforth Castle

MAP Page 345 (4F)
OS Map 104, 289/297: SE314451

CHURCH OF ST JOHN THE EVANGELIST, LEEDS
W. YORKSHIRE – LS2 8JD

© CCT

The oldest church in Leeds. The glory of the church lies in its magnificent fittings, particularly the fabulously detailed wooden screen. Monuments commemorate the citizens of Leeds, while brightly painted angels play instruments in the roof, looking down to the wonderfully carved pews below.

Owned and managed by The Churches Conservation Trust.

OPENING TIMES

Tue-Sat	11am-3pm

VISIT US

Train: Leeds 1 mile

Bus: Many bus services pass close to the church

30 mins from Steeton Hall Gateway

MAP Page 345 (4F)
OS Map 104, 289: SE302338

DISCOUNTED ATTRACTIONS:

Use your membership to get exclusive discounts at these independent attractions in Yorkshire. Please remember to show your card as proof of membership.

BARLEY HALL
North Yorkshire YO1 8AR
Discover the town house of a medieval Lord Mayor of York. Rediscovered under a relatively modern façade, this stunning building has beautiful exposed timber frames and high roofs.
www.barleyhall.co.uk
Tel. 01904 615505

CASTLE HOWARD
North Yorkshire YO60 7DA
Magnificent 18th-century house built by Sir John Vanbrugh for the 3rd Earl of Carlisle, set within spectacular parkland. With exhibitions, events, adventure playground, shops and cafés.
www.castlehoward.co.uk
Tel. 01653 648333

DIG
AN ARCHAEOLOGICAL ADVENTURE
North Yorkshire YO1 8NN
DIG offers you a unique adventure to get you on your way to becoming a real archaeologist.
www.digyork.com
Tel. 01904 615505

DUNCOMBE PARK
North Yorkshire YO62 5EB
A masterpiece of landscape gardening with long sweeping terraces, towering veteran trees, classical temples and breathtaking views over the Rye valley.
www.duncombepark.com
Tel. 01439 770213

FOUNTAINS ABBEY & STUDLEY ROYAL WATER GARDEN
North Yorkshire HG4 3DY
Spectacular World Heritage Site including 12th-century abbey ruins and stunning Georgian water garden.
www.nationaltrust.org.uk/fountainsabbey
Tel. 01765 608888

HAREWOOD HOUSE
West Yorkshire LS17 9LG
See how Harewood inspired Turner, Chippendale and Capability Brown. A great family day out boasting award winning gardens, adventure playground and exotic bird garden.
www.harewood.org
Tel. 0113 2181010

YORKSHIRE

Discount applies to:

KEY ⊞ MEMBERS　OVP OVP HOLDERS　👪? NO. OF MEMBER'S CHILDREN

Terms and conditions may apply, so make sure you check the individual pages on our website or call the individual property for more details.

⊞ OVP 👪 6
JORVIK VIKING CENTRE
North Yorkshire YO1 9WT
Experience life as it was 1000 years ago as you explore the Viking-age city of York at the world-famous Jorvik Viking Centre.

www.jorvik-viking-centre.co.uk
Tel. 01904 615505

⊞ OVP 👪 6
KELHAM ISLAND MUSEUM
South Yorkshire S3 8RY
Discover the story of life and work in Sheffield. Learn how steelmaking forged the city of today and its impact on the world!

www.simt.co.uk
Tel. 0114 272 2106

⊞ OVP 👪 6
MERCHANT ADVENTURERS' HALL
North Yorkshire YO1 9XD
The Merchant Adventurers' Hall is one of York's medieval marvels, constructed in 1357. Discover this stunning building and its unique collections.

www.theyorkcompany.co.uk
Tel. 01904 654818

⊞ OVP 👪 6
MICKLEGATE BAR MUSEUM
North Yorkshire YO1 6JX
Visit the ancient Micklegate Bar to explore the pageantry and barbaric history that has unfolded within York's historic walls.

www.micklegatebar.com
Tel. 01904 615505

⊞
NORTH YORKSHIRE MOORS RAILWAY
North Yorkshire YO18 7JF
Climb aboard a steam train and ride like Harry Potter for the ultimate trip through Heartbeat Country. Trains run between Pickering and Whitby.

www.nymr.co.uk
Tel. 01751 472508

⊞ 👪 6
YORK MINSTER
North Yorkshire YO1 7HH
Take a 2000-year journey through interactive underground chambers and view stained glass masterpieces in The Orb, while exploring one of the world's most magnificent cathedrals.

www.yorkminster.org
Tel. 01904 557200

NORTH WEST

Stott Park Bobbin Mill

Keep up to date with events, news and offers www.english-heritage.org.uk/newsletter

Carlisle Castle

Hadrian's Wall

16

9

23

Carlisle

Cumbria

Workington

15

18 Penrith

Keswick 10

17 12

11

8 21

7

14 5

20

Windermere

22

Ulverston

13

Barrow 6 26

in-Furness

19

Lancaster

Lancashire 25

Blackpool

27 Burnley

Preston Blackburn

24

Southport

Wigan Bolton Oldham

Merseyside St Helens Greater Manchester

Liverpool Manchester

Birkenhead

Warrington

Cheshire Macclesfield

Chester

3 1 4

Crewe

Details of local public transport information in England are available from Traveline
www.traveline.org.uk
or call 0871 200 2233.

HIGHLIGHTS FOR 2014/15 IN THE **NORTH WEST**

p.262

p.266

p.273

Beeston Castle & Woodland Park: an impressive crag-top medieval fortress amid delightful woodland walks, with astonishing views from the battlements.

Carlisle Castle: trace the long and turbulent history of this stern Border guardian, vividly retold in a recently-installed display.

Stott Park Bobbin Mill: tour this fully-operational bobbin factory in a lovely Lakeland setting. Working steam weekends every month.

PROPERTIES

CHESHIRE
1 Beeston Castle and Woodland Park
2 Chester Castle: Agricola Tower and Castle Walls
3 Chester Roman Amphitheatre
4 Sandbach Crosses

CUMBRIA
5 Ambleside Roman Fort
6 Bow Bridge
7 Brough Castle
8 Brougham Castle
9 Carlisle Castle
10 Castlerigg Stone Circle
11 Clifton Hall
12 Countess Pillar
13 Furness Abbey
14 Hardknott Roman Fort
15 King Arthur's Round Table
16 Lanercost Priory
17 Mayburgh Henge
18 Penrith Castle
19 Piel Castle
20 Ravenglass Roman Bath House
21 Shap Abbey
22 Stott Park Bobbin Mill
23 Wetheral Priory Gatehouse

LANCASHIRE
24 Goodshaw Chapel
25 Sawley Abbey
26 Warton Old Rectory
27 Whalley Abbey Gatehouse

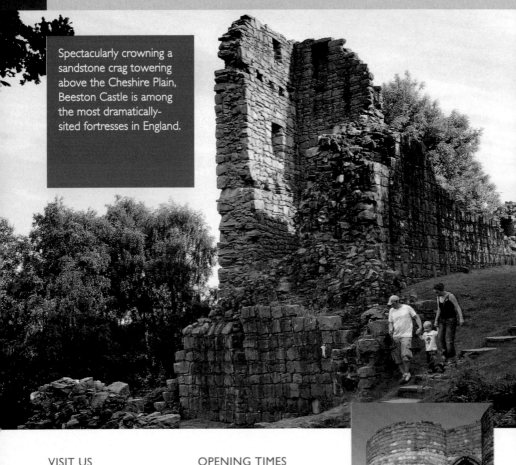

Spectacularly crowning a sandstone crag towering above the Cheshire Plain, Beeston Castle is among the most dramatically-sited fortresses in England.

VISIT US

Address: Beeston Castle, Chapel Lane, Beeston, Cheshire

Direction: Located 11 miles SE of Chester, on minor road off A49

Train: Chester 14 miles

Bus: GHA service 83 (Tue) to Beeston; Otherwise GHA service 56 (Thu & Sat) to Bunbury Heath (then 1 mile walk) or Arriva service 84 to Tarporley (2½ miles)

Tel: 01829 260464

Local Tourist Information
Chester: 01244 402111

NON-MEMBERS

Adult	£6.10
Concession	£5.50
Child	£3.70
Family	£15.90

OPENING TIMES

1 Apr-30 Sep, daily	10am-6pm
1 Oct-2 Nov, daily	10am-5pm
3 Nov-15 Feb, Sat-Sun	10am-4pm
16-20 Feb, daily	10am-4pm
21 Feb-29 Mar, Sat-Sun	10am-4pm
24-26 Dec, 31 Dec-1 Jan	Closed

ACQ.1959

Please note: Steep climb (no disabled access to the top of the hill). Boots or stout footwear recommended.

Parking: charges apply, may vary on event days. Car park not managed by English Heritage.

MAP Page 344 (7D)
OS Map 117, 257/258: SJ537593

The extensive wooded surroundings, rich in wildlife, are fascinating to explore. Visitors can experience some of the best views in Cheshire from within the castle.

Naturally defended by steep cliffs on three sides, Beeston's crag attracted prehistoric settlers. It became an important Bronze Age metal-working site and later an immense Iron Age hillfort, whose earthwork defences were adapted by medieval castle-builders.

The 'Castle of the Rock' – its medieval title – was begun in the 1220s by Ranulf, Earl of Chester, one of the greatest barons of Henry III's England. A defence against aristocratic rivals and a proclamation of Ranulf's power, his fortress is approached via a ruined gatehouse in a multi-towered outer wall, defining a huge outer bailey climbing steadily up the hill.

At its summit is the crowning glory of Beeston, the inner bailey, defended by a deep rock-cut ditch and a mighty double-towered gatehouse. The best-preserved part of the castle, the inner bailey commands astounding views across eight counties, from the Welsh Mountains to the west, to the Pennines in the east. It also contains the famous castle well, which is over 100 metres deep and according to legend was the hiding place of Richard II's treasure.

Beeston Castle experienced a final blaze of glory as an important English Civil War stronghold, which finally surrendered to Parliament in November 1645 after a long and eventful siege. Thereafter it became the romantic ruin which caught the attention of wealthy Victorian John Tollemache, who promoted Beeston as a tourist attraction, even stocking its grounds with kangaroos.

English Heritage's management of the castle's wooded slopes makes the site a paradise for walkers, nature-lovers and adventurous children. A circular Woodland Walk leads fairly gently downhill from near the outer bailey gate. Winding around the base of the crag through wildlife-thronged woods, the path provides glimpses of the castle above, before reaching another of Beeston's attractions, the sandstone caves, one of which appeared as 'Robin Hood's Cave' in a 1992 film. The caves can also be reached via a shorter walk from the Visitor Centre, where the *Castle of the Rock* display vividly recounts Beeston's 4000 years of history.

Visit the website for details of special events.

CHESTER CASTLE: AGRICOLA TOWER AND CASTLE WALLS
CHESHIRE

The original gateway to Chester Castle, this 12th-century tower houses a chapel with exceptionally fine wall-paintings of c. 1220, rediscovered in the 1980s. An access stair to the castle's wall-walk is nearby.

OPENING TIMES
Castle and Agricola Tower open for guided tours only. Tours from the Town Hall Square visitor centre, charged and organised by the Museum Service in Chester, can be booked online. For group and school visits call 01244 972120

VISIT US
Direction: Access via Assizes Court car park on Grosvenor St

Train: Chester 1 mile

Bus: Arriva 1, 3, 3A, 4, 4A, X11, 12, 13, X44, X55; GHA services X1 & 11A pass close to the site

ACQ.1912

MAP Page 344 (7C)
OS Map 117, 266: SJ405657

CHESTER ROMAN AMPHITHEATRE
CHESHIRE

The largest Roman amphitheatre in Britain, used for entertainment and military training by the 20th Legion, based at the fortress of 'Deva' (Chester). Excavations by English Heritage and Chester City Council in 2004-05 revealed two successive stone-built amphitheatres with wooden seating. The first included access to the upper tiers of seats via stairs on the rear wall, as at Pompeii, and had a small shrine next to its north entrance. The second provided seat access via vaulted stairways. The two buildings differed both from each other and from all other British

amphitheatres, underlining the importance of Roman Chester.

Managed by Cheshire West and Chester Council.

OPENING TIMES
Any reasonable daylight hours

VISIT US
Direction: On Vicars Lane, beyond Newgate, Chester

Train: Chester ¾ mile

Bus: From surrounding areas

ACQ.1964
Disabled access (no access to amphitheatre floor).

MAP Page 344 (7C)
OS Map 117, 266: SJ408662

SANDBACH CROSSES
CHESHIRE

The two massive Saxon stone crosses, elaborately carved with animals and Biblical scenes including the Nativity of Christ and the Crucifixion, dominate the cobbled market square of Sandbach. Probably dating from the 9th century and originally painted as well as carved, they are among the finest surviving examples of Anglo-Saxon high crosses.

OPENING TIMES
Any reasonable daylight hours

VISIT US
Direction: Market Sq, Sandbach

Train: Sandbach 1½ miles

Bus: Bakerbus 32; Arriva 37, 37E; Arriva/D&G 38; D&G 78, SB1, SB2 & SB3; GHA X81 (Wed & Fri only)

ACQ.1937

MAP Page 344 (7D)
OS Map 118, 268: SJ759608

NEW FOR 2014
New interpretation, podcasts and a 360° panorama.

CUMBRIA

AMBLESIDE ROMAN FORT
CUMBRIA

The foundations of a 2nd-4th century Roman fort, in a meadow beside Windermere. Built under Hadrian's rule, its large granaries suggest use as a supply base for troops policing the Lake District.

Managed by the National Trust.

OPENING TIMES
Any reasonable daylight hours

VISIT US
Direction: In Borrans Field, beside A5075 on south-western outskirts of Ambleside. 182 metres W of Waterhead car park

Train: Windermere 5 miles

Bus: Stagecoach Cumbria 505, 516, 555, 599, X8 then ½ mile walk

ACQ.1978
No parking at site. Farm stock may be present in meadow. Stout footwear advised.

MAP Page 346 (6D)
OS Map 90, OL7: NY372034

BOW BRIDGE
CUMBRIA

This narrow 15th-century stone bridge across Mill Beck carried an old packhorse route to nearby Furness Abbey (see p.268).

OPENING TIMES
Any reasonable daylight hours

VISIT US
Direction: Located ½ mile N of Barrow-in-Furness, on minor road off A590; near Furness Abbey

Train: Barrow-in-Furness 1½ miles

Bus: Stagecoach in Cumbria service 6 & X6 to within ¾ mile

ACQ.1950

MAP Page 346 (7D)
OS Map 96, OL6: SD224715

BROUGH CASTLE
CUMBRIA

Starkly impressive Brough Castle stands on a ridge commanding strategic Stainmore Pass, on the site of a Roman fort. Frequently the target of Scots raids, its towering keep dates from c. 1200. More comfortable living quarters were later added by the Clifford family, only to be accidentally burnt following a 'great Christmas' party in 1521. Like so many other castles hereabouts, Brough was restored in the 17th century by Lady Anne Clifford, traces of whose additions can still be seen.

St Michael's Parish Church, in pretty Church Brough near the castle, displays an exhibition about the region. This living church is open 10am-4pm daily (not English Heritage).

OPENING TIMES
1 Apr-30 Sep, daily	10am-5pm
1 Oct-29 Mar, daily	10am-4pm
24-26 Dec & 1 Jan	Closed

VISIT US
Direction: 8 miles SE of Appleby S of A66

Train: Kirkby Stephen 10 miles

Bus: Classic service 352; Grand Prix service 563, 564; Cumbria Classic Bus 572 (Wed)

ACQ. 1919

Please note: approach may be muddy, stout footwear recommended.

Guidebook available at Brougham Castle.

MAP Page 347 (6F)
OS Map 91, OL19: NY791141

BROUGHAM CASTLE
CUMBRIA – CA10 2AA

BROUGHAM CASTLE

In a picturesque setting beside the crossing of the River Eamont, Brougham Castle was founded in the early 13th century by King John's agent Robert de Vieuxpont. His great keep largely survives amid many later buildings – including the unusual double gatehouse and impressive 'Tower of League' – added by the powerful Clifford family, Wardens of the Marches. Both a formidable barrier against Scots invaders and a prestigious residence, their castle welcomed Edward I in 1300.

A complex of passages and spiral stairways makes Brougham a fascinating castle to explore, as well as an ideal picnic setting: the keep top provides panoramic views over the Eden Valley and the earthworks of the adjacent Roman fort of Brocavum. Having fallen into decay after James I's visit in 1617, the castle was restored by the indomitable Lady Anne Clifford (see also Brough Castle and Countess Pillar). She often visited with her travelling 'court', and died here in 1676. An exhibition highlights her remarkable life and includes carvings from the Roman fort. There is good wheelchair access to most of the site (excluding the keep).

NON-MEMBERS
Adult	£4.20
Concession	£3.80
Child	£2.50
Family	£10.90

OPENING TIMES
1 Apr-30 Sep, daily	10am-6pm
1 Oct-2 Nov, daily	10am-4pm
3 Nov-29 Mar, Sat-Sun	10am-4pm
24-26 Dec, 31 Dec-1 Jan	Closed

BROUGHAM CASTLE

VISIT US
Direction: 1½ miles SE of Penrith, off A66

Train: Penrith 2 miles

Bus: Stagecoach service 104 and Grand Prix service 563 pass the castle on the A66, but the nearest official stop is at Whinfell Park (about 1 mile east). Fellrunner 132 (Fri) & 562 (Tue) serve Brougham village

Local Tourist information
Penrith: 01768 867466;
Rheged: 01768 860034

Tel: 01768 862488

 ACQ.1920

OVP

Please note: Car parking limited, in 'no through road' opposite castle entrance.

MAP Page 346 (5E)
OS Map 90, OL5: NY537290

CARLISLE CASTLE
SEE FEATURE – PAGE 266

CASTLERIGG STONE CIRCLE
CUMBRIA

Dramatically sited with the mountains of Helvellyn and High Seat as a backdrop, Castlerigg is among the most dramatic stone circles in Britain, probably built in the later Neolithic period.

Managed by the National Trust.

OPENING TIMES
Any reasonable daylight hours

VISIT US
Direction: 1½ miles E of Keswick

Train: Penrith 16 miles

Bus: Stagecoach 'Caldbeck Rambler' service 73A (Sat only) passes the site. Otherwise Stagecoach 555 or X8 (Sat only) to Castle Lane then a 1m walk

ACQ.1883

MAP Page 346 (5D)
OS Map 89/90, OL4: NY291236

CARLISLE CASTLE Cumbria – CA3 8UR

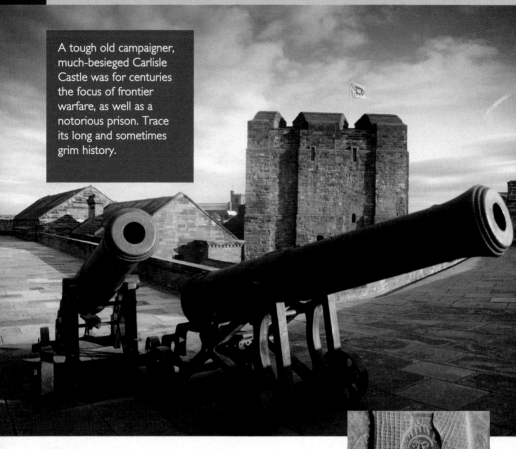

A tough old campaigner, much-besieged Carlisle Castle was for centuries the focus of frontier warfare, as well as a notorious prison. Trace its long and sometimes grim history.

VISIT US

Address: Carlisle Castle, Castle Way, Carlisle, Cumbria

Direction: In Carlisle city centre. Follow Castle Street, past Carlisle Cathedral on left. At main road, take underpass to the castle

Train: Carlisle ½ mile

Bus: Stagecoach 38, 39, 60, 60A, 61, 61A, 67, 68, 71, 93, 300, 301, 554, 600. Also Reay's Coaches service 75 (Mon-Sat)

Tel: 01228 591922

Local Tourist Information: 01228 598596

NON-MEMBERS

Adult	£5.90
Concession	£5.30
Child	£3.50

OPENING TIMES

1 Apr-30 Sep, daily	10am-6pm
1 Oct-2 Nov, daily	10am-5pm
3 Nov-8 Feb, Sat-Sun	10am-4pm
9-20 Feb, daily	10am-4pm
21 Feb-29 Mar, Sat-Sun	10am-4pm
24-26 Dec, 31 Dec-1 Jan	Closed

Disabled access (limited).

Dogs on leads (restricted areas only).

Guided tours available to pre-book at a small extra charge.

Parking (disabled only, but signposted city centre car parks nearby).

MAP Page 346 (4D)
OS Map 85, 315: NY396562

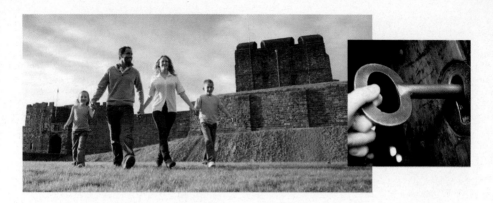

A mighty presence in the city it has dominated for nine centuries, Carlisle Castle was a constantly updated working fortress until well within living memory. Now its rich and varied visitor attractions reflect its long and eventful history, vividly retold in a recently-installed exhibition celebrating Carlisle's fame as the most besieged town in Britain.

Even before the medieval castle was begun, this site was an important Roman fortress. The commanding keep, begun during the 12th century by King Henry I of England and completed by King David I of Scotland, is both the oldest part of the castle and a reminder that Carlisle was for centuries a disputed frontier fortress, commanding the especially turbulent western end of the Anglo-Scottish border.

The castle's violent history included medieval assaults, skirmishes with Elizabethan Border Reivers, a Civil War siege – the longest siege of a town in English history – and Bonnie Prince Charlie's Jacobite Rising of 1745-46. Carlisle was then the very last English fortress ever to suffer a siege: overwhelmed by the Duke of Cumberland's Hanoverian army, its Jacobite garrison were imprisoned in the keep's dank basement, where visitors can see the legendary 'licking stones', which they supposedly licked for life-giving moisture. Equally famous are the strange and fantastic carvings on the keep's second floor, probably cut in the 1460-70s.

All this and more is highlighted in 'Besieged', a striking interactive display which includes examples of the weapons used during Carlisle's many sieges; a reconstruction graphic of the interior of the keep; and a retelling of the daring rescue from the castle of the Border Reiver Kinmont Willie Armstrong. There are also children's dressing-up clothes, and the opportunity to take a 360 degree virtual tour of the castle.

By the time Mary Queen of Scots was imprisoned here in 1568, Henry VIII's updating for heavy artillery had left its mark on Carlisle, including the keep's rounded 'shot-deflecting' battlements and the Half Moon Battery defending the Captain's Tower gatehouse. The interior rooms of this gatehouse, begun in the 12th century and one of the best-preserved in England, are now open to the public for the first time.

The castle's military career did not end after the Jacobite Rising: fear of a radical revolution made it a permanently occupied garrison from the 1820s, when the barrack blocks lining the outer ward were begun. Indeed, the castle remained the headquarters of the Border Regiment until 1959, and the 300-year history of this famous local infantry regiment is vividly told here in Cumbria's Military Museum.

Carlisle Castle is on the Richard III trail (see Middleham Castle, p.239).

FURNESS ABBEY CUMBRIA – LA13 0PJ

Much the grandest monastic ruins in the North West, set in a lovely wooded valley. Furness Abbey was founded by Stephen, later King of England, and became (after Fountains Abbey) the second richest Cistercian abbey in all England. Dating principally from the 12th and 13th centuries, its very extensive red sandstone ruins reflect this prosperity. They include the imposing east end of the great church with its soaring pillars, and its western tower; the chapter house with its fine carved decoration; almost the entire east range of the cloister; the infirmary chapel; and many of the watercourses which drained the kitchens and latrines.

The visitor centre houses an exhibition about the abbey's history, and a large collection of sculpture from the ruins, including striking and distinctive effigies of knights.

English Heritage is currently addressing severe structural problems at the east end of the church, at present supported by a spectacular steel frame – a sight worth seeing in itself.

NEW FOR 2014

The Furness Crosier
A beautiful and rare crosier belonging to the Abbots of Furness goes on permanent display for the first time.

NON-MEMBERS

Adult	£4.20
Concession	£3.80
Child	£2.50

OPENING TIMES

1 Apr-30 Sep, daily	10am-6pm
1 Oct-2 Nov, daily	10am-5pm
3 Nov-29 Mar, Sat-Sun	10am-4pm
24-26 Dec, 31 Dec-1 Jan	Closed

VISIT US

Direction: Located 1½ miles N of Barrow-in-Furness, off A590

Train: Dalton and Roose 2 miles, Barrow-in-Furness 2 miles

Bus: Stagecoach in Cumbria service 6 & X6 to within within ¾ mile

Tel: 01229 823420

ACQ.1923

Dogs on leads (restricted areas only).

MAP Page 346 (7D)
OS Map 96, OL6: SD218717

CLIFTON HALL CUMBRIA

This fortified tower, built in about 1500, is the sole surviving and most important part of the manor house of the Wybergh family. It displays fascinating clues about the changing appearance of the house in the late medieval period.

OPENING TIMES

Check website for the latest opening times

VISIT US

Direction: Next to Clifton Hall Farm; 2 miles S of Penrith, on A6

Train: Penrith 2½ miles

Bus: Reay's/Grand Prix/Kirby Lonsdale Coach Hire services 106 & Alba service 111

ACQ.1973

MAP Page 346 (5E)
OS Map 90, OL5: NY530271

COUNTESS PILLAR, BROUGHAM CUMBRIA

A monument erected in 1656 by Lady Anne Clifford of nearby Brougham Castle, to commemorate her final parting here from her mother. On the low stone beside it, money was given to the poor each anniversary of their parting.

OPENING TIMES

Any reasonable daylight hours

VISIT US

Direction: ¼ mile E of Brougham. A new access route has also been created which runs from the B6262 (to Brougham) and starts near the junction with the A66

Train: Penrith 2½ miles

Bus: Stagecoach service 104 and Grand Prix service 563 pass the castle on the A66, but the nearest official stop is at Whinfell Park (about 1 mile east). Fellrunner 132 (Fri only) & 562 (Tue only) serve Brougham village

COUNTESS PILLAR, BROUGHAM

 ACQ.1977

Warning: site on a very busy main road. Parking on B6262, close to the junction with A66. Safe access by footpath.

MAP Page 346 (5E)
OS Map 90, OL5: NY546289

FURNESS ABBEY
SEE OPPOSITE

HADRIAN'S WALL
SEE PAGE 276

HARDKNOTT ROMAN FORT
CUMBRIA

Among the remotest, most atmospheric and most spectacularly-sited Roman forts in England, Hardknott guarded the precipitous pass carrying the Roman road from Ravenglass to Ambleside through the high Cumbrian fells. Its complete perimeter walls, headquarters building and granaries are clearly visible, with its bath house and circular 'sauna' nearby.

Managed by the National Trust.

OPENING TIMES
Any reasonable daylight hours

VISIT US
Direction: 9 miles NE of Ravenglass; at W end of Hardknott Pass, via short uphill path from unclassified road

---

HARDKNOTT ROMAN FORT

Train: Dalegarth (Ravenglass & Eskdale) 3 miles or Ravenglass 10 miles

Bus: Closest by bus is Stagecoach service 6 (Mon-Sat) or Stagecoach/3D service X6 (Sun only) to Ravenglass or Muncaster Mill then R&ER Dalegarth and then 3½ mile walk

ACQ.1949 P

Very limited parking in lay-by. More parking at Jubilee Bridge, ½ mile to west. Access hazardous in winter months or bad weather. Stout footwear essential.

Visitors are strongly advised to approach from the western (Eskdale) direction: the road from Ambleside over the Wrynose and Hardknott passes is hazardous in poor weather, with hairpin bends and 1-in-3 gradients.

MAP Page 346 (6C)
OS Map 89/90, OL6: NY218015

KING ARTHUR'S ROUND TABLE CUMBRIA

A Neolithic earthwork henge, dating from c. 2500 BC, but much later believed to be King Arthur's jousting arena. Mayburgh Henge is adjacent.

OPENING TIMES
Any reasonable daylight hours

VISIT US
Direction: Located at Eamont Bridge, 1 mile S of Penrith. Mayburgh Henge is nearby

Train: Penrith 1½ miles

Bus: Stagecoach service 108; Reay's Grand Prix/Kirby Lonsdale Coach Hire services 106; Alba service 111 (Tue only) and Fellrunner services 132 (Fri only) & 562 (Tue only)

ACQ.1884

MAP Page 346 (5E)
OS Map 90, OL5: NY523284

LANERCOST PRIORY
SEE FEATURE – PAGE 270

MAYBURGH HENGE
CUMBRIA

A large and impressive Neolithic henge, much better preserved than neighbouring King Arthur's Round Table. Its banks stand up to 3 metres (10 feet) high and unusually are constructed of pebbles collected from the nearby river. Near the centre is a single standing stone: old drawings suggest that it was one of a group of four here, four more having been removed from the entranceway.

OPENING TIMES
Any reasonable daylight hours

VISIT US
Direction: 1 mile S of Penrith off A6

Train: Penrith 1½ miles

Bus: Stagecoach service 108; Reay's/Grand Prix/Kirby Lonsdale Coach Hire services 106; Alba service 111 (Tue only) and Fellrunner services 132 (Fri only) & 562 (Tue only) then very short walk

ACQ.1884

MAP Page 346 (5E)
OS Map 90, OL5: NY519284

VISIT US

Direction: Off a minor road S of Lanercost; 2 miles NE of Brampton

Train: Brampton 3 miles

Bus: Alba/Classic Hadrian's Wall Bus AD122 Spring-Autumn. Otherwise Stagecoach/Arriva service 685 to within 2½ miles

Tel: 01697 73030

NON-MEMBERS

Adult	£3.60
Concession	£3.20
Child	£2.20

OPENING TIMES

1 Apr-30 Sep, daily	10am-6pm
1 Oct-2 Nov, daily	10am-5pm
3 Nov-15 Feb, Sat-Sun	10am-4pm
16-20 Feb, daily	10am-4pm
21 Feb-29 Mar, Sat-Sun	10am-4pm
24-26 Dec, 31 Dec-1 Jan	Closed

ACQ.1930 🐕 f P ⛱ 📷 🏪

⚠ OVP

Lanercost tearoom and farm shop is open every day except 25 and 26 Dec. www.lanercost.co.uk Tel: 016977 41267 (not managed by English Heritage).

MAP Page 346 (4E)
OS Map 86, 315: NY556637

The beautiful and now tranquil setting of Augustinian Lanercost Priory belies an often troubled history. Standing less than half a mile from Hadrian's Wall, it suffered frequent attacks during the long Anglo-Scottish wars, once by Robert Bruce in person. The mortally sick King Edward I rested here for five months in 1306-07, shortly before his death on his final campaign. Yet there is still much to see in this best-preserved of Cumbrian monasteries. The east end of the noble 13th-century church survives to its full height, housing within its dramatic triple tier of arches some fine monuments. The nave, with its lofty west front, is still in full use as the parish church.

Lanercost's cloisters include a beautiful vaulted 13th-century refectory undercroft. They partly owe their preservation to their conversion, after the priory's suppression, into the Tudor mansion of the Dacre family. The west range includes the four-storey Dacre Tower, a pele tower adapted from the monastic kitchen, and the Dacre Hall (used as the village hall so not always open to the public). This displays fragments of 16th-century wall-painting and a splendidly carved Jacobean chimneypiece, recently returned here from its travels.

Set beside an ancient vicarage, and 'vicar's pele tower' (viewable only from outside), Lanercost Priory's extensive remains make an unforgettable ensemble. The English Heritage ticket office and gift shop is next to the church.

Nearby farm buildings have been converted into a visitor centre, with a restaurant/ tearoom and display about Hadrian's Wall. The parish church, Dacre Hall and visitor centre are not managed by English Heritage.

PENRITH CASTLE CUMBRIA

Penrith Castle was begun at the end of the 14th century by William Strickland, Bishop of Carlisle. Later acquired by Ralph Neville, who played a key role in defending this area against the Scots. It was then transformed into a luxurious residence by Richard, Duke of Gloucester (subsequently Richard III). Surviving in places to their full height, the castle walls stand in a public park. Graphic panels tell the story of the castle.

OPENING TIMES

Park:

Summer	7.30am-9pm
Winter	7.30am-4.30pm

VISIT US

Direction: Opposite Penrith railway station

Train: Penrith (adjacent)

Bus: From surrounding areas

ACQ.1913

MAP Page 346 (5E)
OS Map 90, OL5: NY513299

PIEL CASTLE CUMBRIA

A visit to Piel Castle is a memorable adventure. Accessible only via small boat ferry, this still-impressive fortress shares its little island at the mouth of Barrow harbour with abundant wildlife and a famous pub. Its strong keep and towered outer defences were built in the 14th century by the Abbot of Furness, mainly as a refuge from pirates and Scots raiders. Lambert Simnel, pretender to Henry VII's throne, landed here with his army in 1487.

OPENING TIMES

Any reasonable daylight hours. Access by ferry boat not managed by English Heritage

VISIT US

Direction: Via ferry from Roa Island, accessible by road 3¼ miles SE of Barrow-in-Furness

By small boat: From Easter until September, approx. 11am until 6pm daily, two ferries operate services from Roa Island to Piel Island (subject to tides and weather). Call in advance Steve Chattaway (Ship Inn) on 07516 453784 or Alan Cleasby on 07798 794550. There is a charge for the ferry

PIEL CASTLE

Train: Barrow-in-Furness 4 miles

Bus: Blueworks Taxis service 11 Barrow-in Furness – Ulverston Roa Island and then ferry to Piel Castle

ACQ.1973

Public house refreshments (not managed by EH).

MAP Page 346 (7D)
OS Map 96, OL6: SD233636

RAVENGLASS ROMAN BATH HOUSE CUMBRIA

Among the tallest surviving Roman structures in northern Britain, the unusually well-preserved walls of this bath house stand up to 4 metres (13 feet) high, complete with remains of plasterwork and elegant niches for statues. It served Ravenglass Roman fort, whose earthworks can be traced on private land across the track. Guarding a useful harbour, the fort was once garrisoned by troops from Hadrian's fleet.

OPENING TIMES

Any reasonable daylight hours

VISIT US

Direction: ½ mile SE of Ravenglass station, via signposted footpath from village car park and then private road. No vehicular access or parking at site

Train: Ravenglass (nearby)

Bus: Stagecoach service 6 (Mon-Sat) or Stagecoach/3D service X6 (Sun only)

ACQ.1980

MAP Page 346 (6C)
OS Map 96, OL6: SD088959

STOT PARK BOBBIN MILL
SEE FEATURE – OPPOSITE

SHAP ABBEY CUMBRIA

The impressive full-height 15th-century tower and other remains of a remote abbey of Premonstratensian 'white canons'.

Information panels guide you round the abbey and illustrate daily monastic life.

OPENING TIMES
Any reasonable daylight hours

VISIT US
Direction: 1½ miles W of Shap, on the bank of the River Lowther

Train: Penrith 10 miles

Bus: Alba service 111 (Tue only) passes the approach road; Reay's/Grand Prix/Kirby Lonsdale service 106 Penrith-Kendal passes within 1½ miles

ACQ.1948 ⊠ P &

Disabled access (limited views from outside the site).

Steep access road is unsuitable in wintry weather.

MAP Page 346 (6E)
OS Map 90, OL5: NY548152

ST NINIAN'S, BROUGHAM
CUMBRIA – CA10 2AD

© CCT

The originally Norman St Ninian's Church was rebuilt in the 17th century by Lady Anne Clifford, who inherited Brougham Castle. The simple interior is whitewashed, with clear glass windows, stone flagged floor, box pews, an elegant screen, and a three-decker pulpit.

Owned and managed by The Churches Conservation Trust.

OPENING TIMES
Open daily during daylight hours

VISIT US
Train: Penrith 3 miles

Bus: Stagecoach service 104 and Grand Prix service 563 pass the site on the A66, but the nearest official stop is at Whinfell Park (about 1 mile east)

Nr Brougham Castle

MAP Page 346 (5E)
OS Map 90, OL05: NY557289

WETHERAL PRIORY GATEHOUSE CUMBRIA

Well-preserved 15th-century gatehouse, the sole survivor of a small Benedictine priory. A miniature 'pele-tower' containing two storeys of comfortable rooms, it later became a fortified vicarage, a defence against border raiders.

OPENING TIMES
1 Apr-30 Sep, daily	10am-5pm
1 Oct-29 Mar, daily	10am-4pm
24-26 Dec & 1 Jan	Closed

VISIT US
Direction: Near Wetheral village; 6 miles E of Carlisle, on B6263

Train: Wetheral ½ mile

Bus: Reay's/Stagecoach in Cumbria services 75 to Wetheral then short walk

ACQ.1978 ⊠

MAP Page 346 (4E)
OS Map 86, 315: NY468541

VISIT US

Direction: Located 1½ miles N of Newby Bridge, off A590

Train: Grange-over-Sands 8 miles; Lakeside Station (Lakeside & Haverthwaite railway) ¾ mile

Bus: Lecks 538 (Thu only) passes the site. Alternatively Stagecoach service X6 & Lecks 518 or Blueworks summer service X32 to Newby Bridge and then 1½ mile walk. Lakeside and Haverthwaite Railway's Lakeside terminus is ¾ mile walk

Boat: Windermere Lake Cruises from Ambleside or Bowness to Lakeside, then ¾ mile walk

Tel: 01539 531087

Local Tourist Information
Hawkshead: 01539 436946

NON-MEMBERS

Adult	£6.60
Concession	£5.90
Child	£4.00
Family	£17.20

OPENING TIMES

1 Apr-18 Jul, Wed-Sun	10am-5pm
19 Jul-31 Aug, daily	10am-5pm
1 Sep-2 Nov, Wed-Sun	10am-5pm
3 Nov-29 Mar	Closed

Please call for details of steam days

Disabled access (ground floor only. Specific interpretation for visually impaired visitors).

Lower car park for disabled parking (short downhill path to mill).
Upper car park for general parking.

Disabled visitors can be dropped off at the mill gates (with level access to site) before cars are parked. Please phone site in advance to arrange.

Dogs welcome on leads.

MAP Page 346 (6D)
OS Map 96/97, OL7: SD372881

Stott Park is one of English Heritage's most unusual and fascinating attractions: there is perhaps nowhere in the country where the Industrial Revolution is more vividly brought to life.

In a lovely wooded setting near Lake Windermere, this fully-working mill is a unique survivor of the many Lakeland mills which turned bobbins for the Lancashire textile industry. Using timber coppiced from the surrounding woodlands, it operated commercially from 1835 until 1971, diversifying into products from cotton reels to rungs for naval rope ladders and toggles for Second World War duffel coats.

Powered first by water and later by a magnificent steam engine – which still operates on working steam weekends – and finally by electricity, it retains much of the belt-operated machinery in its scarcely-altered workshops. Close-up demonstrations of the whole fascinating process of bobbin-making are given by friendly and knowledgeable staff during guided tours. Guided tours are included in the admission charge: the last tour begins ½ hour before closing.

Recently-installed undercover displays tell the stories of the people who worked the mill, and illustrate the intriguing process of coppicing timber. Interpretation panels help visitors to take self-guided tours of the mill's surroundings. Working steam displays are held on the first weekend of every month, Apr-Oct. Call site for details.

LANCASHIRE

GOODSHAW CHAPEL
LANCASHIRE

English Heritage's only Nonconformist place of worship, this atmospheric Baptist chapel displays a complete set of box-pews, galleries and pulpit dating from c. 1742 to 1809. A festival of hymns and sermons is held on the first Sunday in July.

OPENING TIMES
Please call the keykeeper for details. Tel: 01706 227333

VISIT US
Direction: In Crawshawbooth, 2 miles N of Rawtenstall via A682 (in Goodshaw Ave – turning off A682 opp. Jester public house). Chapel approx. 1½ miles from main road

Train: Burnley Manchester Road 4½ miles

Bus: Transdev Burnley & Pendle 'Witch Way' services X43/4

ACQ.1976

MAP Page 344 (4E)
OS Map 103, OL21: SD814261

SAWLEY ABBEY
LANCASHIRE

SAWLEY ABBEY

The remains of a Cistercian abbey founded in 1148, set on the banks of the Ribble against a backdrop of dramatic hills. After its dissolution in 1536, the monks were briefly returned to the abbey during the Pilgrimage of Grace. They remained in possession until the insurrection's collapse and the execution of their abbot.

Managed by the Heritage Trust for the North West.

OPENING TIMES

1 Apr-31 Oct, daily	10am-5pm
1 Nov-29 Mar, daily	10am-4pm
24-26 Dec & 1 Jan	Closed

VISIT US
Direction: Located at Sawley; 3½ miles N of Clitheroe, off A59

Train: Clitheroe 4 miles

Bus: Transdev Lancashire United (of Blackburn) services 280 & X80 stop nearby

ACQ.1951

MAP Page 344 (4D)
OS Map 103, OL41: SD777464

WARTON OLD RECTORY
LANCASHIRE

A rare survival of a large 14th-century stone house with great hall and chambers. It served as a residence and courthouse for the wealthy and powerful rectors of Warton.

WARTON OLD RECTORY

Managed by the Heritage Trust for the North West.

OPENING TIMES

1 Apr-30 Sep, daily	10am-6pm
1 Oct-29 Mar, daily	10am-4pm
24-26 Dec & 1 Jan	Closed

VISIT US
Direction: At Warton; 1 mile N of Carnforth, on minor road off A6

Train: Carnforth 1 mile

Bus: Stagecoach in Lancashire service 51 & 55

ACQ.1969

MAP Page 344 (3D)
OS Map 97, OL7: SD499723

WHALLEY ABBEY GATEHOUSE LANCASHIRE

The 14th-century gatehouse of the nearby Cistercian abbey, the second wealthiest monastery in Lancashire, beside the River Calder. The first floor was probably a chapel.

OPENING TIMES
Any reasonable daylight hours

VISIT US
Direction: In Whalley; 6 miles NE of Blackburn, on minor road off A59

Train: Whalley ¼ mile

Bus: From surrounding area

ACQ.1971

MAP Page 344 (4D)
OS Map 103, 287: SD729362

DISCOUNTED ATTRACTIONS: **NORTH WEST**

Use your membership to get exclusive discounts at these independent attractions in the North West. Please remember to show your card as proof of membership.

Discount applies to:

KEY	⊞ MEMBERS	OVP OVP HOLDERS	👥? NO. OF MEMBER'S CHILDREN

Terms and conditions may apply, so make sure you check the individual pages on our website or call the individual property for more details.

⊞ OVP

LOWTHER CASTLE
Cumbria CA10 2HH
The gardens at Lowther are really unique. 130 acres of historical lost gardens lie in the grounds of a ruined castle in an idyllic pastoral landscape unchanged for hundreds of years.
www.lowthercastle.org
Tel. 01931 712192

⊞ OVP 👥 6

NORTON PRIORY MUSEUM & GARDENS
Cheshire WA7 1BD
Explore medieval priory remains, woodlands and beautiful Georgian walled garden. Museum offers tearoom and shop.
www.nortonpriory.org
Tel. 01928 569895

⊞ 👥 6

PENDLE HERITAGE CENTRE
Lancashire BB9 6JQ
Historic farmhouse, restored using traditional building skills. Exhibitions, 18th-century walled garden, shop and café.
www.htnw.co.uk
Tel. 01282 677150

⊞ 👥 6

SMITHILLS HALL
Lancashire BL1 7NP
Set in over 2200 acres of woodland, on the edge of the West Pennine Moors, Smithills Hall is one of the oldest and best preserved manor houses in the North West.
www.boltonmuseums.org.uk
Tel. 01204 332377

⊞ OVP 👥 1

STRETTON WATERMILL
Cheshire SY14 7JA
Step back in time and visit a working mill in beautiful rural Cheshire. See one of the country's best preserved demonstration water-powered corn mills.
www.strettonwatermill.blogspot.com
Tel. 01606 271640

⊞ OVP 👥 1

WEAVER HALL MUSEUM AND WORKHOUSE
Cheshire CW9 8AB
Discover the hidden history of Cheshire from the salt industry to archaeological treasures, all housed in a former Victorian workhouse.
www.weaverhallmuseum.org.uk
Tel. 01606 271640

HADRIAN'S WALL

Marching 73 miles from sea to sea across some of the wildest and most dramatic country in England, this celebrated World Heritage Site was the north-west frontier of the whole Roman Empire. Walk along the Wall to discover 2000 years of history at our many forts, museums, and even a high street of a once-thriving Roman town.

Scotland

Lanercost Priory
See feature on page 270

Brampton

Carlisle Castle
See feature on page 266

Carlisle

Cumbria

Birdoswald Roman Fort
See feature on page 284

Haltwhistle

Hexham

Northumberland

CARING FOR THE HADRIAN'S WALL WORLD HERITAGE SITE AND NATIONAL TRAIL

Whilst planning your holiday or visit, please remember to observe 'Every Footstep Counts' – the World Heritage Site's own country code. As you will appreciate, Hadrian's Wall is a fragile environment and the archaeology is easily damaged.

You can help protect this great Wonder of the World by following the general advice:

- Always keep to the signed paths.
- Visit the organised paying sites, which are more robust and can accommodate visitors, but please avoid walking alongside the Wall when the ground is very wet. The buried archaeology underfoot is particularly vulnerable to damage in the wet winter months between November and April. Ask about the winter walking passport.
- Avoid walking on the Wall as this may cause it to collapse.
- Respect livestock and land.
- Keep dogs on a lead and under close control.
- Use public transport whenever you can.
- Please note, Hadrian's Wall Path National Trail is a footpath only. Please cycle on legal routes only i.e. bridgeways, byways, roads and cyclepaths.

Newcastle-upon-Tyne
Corbridge
Gateshead
Tyne and Wear
Durham

① HARE HILL

A short length of Wall still stands 2.7 metres (8.8 feet) high.

VISIT US
Direction: ¾ mile NE of Lanercost

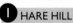 ACQ.1972

OS Map 86, 43: NY564646

② BANKS EAST TURRET

Imposing and well-preserved turret with adjoining stretches of Hadrian's Wall.

VISIT US
Direction: On minor road E of Banks village; 3½ miles NE of Brampton

ACQ.1934 🅿️ ♿ ⚠️

OS Map 86, 315: NY575647

③ PIKE HILL SIGNAL TOWER

The remains of one of a network of signal towers predating Hadrian's Wall, Pike Hill was later joined to the Wall at an angle of 45 degrees.

VISIT US
Direction: On minor road E of Banks village

ACQ.1971 🅿️

OS Map 86, 315: NY577648

④ LEAHILL TURRET & PIPER SIKE TURRET

Turrets west of Birdoswald: Piper Sike has a cooking-hearth.

VISIT US
Direction: On minor road 2 miles W of Birdoswald Fort

ACQ.1952

OS Map 86, OL43/315: NY586652

⑤ BIRDOSWALD ROMAN FORT

See feature on page 284

⑥ HARROWS SCAR MILECASTLE & WALL

A mile-long section of the Wall, rebuilt in stone later in Hadrian's reign. It is linked to Birdoswald Roman Fort (see p.284).

VISIT US
Direction: ¼ mile E of Birdoswald, on minor road off B6318

ACQ.1946 🅿️

Parking at Birdoswald.

OS Map 86, OL43: NY620664

f 🐦 For updates on Hadrian's Wall, don't forget to follow on Facebook and Twitter.

Scotland

Lanercost Priory
See feature on page 270

① ② ③ ⑦ ⑧ ⑨ ⑩ ⑪ ⑫ ⑬ ⑭ ⑮ ⑯ ⑰ ⑱ ⑲ ⑳

④ ⑤ ⑥

Haltwhistle

Hexham

Brampton

Carlisle Castle
See feature on page 266

Carlisle

Cumbria

Birdoswald Roman Fort
See feature on page 284

Northumberland

⑦ WILLOWFORD WALL, TURRETS AND BRIDGE

A fine 914 metre (2999 feet) stretch of Wall, including two turrets and impressive bridge remains beside the River Irthing. Linked by a bridge to Birdoswald Roman Fort (see p.284).

VISIT US

Direction: W of minor road, ¾ mile W of Gilsland

ACQ.1946

OS Map 86, OL43: NY627664

Don't forget to check opening times online before you visit.

www.english-heritage.org.uk/daysout/properties

⑧ POLTROSS BURN MILECASTLE

One of the best-preserved milecastles on Hadrian's Wall, Poltross includes an oven, a stair to the rampart walk, and the remains of its north gateway. Known locally as 'the King's Stables'.

VISIT US

Direction: On minor road E of Banks village. Immediately SW of Gilsland village, by old railway station

ACQ.1938 P

Parking (near the Station Hotel).

OS Map 86, OL43: NY634662

⑨ WALLTOWN CRAGS

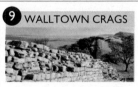

One of the best places of all to see the Wall, dramatically snaking and diving along the crags of the Whin Sill.

VISIT US

Direction: 1 mile NE of Greenhead, off B6318

ACQ.1939

OS Map 86/87, 43: NY674663

⑩ CAWFIELDS ROMAN WALL

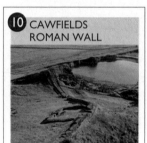

A fine stretch of Hadrian's Wall on a steep slope, with turrets and an impressive milecastle, probably built by the Second Legion.

VISIT US

Direction: 1¼ miles N of Haltwhistle, off B6318

ACQ.1960 🚶 ♿ P

Parking not operated by EH. Parking charge applies (payable to Northumberland National Park).

OS Map 86/87, OL43: NY716667

⑪ WINSHIELDS WALL

The highest point on the Wall, in rugged country with spectacular views.

VISIT US

Direction: W of Steel Rigg car park; on minor road off B6318

ACQ.1937

OS Map 86/87, 43: NY742676

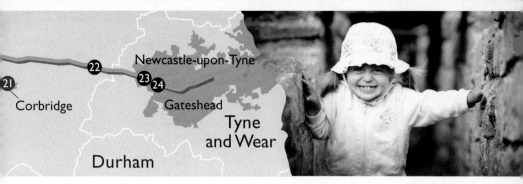

Newcastle-upon-Tyne

Corbridge

Gateshead

Tyne and Wear

Durham

12 ROMAN VINDOLANDA

See Associated Attractions on page 289

13 HOUSESTEADS ROMAN FORT

See feature on page 287

14 SEWINGSHIELDS WALL

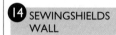

A length of Wall with milecastle remains, impressively sited along the Whin Sill, commanding fine views of many prehistoric and later earthworks to the north.

VISIT US

Direction: N of B6318; 1½ miles E of Housesteads Fort

ACQ.1946

OS Map 86/87, OL43: NY805702

15 TEMPLE OF MITHRAS, CARRAWBURGH

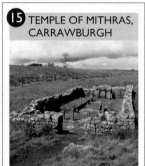

Near Carrawburgh fort stands a fascinating temple to the eastern god Mithras, with facsimiles of altars found during excavation. Sited like many Mithraic temples near a military base, it was founded in the 3rd century and eventually desecrated, probably by Christians. Nearby, but no longer visible, was the shrine of the water nymph Coventina.

VISIT US

Direction: 3¾ miles W of Chollerford, on B6318

ACQ.1953 P

Parking charge payable to Northumberland National Park.

OS Map 87, 43: NY859711

16 BLACK CARTS TURRET

A 460 metre (1509 feet) length of Hadrian's Wall including one turret. **Please note:** It is not possible for visitors to park here.

VISIT US

Direction: On minor road E of Banks village; 3½ miles NE of Brampton

ACQ.1970

OS Map 86, 315: NY575647

17 CHESTERS ROMAN FORT AND MUSEUM

See feature on page 285

 For updates on Hadrian's Wall, don't forget to follow on Facebook and Twitter.

Scotland

Lanercost Priory
See feature on page 270

① ② ③ ⑦ ⑧ ⑨ ⑩ ⑪ ⑫ ⑬ ⑭ ⑮ ⑯ ⑰ ⑱ ⑲ ⑳

④ ⑤ ⑥

Brampton

Haltwhistle

Hexham

Carlisle Castle
See feature on page 266   Carlisle

Birdoswald Roman Fort
See feature on page 284

Cumbria   Northumberland

---

⑱ CHESTERS BRIDGE ABUTMENT

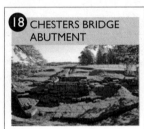

Close to Chesters Roman Fort are the remains of a bridge which carried Hadrian's Wall across the North Tyne. Visible on both river banks, they are most impressive on the eastern side.

VISIT US

Direction: ½ mile S of Low Brunton, on A6079

ACQ.1946

OS Map 87, 43: NY914701

---

⑲ BRUNTON TURRET

Wall section and a surviving piece of turret 2½ metres (8.2 feet) high, built by men of the Twentieth Legion.

VISIT US

Direction: ¼ mile S of Low Brunton, off A6079

ACQ.1947 🐕

OS Map 87, OL43: NY922698

---

⑳ PLANETREES ROMAN WALL

A 15 metre (49 feet) length of narrow Wall on broad foundations, reflecting a change of policy concerning the thickness of the Wall during construction.

VISIT US

Direction: 1 mile SE of Chollerford on B6318

ACQ.1945

OS Map 87, OL43: NY929696

㉑ CORBRIDGE ROMAN TOWN

See feature on page 286

㉒ HEDDON-ON-THE-WALL

A consolidated stretch of Wall, up to 2 metres (6½ feet) thick in places.

VISIT US

Direction: Immediately E of Heddon village; S of A69

ACQ.1935

OS Map 88, 316: NZ137669

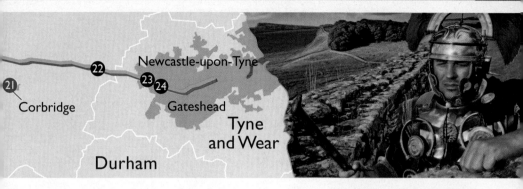

Newcastle-upon-Tyne

22

23 24

21

Corbridge

Gateshead

Tyne and Wear

Durham

23 DENTON HALL TURRET

The foundations of a turret and a 65-metre (213 feet) length of Wall.

VISIT US

Direction: 4 miles W of Newcastle-upon-Tyne city centre, located immediately SE of A69

ACQ.1934

OS Map 88, 316: NZ198655

M. BUONARROTI

24 BENWELL ROMAN TEMPLE

The remains of a small temple to the native god 'Antenociticus', in the 'vicus' (civilian settlement) which stood outside Benwell fort.

VISIT US

Direction: Temple located immediately SE of A69, at Benwell in Broomridge Ave; Vallum Crossing in Denhill Park

ACQ.1936

OS Map 88, 316: NZ217647

BENWELL VALLUM CROSSING

A stone-built causeway, where the road from the south crossed the Vallum earthwork on its way to Benwell fort.

ACQ.1934

OS Map 88, 316: NZ216646

The Hadrian's Wall Bus (AD122) runs throughout the spring and summer months between Newcastle, Hexham and Carlisle, and is an excellent way to see the stunning scenery in this part of England. It stops at Corbridge, Chesters, Housesteads, Vindolanda and Birdoswald Roman Sites – as well as main railway stations, market places, towns and villages along the way.

For updates on Hadrian's Wall, don't forget to follow on Facebook and Twitter.

BIRDOSWALD ROMAN FORT
Cumbria – CA8 7DD

VISIT US

Direction: 4 miles west of Greenhead off B6318. Signposted from A69 Carlisle-Hexham road at Brampton roundabout

Train: Brampton 8 miles, Haltwhistle 7 miles

Bus: Alba service AD122 Carlisle – Hexham ⊛ (Apr-Oct)

Tel: 01697 747602

Haltwhistle Tourist Information 01434 322002

NON-MEMBERS

Adult	£5.60
Concession	£5.00
Child	£3.40

OPENING TIMES

1 Apr-30 Sep, daily	10am-6pm
1 Oct-2 Nov, daily	10am-5pm
3 Nov-15 Feb, Sat-Sun	10am-4pm
16-20 Feb, daily	10am-4pm
21 Feb-29 Mar, Sat-Sun	10am-4pm
24-26 Dec, 31 Dec-1 Jan	Closed

ACQ.1946

Parking: Pay and display parking refunded to all visitors and members who visit the site.

Disabled access (to visitor centre, toilets, shop, tearoom and part of site. Disabled parking on site).

MAP Page 346 (4E)
OS Map 86, OL43: NY615663

Birdoswald is one of the best places to gain an overview of Hadrian's Wall at one single site. A Roman fort, turret and milecastle can all be seen here, with nearby the longest continuous stretch of Wall visible today. The visitor centre illustrates the history of the Wall, and tells the story of Birdoswald and its people over the past 2000 years.

Known as 'Banna', Birdoswald likewise has the best preserved defences of any of the major Hadrian's Wall forts. Three main gates, perimeter walls, angle towers, granaries and drill hall are all still traceable.

Another distinctive feature is the traces of the buildings successively raised here after the Roman withdrawal: including a large 5th-century timber hall, perhaps for a local British chieftain; a medieval fortified tower; an Elizabethan 'bastle house', a defence against 'Border Reivers'; and finally the present turreted farmhouse. Adjacent buildings now house a tearoom, a shop and a small exhibition.

The fort stands on the Hadrian's Wall Path National Trail. Guided tours for groups are available at a small additional fee. Please contact the site for details and bookings.

Accommodation
If you would like to stay within the walls of the fort, a 39-bed farmhouse can be booked for groups. Please call 01697 747602 or email birdoswald.accommodation@english-heritage.org.uk

VISIT US

Direction: ¼ mile W of Chollerford, on B6318

Train: Hexham 5½ miles

Bus: Alba/Classic service AD122 Carlisle – Hexham (Apr-Oct); also Tyne Valley/Snaith service 880 from Hexham

Tel: 01434 681379

Local Tourist Information
Hexham: 01434 652220

NON-MEMBERS

Adult	£5.60
Concession	£5.00
Child	£3.40

OPENING TIMES

1 Apr-30 Sep, daily	10am-6pm
1 Oct-2 Nov, daily	10am-5pm
3 Nov-15 Feb, Sat-Sun	10am-4pm
16-20 Feb, daily	10am-4pm
21 Feb-29 Mar, Sat-Sun	10am-4pm
24-26 Dec, 31 Dec-1 Jan	Closed

ACQ.1954

Disabled access (companion recommended). Disabled parking and toilets.

Dogs on leads (restricted areas only).

Tearoom (summer only; not managed by English Heritage).

Parking (pay and display. Charge refundable upon admission).

MAP Page 347 (4F)
OS Map 87, OL43: NY912702

Picturesquely set in the beautiful valley of the River North Tyne, Chesters is the best-preserved example of a Roman cavalry fort in Britain. The site also features a museum containing an amazing collection of archaeological discoveries.

Known as 'Cilurnum', Chesters was one of the series of permanent forts added during the construction of the Wall. It housed a garrison of some 500 troops, by the 3rd century a cavalry regiment originating from Asturias in northern Spain. There is much still to see, including remains of all four principal gates; the headquarters building with courtyard, hall and regimental shrine; and the elaborate and luxurious commandant's house.

Even better preserved, between the fort and the river, is the garrison's bath house. This still displays the complex of rooms which offered soldiers hot, cold or steam baths, as well as a changing-room-cum-clubhouse.

Hundreds of Roman finds from the central section of the Wall – retrieved by the Victorian antiquarian, John Clayton – are crowded into Chesters' highly distinctive museum, which has been restored to its Victorian glory with its original colour-scheme and 'traditional' museum layout. Recent additions include a portrait of John Clayton: and outside, a tactile model of the site, ramped access to the museum, and a viewing platform overlooking the river.

NEW FOR 2014

Coventina's Eagle. Find out what links a Roman Well and a bronze eagle statue.

CORBRIDGE ROMAN TOWN
Northumberland – NE45 5NT

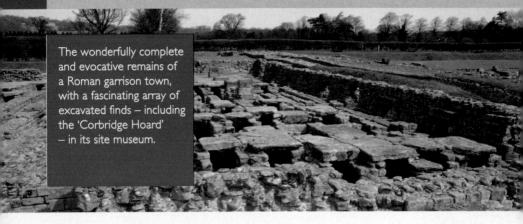

The wonderfully complete and evocative remains of a Roman garrison town, with a fascinating array of excavated finds – including the 'Corbridge Hoard' – in its site museum.

VISIT US

Direction: ½ mile NW of Corbridge, on minor road, then signposted

Train: Corbridge 1¼ miles

Bus: Alba/Classic AD122 (Apr-Oct), Go North East 10, X84 & X85; Arriva/Stagecoach in Cumbria services 685, Wrights service 888

Tel: 01434 632349

Local Tourist Information
Corbridge: 01434 632815

NON-MEMBERS

Adult	£5.60
Concession	£5.00
Child	£3.40

OPENING TIMES

1 Apr-30 Sep, daily	10am-6pm
1 Oct-2 Nov, daily	10am-5pm
3 Nov-15 Feb, Sat-Sun	10am-4pm
16-20 Feb, daily	10am-4pm
21 Feb-29 Mar, Sat-Sun	10am-4pm
24-26 Dec, 31 Dec-1 Jan	Closed

ACQ.1933

New guidebook.

Dogs on leads (restricted areas only).

Disabled access (parking, toilet, audio tour, access to the museum and perimeter of site).

MAP Page 347 (4F)
OS Map 87, OL43: NY982648

Corbridge Roman Town is the only place in Britain where visitors can walk along the original surface of a Roman 'high street', flanked by the excavated remains of granaries, fountain, markets, workshops and temples.

Astride the intersection of the Roman Dere Street and Stanegate roads, Corbridge was initially the site of a series of important forts: but after Hadrian's Wall was fully commissioned it developed into a prosperous garrison town, a tempting leave-centre for off-duty Wall soldiers. Abandoned after the collapse of Roman rule in Britain, the site of the settlement moved to the present Corbridge town, the Saxon tower of whose church – partly built with recycled Roman masonry – can clearly be seen from here.

The Roman town centre has been systematically excavated, producing the array of finds now most attractively displayed in the site museum. Covering every aspect of Roman life, artefacts include the tombstone of little Ertola, who 'lived most happily four years and sixty days', shown still playing with her ball; and the famous Corbridge lion carving. His modern counterpart, Grricola the Roman lion, takes younger visitors on a trail around the museum.

A recently-installed display showcases the Corbridge Hoard, one of the most significant finds from Roman Britain. Buried in the early 2nd century and rediscovered in 1964, this chest contained an extraordinary collection of weapons, tools, and personal possessions, including a soldier's iron bowl and a huge wooden tankard. Most importantly, it also included sections of 'lorica segmentata', articulated Roman armour. These allowed archaeologists to reconstruct how this complex armour – previously known only from depictions – actually worked. A touch-screen display allows visitors to explore the Hoard at many levels of detail.

NEW FOR 2014

Honour, loss and religion: new presentation of stone sculpture and inscription.

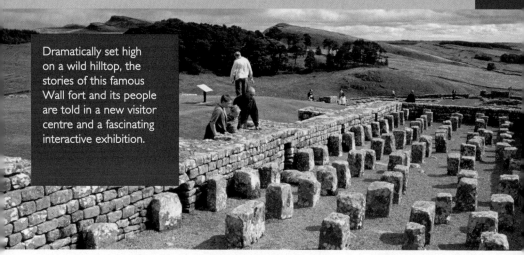

Dramatically set high on a wild hilltop, the stories of this famous Wall fort and its people are told in a new visitor centre and a fascinating interactive exhibition.

VISIT US

Address: Housesteads Roman Fort, Haydon Bridge, Hexham, Northumberland

Direction: Bardon Mill 4 miles

Bus: Alba service AD122 Carlisle – Hexham ⬛ (Apr-Oct)

Tel: 01434 344363

Local Tourist Information Hexham: 01434 652220

Disabled access to the museum (companion recommended). Limited access to site. 750 metre walk up a steep gradient. Disabled parking available at the top of the hill. Please enquire at the visitor centre in the bottom car park to arrange disabled parking. Guide dogs only in the museum.

Car park not operated by English Heritage (charge payable to Northumberland National Park).

NON-MEMBERS

Adult	£6.40
Concession	£5.80
Child	£3.80
Free to National Trust members	

OPENING TIMES

1 Apr-30 Sep, daily	10am-6pm
1 Oct-2 Nov, daily	10am-5pm
3 Nov-29 Mar, daily	10am-4pm
24-26 Dec & 1 Jan	Closed

MAP Page 347 (4F)
OS Map 86/87, OL43: NY790688

Among the most popular sites on Hadrian's Wall, Housesteads is also the most complete example of a Roman fort anywhere in Britain. It stands high on the wild Whin Sill escarpment, flanked by dramatic stretches of the Wall. Now 'the Grandest Station' on the Wall – as a Georgian visitor called it – boasts an outstanding exhibition, vividly interpreting life here on the northern edge of the Roman Empire.

Begun in about AD 124 as one of twelve permanent forts supporting Hadrian's frontier system, Housesteads was known as 'Vercovicium'. It was garrisoned by around 800 infantry (for most of its existence Tungrians from what is now eastern Belgium) later reinforced by a warband of Frisian cavalry. The big five-acre fort displays the remains of four gateways and a turreted curtain wall: within are a host of clearly traceable buildings, including the headquarters, commandant's house, baths, hospital – and the renowned multi-seater communal latrines. Served by an ingenious drainage system, these even retain the water channel used for washing hands.

The Roman south gate nearby was much later adapted into a 'bastle' farmhouse, fortified

CONTINUED ▶

against the 'rank robbers hereabouts', the Border Reivers who scared off Elizabethan travellers. Beyond it, outside the fort wall, are the excavated foundations of the Roman 'vicus' or civilian settlement, one of whose houses produced in the 1930s evidence of a gruesome Roman double murder.

The story of Housesteads and its people is now clearly and fascinatingly retold in a new multi-media display in the site museum. A short film traces the history of the fort and recreates its original appearance, also demonstrated by a fine model. Every aspect of Roman life here – what the soldiers wore; the tools and weapons they used; how they were cared for when sick; and gods they worshipped, including trios of 'Hooded Gods' and 'Mother Goddesses' – is illuminated by interpretative displays. These feature many locally excavated artefacts returning to the fort for the first time for centuries, most strikingly a winged Victory statue from a fort

gateway. The exhibition includes a dressing-up 'Discovery Box', and incorporates touchable replicas of Roman objects set at child-height, and explained by Felix the Roman soldier. Felix can also be followed on the new interpretation panels which guide visitors round the fort itself.

The fort stands uphill from the car park (via a fairly strenuous 10-minute walk, which also gives access to Hadrian's Wall Path National Trail). Owned by the National Trust, Housesteads is managed by English Heritage. A new National Trust visitor centre by the extended car park opened in 2013 – the culmination of a joint project by English Heritage and the National Trust to enhance the visitor welcome to Housesteads. The centre offers a new welcome and introduction to the site; a large new 3D map of the Fort; improved retail and catering facilities; glazed outdoor café seating for warm days, and a mezzanine level featuring views and images from all along the Wall.

DISCOUNTED ATTRACTIONS: **HADRIAN'S WALL**

Use your membership to get exclusive discounts at these independent attractions across Hadrian's Wall. Please remember to show your card as proof of membership.

Discount applies to:

| KEY | ⊞ MEMBERS | OVP OVP HOLDERS | 👪? NO. OF MEMBER'S CHILDREN |

Terms and conditions may apply, so make sure you check the individual pages on our website or call the individual property for more details.

20% DISCOUNT ON ENTRY

10% DISCOUNT ON ENTRY

10% DISCOUNT ON ENTRY

⊞ OVP 👪 6

HEXHAM OLD GAOL
Northumberland NE46 1XD
Built 1330-33, this is the earliest recorded purpose-built prison in England. This fully-accessible building introduces you to the history of the gaol, inmates and the Border Reivers of the 1500s.
www.experiencewoodhorn.com
Tel. 01670 624523

⊞ 👪 2

ROMAN VINDOLANDA
Northumberland NE47 7JN
Extensive Roman fort and settlement in the central section of Hadrian's Wall. Active archaeological programme and superb museum.
www.vindolanda.com
Tel. 01434 344277

⊞ OVP 👪 6

SEGEDUNUM ROMAN FORT, BATH HOUSE AND MUSEUM
Wallsend NE28 6HR
Segedunum is the gateway to Hadrian's Wall, providing outstanding views across this World Heritage Site.
www.segedunumromanfort.org.uk
Tel. 0191 236 9347

2 for 1 ENTRY

⊞ OVP 👪 6

SENHOUSE ROMAN MUSEUM
Cumbria CA15 6JD
Discover the unique and intriguing collection recovered from the adjacent Roman fort and civilian settlement.

www.senhousemuseum.co.uk
Tel. 01900 816168

THE HADRIAN'S WALL BUS (AD122)
runs throughout spring and summer between Newcastle, Hexham and Carlisle*.
For timetable details visit **www.hadrians-wall.org/bus**

*Information correct at time of going to press

NORTH EAST

Tynemouth Priory and Castle

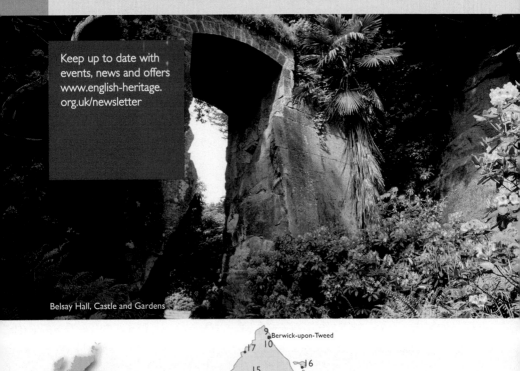

Keep up to date with
events, news and offers
www.english-heritage.
org.uk/newsletter

Belsay Hall, Castle and Gardens

9 Berwick-upon-Tweed
17 10
15 16
13
Alnwick
14
19
12
Northumberland
11
Morpeth
8 Blyth
Newcastle Tynemouth
upon Tyne 23 24
Hadrian's Wall 7 18 21
Hexham Gateshead 22 Tyne and Wear
Consett Sunderland
6
Durham
Peterlee
Durham Hartlepool
1 Billingham
Bishop Auckland Middlesbrough
Barnard 2 Darlington Tees Valley 20
Castle
3 5

Details of local public transport
information in England are
available from Traveline
www.traveline.org.uk
or call 0871 200 2233.

HIGHLIGHTS FOR 2014/15 IN THE **NORTH EAST**

p.298

p.276

p.302

Belsay Hall, Castle and Gardens: this year, meet the 'Wildman of Belsay' in a new display and themed events.

Hadrian's Wall: visit the many forts, museums and other historic places along the famous Roman frontier, a World Heritage Site.

Lindisfarne Priory: venture across to the Holy Island shrine of St. Cuthbert, goal of pilgrims for thirteen centuries.

PROPERTIES

DURHAM
1   Auckland Castle Deer House
2   Barnard Castle
3   Bowes Castle
4   Derwentcote Steel Furnace
5   Egglestone Abbey
6   Finchale Priory

NORTHUMBERLAND
7   Aydon Castle
8   Belsay Hall, Castle and Gardens
9   Berwick-upon-Tweed Barracks and Main Guard

10   Berwick-upon-Tweed Castle and Town Defences
11   Black Middens Bastle House
12   Brinkburn Priory
13   Dunstanburgh Castle
14   Edlingham Castle
15   Etal Castle
16   Lindisfarne Priory
17   Norham Castle
18   Prudhoe Castle
19   Warkworth Castle and Hermitage

REDCAR AND CLEVELAND
20   Gisborough Priory

TYNE AND WEAR
21   Bessie Surtees House
22   Hylton Castle
23   St Paul's Monastery, Jarrow
24   Tynemouth Priory and Castle

HADRIAN'S WALL
See page 276

Remember to check opening times before you visit any of our properties
www.english-heritage.org.uk/daysout

DURHAM

AUCKLAND CASTLE DEER HOUSE DURHAM

A charming Gothic Revival 'eyecatcher' built in 1760 in the park of the Bishops of Durham. It provided deer with shelter and food, and had grounds for picnics and rooms for enjoying the view.

Managed by the Church Commissioners for England.

OPENING TIMES

Park

1 Apr-30 Sep, daily	10am-6pm
1 Oct-29 Mar, daily	10am-4pm
24-26 Dec & 1 Jan	Closed

VISIT US

Direction: Located in Auckland Park, Bishop Auckland; N of town centre on A68

Train: Bishop Auckland 1 mile

Bus: Arriva service 56; Go Ahead 18, X21; Aabat Taxis 104 & Scarlet Band 113 pass closest to the castle gates

ACQ.1952

MAP Page 347 (5G)
OS Map 93, 305: NZ216304

BARNARD CASTLE
DURHAM – DL12 8PR

Barnard Castle is spectacularly set on a high rock above the River Tees, on the fringe of an attractive market town. Taking its name from its 12th-century

---

BARNARD CASTLE

founder, Bernard de Balliol, this huge and imposing fortress was later developed by the Beauchamp family and Richard III. Richard's boar emblem is carved above a window in the inner ward, the castle's chief strength: here loyalist forces were besieged during the 1569 Northern Rising against Queen Elizabeth I, before surrendering to 5000 rebels. There are fine views over the Tees Gorge, and a 'sensory garden' of scented plants and tactile objects. Barnard Castle is on the Richard III trail (see Middleham Castle, p.239).

NON-MEMBERS

Adult	£4.60
Concession	£4.10
Child	£2.80

OPENING TIMES

1 Apr-30 Sep, daily	10am-6pm
1 Oct-2 Nov, daily	10am-5pm
3 Nov-29 Mar, Sat-Sun	10am-4pm
24-26 Dec, 31 Dec-1 Jan	Closed

VISIT US

Direction: In Barnard Castle town

Bus: Arriva services 75 & 76; Classic service 352; Hodgson services 70, 71, 72, 73, 79 & 79X; Cumbria Classic 572; Scarlet Band services 83, 84, 95 & 96

Tel: 01833 638212

ACQ.1952

Parking (pay and display in town centre).

MAP Page 347 (6G)
OS Map 92, OL31: NZ049165

BOWES CASTLE DURHAM

The impressive ruins of Henry II's 12th-century keep, on the site of a Roman fort guarding the

---

BOWES CASTLE

approach to strategic Stainmore Pass over the Pennines.

OPENING TIMES
Any reasonable daylight hours

VISIT US

Direction: In Bowes Village off A66; 4 miles W of Barnard Castle town

Bus: Hodgsons 72, 79X; Cumbria Classic 572; Classic services 352

ACQ.1931

MAP Page 347 (6F)
OS Map 92, OL30/31: NY992135

DERWENTCOTE STEEL FURNACE DURHAM

Built in the 1730s, Derwentcote is the last surviving cementation steel-making furnace in Britain. It produced high-grade steel for springs and cutting tools.

OPENING TIMES
Any reasonable daylight hours (Grounds only – no access to Furnace)

24-26 Dec & 1 Jan	Closed

VISIT US

Direction: 10 miles SW of Newcastle, on A694; between Rowland's Gill and Hamsterley

Train: Metro Centre, Gateshead, 7 miles

Bus: Go North East Red Kite services 45/6 Newcastle-upon-Tyne – Consett

Tel: 01661 881636 (Sat-Sun)

ACQ.1985

Dogs on leads (restricted areas only).

Parking across main road from site.

MAP Page 347 (4G)
OS Map 88, 307: NZ130566

EGGLESTONE ABBEY
DURHAM

The charming ruins of a small monastery of Premonstratensian 'white canons', picturesquely set above a bend in the River Tees near Barnard Castle. Remains

EGGLESTONE ABBEY

include much of the 13th-century church and a range of living quarters, with traces of their ingenious toilet drainage system.

OPENING TIMES

| 1 Apr-29 Mar, daily | 10am-6pm |
| 24-26 Dec & 1 Jan | Closed |

VISIT US

Direction: 1 mile S of Barnard Castle, on a minor road off B6277

Bus: Hodgsons service 79 & 79X then ½ mile walk

ACQ.1925

Limited free parking available.

MAP Page 347 (6G)
OS Map 92, OL31: NZ062151

FINCHALE PRIORY
DURHAM – DH1 5SH

The very extensive remains of a 13th-century priory, founded on the site of the retired pirate St Godric's hermitage. Part of it later served as a holiday retreat for the monks of Durham Cathedral. Beautifully sited by the River Wear, with delightful riverside walks nearby.

OPENING TIMES

| 1 Apr-29 Mar, daily | 10am-5pm |
| 24-26 Dec & 1 Jan | Closed |

VISIT US

Direction: 3 miles NE of Durham; on minor road off A167

Train: Durham 5 miles

Bus: Arriva/Scarlet Band service 42 from Durham to HMP Frankland and then a short walk

ACQ.1916

Parking (fee applies; not managed by EH).

MAP Page 347 (4G)
OS Map 88, 308: NZ296471

NORTHUMBERLAND

AYDON CASTLE
NORTHUMBERLAND
NE45 5PJ

One of the finest and most unaltered examples of a 13th-century English manor house, Aydon Castle stands in a secluded woodland setting. It was originally built as an undefended residence, but almost immediately fortified on the outbreak of Anglo-Scottish warfare. Nevertheless it was pillaged and burnt by the Scots in 1315, seized by English rebels two years later and again occupied by Scots in 1346. In the 18th century Aydon became a farmhouse, remaining so until 1966. Today the castle is a fantastic place to explore with the family, and you can take advantage of the beautiful walks in the surrounding area.

NON-MEMBERS
Adult	£4.00
Concession	£3.60
Child	£2.40

OPENING TIMES

1 Apr-30 Sep, Wed-Sun & Bank Hols	10am-6pm
1 Oct-2 Nov, Wed-Sun	10am-4pm
3 Nov-29 Mar	Closed

VISIT US

Direction: 1 mile NE of Corbridge, on minor road off B6321 or A68

AYDON CASTLE

Train: Corbridge 4 miles – approach via bridle path from W side of Aydon Road, immediately N of Corbridge bypass

Bus: Alba/Classic service AD122 Apr-Nov. Otherwise closest is Corbridge served by Go North East 10, X84, X85; Stagecoach/Arriva 685 and Wrights 888

Tel: 01434 632450

ACQ.1966

Disabled access (ground floor only).

Dogs on leads (restricted areas only).

MAP Page 347 (4F)
OS Map 87, 316: NZ001663

BELSAY HALL, CASTLE AND GARDENS
SEE FEATURE – PAGE 298

BERWICK-UPON-TWEED BARRACKS AND MAIN GUARD
NORTHUMBERLAND
TD15 1DF

Berwick Barracks, among the first in England to be purpose-built, were begun in 1717, adapting

BERWICK-UPON-TWEED BARRACKS AND MAIN GUARD

a design by the distinguished architect Nicholas Hawksmoor. Today the barracks host a number of attractions, including *By Beat of Drum* – an exhibition on the life of the British infantryman. While there, visit the King's Own Scottish Borderers Museum and the Berwick Museum & Art Gallery.

The Main Guard is a Georgian Guard House near the quay: it displays *The Story of a Border Garrison Town* exhibition.

The Main Guard is managed by Berwick Civic Society.

NON-MEMBERS

Barracks

Adult	£4.20
Concession	£3.80
Child	£2.50

OPENING TIMES

Barracks

1 Apr-30 Sep, Mon-Fri & Bank Hols	10am-6pm
1 Oct-2 Nov, Mon-Fri	10am-4pm
3 Nov-29 Mar	Closed

Main Guard
Please call for details

VISIT US

Direction: On the Parade, off Church St in town centre

Train: Berwick-upon-Tweed ¼ mile

Bus: From surrounding areas

Tel: 01289 304493

Disabled access (Main Guard).

Dogs on leads (restricted areas only).

Parking: pay and display (in town).

MAP Page 347 (1F) OS Map 75, 346
Barracks: NU001531
Main Guard: NU000525

BERWICK-UPON-TWEED CASTLE AND TOWN DEFENCES
NORTHUMBERLAND TD15 1DF

The remains of a medieval castle crucial to Anglo-Scottish warfare, superseded by the most complete and breathtakingly impressive bastioned town defences in England, mainly Elizabethan but updated in the 17th and 18th centuries. Surrounding the whole historic town, their entire circuit can be walked, guided by interpretation panels.

OPENING TIMES

Any reasonable daylight hours

VISIT US

Direction: The castle is adjacent to Berwick-upon-Tweed railway station. The ramparts surround the town (accessed at various points)

Train: Berwick-upon-Tweed, adjacent

Bus: From surrounding areas

ACQ.1931

Disabled access (Ramparts).

Parking: pay and display (in town).

Note: Steep hidden drops. Dangerous after dark.

MAP Page 347 (1F)
OS Map 75, 346 Castle: NT993534
Ramparts: NU003530

Don't forget to check opening times online before you visit.

www.english-heritage.org.uk/daysout/properties

BLACK MIDDENS BASTLE HOUSE NORTHUMBERLAND

A fortified farmhouse with thick stone walls, of a type distinctive to the troubled 16th-century Anglo-Scottish borders. The living quarters were only accessible at first floor level. Set in splendid walking country, on the Reivers Route cycle trail.

OPENING TIMES

Any reasonable daylight hours

VISIT US

Direction: 180 metres N of minor road, 7 miles NW of Bellingham; or along a minor road from A68

Bus: Arriva service 714 (summer Sun only) serves Lanehead (3 miles). Otherwise nearest bus service is Snaith's/Tyne Valley service 880 which links Hexham and Bellingham (7 miles)

ACQ.1978

MAP Page 347 (3F)
OS Map 80, OL42: NY773900

BRINKBURN PRIORY
NORTHUMBERLAND NE65 8AR

The beautiful 12th-century church of the Augustinian priory of Brinkburn survives completely roofed and restored. Picturesquely set by a bend in the River Coquet, it is reached by a scenic 10-minute walk from the car park. Parts of the monastic buildings are

BRINKBURN PRIORY

incorporated into the elegant adjacent manor house.

NON-MEMBERS

Adult	£3.60
Concession	£3.20
Child	£2.20

OPENING TIMES

1 Apr-30 Sep, Mon-Fri & Bank Hols	10am-6pm
1 Oct-2 Nov, Sat-Sun	10am-4pm
3 Nov-29 Mar	Closed

VISIT US

Direction: 4½ miles SE of Rothbury, off B6344

Train: Acklington 10 miles

Bus: Arriva service 14 Morpeth – Thropton (passing ⇌ Morpeth). Nearest stop Brinkburn New Houses then about 1½ mile walk

Tel: 01665 570628

ACQ.1965 🐾 🏛 P 🏠 📷 ⚠ OVP

Picnic area (⅓ mile).

MAP Page 347 (3G)
OS Map 92, 325: NZ116983

DUNSTANBURGH CASTLE
NORTHUMBERLAND
NE66 3TT

Dramatic Dunstanburgh Castle was built at a time when relations between King Edward II and his most powerful baron, Earl Thomas of Lancaster, had become openly hostile. Lancaster began the fortress in 1313, and the latest archaeological research

DUNSTANBURGH CASTLE

carried out by English Heritage indicates that he built it on a far grander scale than was hitherto recognised, perhaps more as a symbol of his opposition to the king than as a military stronghold. The innovative gatehouse, for instance, competed with the new royal castles in Wales.

The earl failed to reach Dunstanburgh when his rebellion was defeated, and was taken and executed in 1322. Thereafter the castle passed eventually to John of Gaunt, who strengthened it against the Scots by converting the great twin towered gatehouse into a keep. The focus of fierce fighting during the Wars of the Roses, it was twice besieged and captured by Yorkist forces, but subsequently fell into decay. Its impressive ruins now watch over a headland famous for seabirds.

Owned by the National Trust, maintained and managed by English Heritage.

NON-MEMBERS

Adult	£4.30
Concession	£3.90
Child	£2.60
Free to National Trust members	

OPENING TIMES

1 Apr-30 Sep, daily	10am-6pm
1-31 Oct, daily	10am-4pm
1 Nov-15 Feb, Sat-Sun	10am-4pm
16-20 Feb, daily	10am-4pm
21 Feb-29 Mar, Sat-Sun	10am-4pm
24-26 Dec, 31 Dec-1 Jan	Closed

VISIT US

Direction: 8 miles NE of Alnwick; on footpaths from Craster or Embleton – 1½ miles rugged coastal walk

Train: Chathill, not Sun, 5 miles from Embleton, 7 miles from Castle;

DUNSTANBURGH CASTLE

Alnmouth, 7 miles from Craster, 8¼ miles from Castle

Bus: Arriva service X18 Travelsure 418. Alight Craster and take coast walk, 1½ miles

Tel: 01665 576231

Local Tourist Information
Craster: 01665 576007

ACQ.1929 🐾 🏛 🏠 📷 ⚠ OVP

Parking (in Craster village; approx. 1½ miles walk. A charge is payable).

Nearest toilets located at car park in Craster Village.

MAP Page 347 (2G)
OS Map 75, 332: NU257219

EDLINGHAM CASTLE
NORTHUMBERLAND

The riverside ruins, principally the solar tower, of a manor house progressively fortified against the Scots during the 14th century.

Managed by the Parochial Church Council of St John the Baptist, Edlingham, with Bolton Chapel.

OPENING TIMES

Any reasonable daylight hours

VISIT US

Direction: At E end of Edlingham village, on minor road off B6341; 6 miles SW of Alnwick

Train: Alnmouth 9 miles

Bus: Closest bus is Glen Valley 473 service to Banktop (2 miles)

ACQ.1975 🐾 ⚠

Note: waterproof footwear is recommended.

MAP Page 347 (2G)
OS Map 81, 332: NU116092

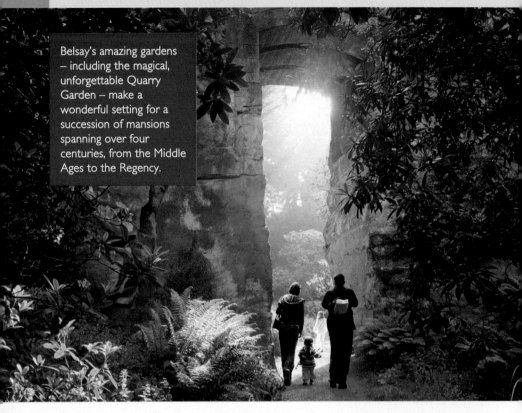

Belsay's amazing gardens – including the magical, unforgettable Quarry Garden – make a wonderful setting for a succession of mansions spanning over four centuries, from the Middle Ages to the Regency.

VISIT US

Address: Belsay Hall, Castle & Gardens, Belsay, Northumberland

Direction: In Belsay; 14 miles NW of Newcastle, on A696

Train: Morpeth 10 miles

Bus: Arriva 508 from 🚉 Newcastle operates to the gardens on Sun and Bank Hols only, (May-Oct); also Arriva Sun and Bank Hol service 714 serves Belsay village; Snaith's 808 from Newcastle

Tel: 01661 881636

Local Tourist Information
Morpeth: 01670 500700

NON-MEMBERS

Adult	£8.00
Concession	£7.20
Child	£4.80
Family	£20.80

OPENING TIMES

1 Apr-30 Sep, daily	10am-6pm
1-31 Oct, daily	10am-5pm
1 Nov-15 Feb, Sat-Sun	10am-4pm
16-20 Feb, daily	10am-4pm
21 Feb-29 Mar, Sat-Sun	10am-4pm
24-26 Dec, 31 Dec-1 Jan	Closed

ACQ.1980 🐕 🍴 🏠 ♿ E f 👐 ❄
🖼 🧑 🌳 P 🎧 📷 ♿ 🛒
🐦 ⚠ OVP

Disabled access (grounds, tearoom and ground floor only; toilets).

Dogs on leads (grounds only not halls).

Tearoom (Apr-Oct, open daily; Nov, Dec & Mar, Sat-Sun).

MAP Page 347 (3G)
OS Map 88, 316: NZ086785

NEW FOR 2014

'The Wildman of Belsay' a display of unique 17th-century statues and an opportunity to 'go wild' with themed events.

The tearoom, in the original Victorian kitchens, provides a perfect setting for a break during your visit.

Belsay has something for everyone. A fine medieval castle, enlarged into a Jacobean mansion; the imposing Greek Revival villa that succeeded it; and the outstanding plant-rich gardens linking the two buildings.

The whole ensemble is the creation of the Middleton family over more than seven centuries. First came the castle, still dominated by its massive 14th-century defensive 'peel tower'. Built as a refuge at a time of Anglo-Scottish warfare, it was also designed to impress: it still displays rare traces of elaborate medieval wall-paintings. In more peaceful times a Jacobean mansion wing was added: here the family lived until Christmas Day 1817, when they moved into Belsay Hall.

Belsay Hall is an elegant Classical Greek Revival villa, now displayed without furnishings to reveal the fine craftsmanship of its construction. Begun in 1807, it was designed by Sir Charles Monck (formerly Middleton), a man inspired by Ancient Greece and the buildings he had seen on his honeymoon in Athens. Despite its austere façade, it had a comfortable interior, arranged round its amazing central 'Pillar Hall'.

The vast gardens which provide a magnificent setting for the castle and hall are also largely Sir Charles's work. His romantic Quarry Garden, created where stone was cut for his hall, has ravines and sheer rock faces inspired by Sicilian quarries. His grandson Sir Arthur Middleton, likewise a pioneering plantsman, further embellished the Quarry with the exotic species which thrive in its micro-climate and added the Winter Garden, Yew Garden, and Magnolia Terrace.

SPRING

A white carpet of thousands of Snowdrops, followed by a riot of colour from Daffodils, Spring Snowflakes and Dog's Tooth Violets. Rhododendrons and large Magnolias.

SUMMER

Rhododendrons (May & June). Giant Himalayan Lilies up to nine feet tall, and other species of lilies. A NCCPG National Collection of Iris can be seen, as well as the Pocket Handkerchief Tree.

AUTUMN

Amazing autumn colours of red, yellow and orange foliage. The fallen leaves of Cercidiphyllum Japonicum smell of burnt sugar!

WINTER

Spectacular Rhododendrons flower, and frosted spiders' webs frame the topiary in the Yew Garden. Scented Viburnums and Jasmines and the appropriately titled Christmas Box (Sarcococca) can be found in the Winter Garden.

ETAL CASTLE NORTHUMBERLAND – TD12 4TN

NORHAM CASTLE
NORTHUMBERLAND TD15 2JY

Commanding a vital ford over the River Tweed, Norham was one of the strongest of all the border castles, and the most often attacked by the Scots. Besieged at least thirteen times – once for nearly a year by King Robert Bruce in 1318 – it was called 'the most dangerous and adventurous place in the country'.

But even its powerful 12th-century keep and massive towered bailey walls could not resist James IV's heavy cannon, and it fell to him in 1513, shortly before his disastrous defeat at Flodden. Quickly recaptured, it was extensively rebuilt as a powerful artillery fortress.

Graphic panels guide you round the castle, and a free audio tour can be downloaded from our website.

OPENING TIMES

1 Apr-30 Sep, daily	10am-5pm

VISIT US

Direction: In Norham village; 6 miles SW of Berwick-upon-Tweed, on minor road off B6470 (from A698)

Train: Berwick-upon-Tweed 7½ miles

Bus: Perryman's 67 🚆 Berwick-upon-Tweed – Galashiels

ACQ.1923 🍴 P 🏕 🚻 ⚠

Disabled access (excluding keep).

Etal Castle was begun in the early 14th century by Robert Manners as a tower house, in a strategic position by a ford over the River Till on the Anglo-Scottish border. Thus intensely vulnerable to attack by raiders, it was soon provided with a curtain wall with corner towers and a large gatehouse.

In 1513 the castle was suddenly thrust into the forefront of history, when the flamboyant King James IV of Scotland invaded Northumberland with the largest Scots army ever to invade England. He quickly captured Etal Castle, but was outmanoeuvred by the wily English veteran the Earl of Surrey, and lured from his strong position on nearby Branxton Hill. In the ensuing Battle of Flodden, the most disastrous defeat ever inflicted by the English on the Scots, King James was killed along with nine Scots earls, fourteen lords, and thousands of his men.

An award-winning exhibition tells the story of Flodden

and the long border warfare between the two nations. The Flodden battlefield is nearby, and can also be visited.

NON-MEMBERS

Adult	£4.10
Concession	£3.70
Child	£2.50
Family	£10.70

OPENING TIMES

1 Apr-30 Sep, daily	10am-6pm
1 Oct-2 Nov, daily	10am-4pm
3 Nov-29 Mar	Closed

VISIT US

Direction: In Etal village, 10 miles SW of Berwick

Train: Berwick-upon-Tweed 10½ miles

Bus: Glen Valley/Perrymans service 267 Berwick-upon-Tweed – Wooler

Tel: 01890 820332

ACQ.1975 🍴 🏕 🛡 ⚒ 🖥 🚶 👤 P 🏕 📷 ♿ OVP

Dogs on leads (restricted areas only).

Toilets (in car park).

MAP Page 347 (1F)
OS Map 74/75, 339: NT925393

MAP Page 347 (1F)
OS Map 74/75, 339: NT906476

LINDISFARNE PRIORY
SEE FEATURE – PAGE 302

ST ANDREW'S CHURCH, BYWELL
NORTHUMBERLAND
NE43 7AD

© CCT

The tall Saxon tower of St Andrew's dates from about 850, and its massive walls are 5m thick. The body of the church is 13th century, but the mosaic sanctuary floor, glittering reredos and fine stained glass were restored in 1871. There are also some boldly carved medieval grave slabs.

Owned and managed by The Churches Conservation Trust.

OPENING TIMES
Open daily during daylight hours

VISIT US
Train: Stocksfield 1 mile

Bus: Go Ahead service 10, then 1 mile walk

10 mins from Prudhoe Castle (or 15 mins from Corbridge Roman Town)

MAP Page 347 (4G)
OS Map 87, 316: NZ048614

Don't forget to check opening times online before you visit.

www.english-heritage.org.uk/daysout/properties

PRUDHOE CASTLE NORTHUMBERLAND – NE42 6NA

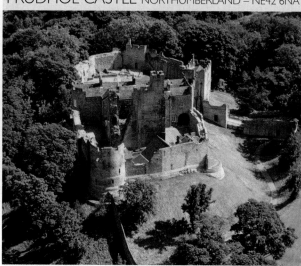

Begun between 1100 and 1120 to defend a strategic crossing of the River Tyne against Scottish invaders, Prudhoe Castle has been continuously occupied for over nine centuries. After two sieges during the 1170s – the Scots attackers reportedly declaring 'as long as Prudhoe stands, we shall never have peace' – the mighty stone keep and a great hall were added, followed in about 1300 by two strong towers. Passing from its original Umfraville owners to the powerful Percy family in 1398, it was again updated with a fashionable new great hall.

Even after its last military action against the Scots in 1640, Prudhoe's importance as the centre of a great landed estate continued. Early in the 19th century the Percys restored it, building a fine new manor house within its walls. All these developments are now vividly interpreted in a family-friendly exhibition including site finds, helping visitors to explore and understand the extensive remains of this formidable and long-lived fortress.

NON-MEMBERS
Adult	£4.60
Concession	£4.10
Child	£2.80

OPENING TIMES
1 Apr-30 Sep, Wed–Sun & Bank Hols	10am-6pm
1 Oct-2 Nov, Wed–Sun	10am-4pm
3 Nov-29 Mar	Closed

VISIT US
Direction: In Prudhoe, on minor road off A695

Train: Prudhoe ¼ mile

Bus: Go North East 10, 11A, 686

Tel: 01661 833459

Dogs on leads (restricted areas only).
Toilets with disabled access on site.

MAP Page 347 (4G)
OS Map 88, 316: NZ091634

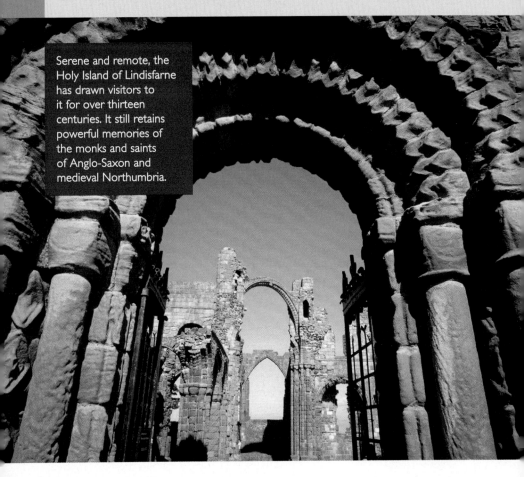

Serene and remote, the Holy Island of Lindisfarne has drawn visitors to it for over thirteen centuries. It still retains powerful memories of the monks and saints of Anglo-Saxon and medieval Northumbria.

VISIT US

Address: Lindisfarne Priory, Holy Island, Berwick Upon Tweed, Northumberland

Direction: On Holy Island, only reached at low tide across causeway; tide tables at each end, or from Tourist Information Centre

Train: Berwick-upon-Tweed 14 miles, via causeway

Bus: Perrymans service 477 from Berwick-upon-Tweed (passes close ⊠ Berwick-upon-Tweed). Times vary with tides

Tel: 01289 389200

Tourist Information Centre
01289 330733

NON-MEMBERS

Adult	£5.40
Concession	£4.90
Child	£3.20

OPENING TIMES

1 Apr-30 Sep, daily	10am-6pm
1-31 Oct, daily	10am-5pm
1 Nov-15 Feb, Sat-Sun	10am-4pm
16-20 Feb, daily	10am-4pm
21 Feb-29 Mar, Sat-Sun	10am-4pm
24-26 Dec, 31 Dec-1 Jan	Closed

The causeway floods at high tide, so it is very important to check the tide times before crossing

ACQ. 1913

Dogs on leads (restricted areas only).

Parking and toilets in the village. Parking pay and display operated by Northumberland County Council.

Access (limited in some areas of priory grounds).

MAP Page 347 (1G)
OS Map 75, 340: NU126417

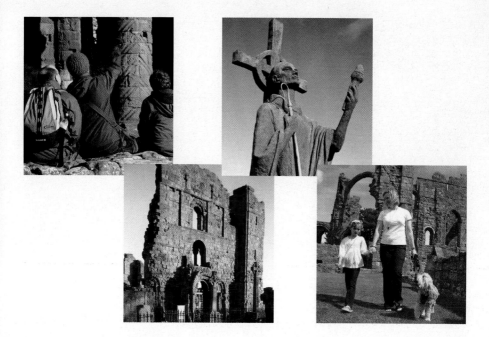

Founded in AD 635 and still a place of pilgrimage today, Lindisfarne Priory on Holy Island was one of the most important centres of early Christianity in Anglo-Saxon England. The dramatic approach to the island across the causeway only emphasises the serene appeal of this atmospheric site.

St Cuthbert, Prior of Lindisfarne, is the most celebrated of the priory's many holy men. After ten years seeking peace as a hermit on lonely Inner Farne Island, he reluctantly became Bishop before retiring to die on Inner Farne in 687. Buried in the priory, his remains were transferred to a pilgrim shrine. After eleven years his coffin was opened and his body found to be undecayed – a sure sign of sanctity.

From the end of the 8th century, the rich monastery was easy prey for Viking raiders. In 875 the monks left, carrying Cuthbert's remains, which after long wanderings were enshrined in Durham Cathedral in 1104, where they still rest. Only after that time did Durham monks re-establish a priory on Lindisfarne. The evocative ruins of the richly decorated priory church they built in c. 1150 still stand, with their famous 'rainbow arch' – a vault-rib of the now-vanished crossing tower.

The priory is likewise renowned for the Lindisfarne Gospels, among England's greatest artistic and religious treasures. They were produced here in the late 7th or early 8th century by Bishop Eadfrith, possibly in honour of St Cuthbert's transference to his pilgrim shrine.

The same Lindisfarne artists may well have produced the fourteen extraordinary 'name stones' discovered around the site. Carved and originally painted and possibly bejewelled versions of the Gospels' manuscript pages, these delicate stones commemorate people who may have known Cuthbert and Eadfrith. The recently-installed 'Inscribed in Stone' display in the site museum celebrates these rare survivals of 8th-century craftsmanship, unique links with the vanished Saxon monastery.

VISIT US

Direction: In Warkworth; 7½ miles S of Alnwick, on A1068

Train: Alnmouth 3½ miles

Bus: Arriva X18 Newcastle – Alnwick & Travelsure 472

Tel: 01665 711423

Local Tourist Information
Amble: 01665 712313

NON-MEMBERS

Castle:

Adult	£5.20
Concession	£4.70
Child	£3.10
Family	£13.50

Hermitage:

Adult	£3.50
Concession	£3.20
Child	£2.10

OPENING TIMES

Castle:

1 Apr-30 Sep, daily	10am-6pm
1-31 Oct, daily	10am-5pm
1 Nov-15 Feb, Sat-Sun	10am-4pm
16-20 Feb, daily	10am-4pm
21 Feb-29 Mar, Sat-Sun	10am-4pm
24-26 Dec, 31 Dec-1 Jan	Closed

Hermitage:

1 Apr-30 Sep, Sun-Mon & Bank Hols	11am-4pm
1 Oct-29 Mar	Closed

Audio tours (also available for the visually impaired and those with learning difficulties).

Disabled access (limited access).

Dogs on leads (restricted areas only).

Parking (Charge payable, which is refundable on admission).

The magnificent cross-shaped keep of Warkworth, crowning a hilltop rising steeply above the River Coquet, dominates one of the largest, strongest and most impressive fortresses in northern England. The castle's most famous owners were the Percy family, whose lion badge can be seen carved on many parts of their stronghold. Wielding almost kingly power in the North, their influence reached its height under the first Percy Earl of Northumberland and his son 'Harry Hotspur', hero of many Border ballads as the bane of Scots raiders and a dominant character in Shakespeare's *Henry IV*. Having helped to depose Richard II, these turbulent 'kingmakers' both fell victim to Henry IV: the next three Percy earls likewise died violent deaths.

Still roofed and almost complete, the uniquely-planned keep dates mainly from the end of the 14th century. It presides over the extensive remains of a great hall, chapel, fine gatehouse and a virtually intact circuit of towered walls.

Half a mile from the castle, tucked away by the Coquet and accessible only by boat, stands a much more peaceful building: the late medieval cave Hermitage and chapel of a solitary holy man.

The Duke's Rooms and the Hermitage are open on Sun, Mon and Bank Holidays from 1 Apr to 30 Sep.

MAP Page 347 (2G)
OS Map 81, 332: NU247058

REDCAR AND CLEVELAND

GISBOROUGH PRIORY
REDCAR AND CLEVELAND

The ruins of an Augustinian priory founded by the Bruce family, afterwards Kings of Scotland. They are dominated by the dramatic skeleton of the 14th-century church's east end.

Managed by Redcar and Cleveland Borough Council.

NON-MEMBERS

Adult	£2.00
Concession	£1.00
Child	£1.00
Family	£4.00

OPENING TIMES

1 Apr-30 Sep, Wed-Sun & Bank Hols	10am-4pm
1 Oct-29 Mar, Wed-Sun	10am-3pm
24 Dec-1 Jan	Closed

VISIT US

Direction: In Guisborough town, next to the parish church

Train: Marske 4½ miles

Bus: Arriva services 5, 5A, 5B, 28, 81, 93, X93. (Arriva service 28 actually passes by)

Tel: 01287 633801

ACQ.1932

Toilets and parking (in town).

MAP Page 347 (6H)
OS Map 94, OL26/306: NZ617160

TYNE AND WEAR

BESSIE SURTEES HOUSE
TYNE AND WEAR – NE1 3JF

These two five-storey, 16th- and 17th-century merchants' houses – which now also house English Heritage's local office – are fine examples of Jacobean domestic architecture, with some splendid period interiors. The Surtees house is best known as the scene of the elopement of Bessie with John Scott, later Lord Chancellor of England. An exhibition illustrating the history of the houses is on the first floor.

OPENING TIMES

All year round, Mon-Fri	10am-4pm
Bank Hols & 24 Dec-2 Jan	Closed

VISIT US

Direction: 41-44 Sandhill, Newcastle-upon-Tyne

Train: Newcastle ½ mile

Metro: Central ½ mile

Bus: From surrounding areas

Tel: 0191 269 1200

ACQ.1989

MAP Page 347 (4G)
OS Map 88, 316: NZ256338

HYLTON CASTLE
TYNE AND WEAR

The distinctive and highly decorative gatehouse-tower of a castle built by the wealthy Sir William Hylton shortly before 1400. Originally containing four floors of self-contained family accommodation, its entrance front displays royal and family heraldry, including Richard II's white hart badge.

OPENING TIMES

1 Apr-29 Mar, daily	10am-4pm
Grounds only – no access to Castle	
24-26 Dec & 1 Jan	Closed

VISIT US

Direction: 3¾ miles W of Sunderland

Train: Seaburn Metro (2½ miles) then bus 99; Pallion Metro then bus 29, 29A, 39 or 39A

Bus: Stagecoach services 3, 13; Go North East services 26 & 56

ACQ.1950

Dogs on leads.
Disabled access (grounds only).

MAP Page 347 (4H)
OS Map 88, 308: NZ358588

ST PAUL'S MONASTERY, JARROW
TYNE AND WEAR

The home of the Venerable Bede, chronicler of the beginnings of English Christianity, Jarrow has become one of the best-understood Anglo-Saxon monastic sites. The Anglo-Saxon church – with the oldest dedication stone in the country, dated AD 685 – partly survives as the chancel of the parish church. A free downloadable audio tour is available from our website.

OPENING TIMES

Monastery ruins any reasonable daylight hours

VISIT US

Direction: In Jarrow, on minor road N of A185; follow signs for Bede's World

Metro: Bede ¾ miles

Bus: Go North East The Crusader services 27

Tel: 0191 489 7052

ACQ.1956

MAP Page 347 (4H)
OS Map 88, 316: NZ339652

VISIT US

Direction: In Tynemouth, near North Pier

Metro: Tynemouth ½ mile

Bus: Arriva Northumbria service 306

Tel: 0191 257 1090

NON-MEMBERS

Adult	£4.80
Concession	£4.30
Child	£2.90
Family	£12.50

OPENING TIMES

1 Apr-30 Sep, daily	10am-6pm
1-31 Oct, daily	10am-4pm
1 Nov-29 Mar, Sat-Sun	10am-4pm
24-26 Dec, 31 Dec-1 Jan	Closed

Gun Battery: Access limited, please ask site staff for details

ACQ.1969

Dogs on leads.

Disabled access (priory only).
Toilets with disabled access on site.
Limited disabled parking avaiable.

Set in an almost impregnable position on a steep headland between the river and the North Sea, Tynemouth has always been as much a fortress as a religious site.

Here stood a 7th-century Anglian monastery, burial place of Oswin, sainted King of Northumbria. After its destruction by Danish raiders, the present Benedictine priory was founded on its site in c. 1090.

The towering east end of the priory church, built in c. 1200 with slender lancet windows and soaring arches, still survives almost to its full height, dominating the headland. Beyond it stands a small but complete and exceptionally well-preserved chapel, with a rose window and an ornately sculpted roof vault. This was built in the mid-15th century as a chantry for the souls of the powerful Percy family, Earls of Northumberland.

Enclosing both headland and monastery, and still surviving in part, were the strong medieval walls which once made Tynemouth among the largest fortified areas in England, and an important bastion against the Scots.

When the priory's 19 monks surrendered Tynemouth to Henry VIII in 1539, it was immediately adopted as a royal castle. Thereafter the fortress headland continued to play an important role in coastal defence from Elizabethan times until the end of the Second World War.

The interactive *Life in the Stronghold* exhibition takes visitors on a journey from Tynemouth's beginnings as an Anglo-Saxon settlement, via its medieval monastery and Tudor fortification, right up to its importance as a Second World War coastal gun battery.

MAP Page 347 (4H)
OS Map 88, 316: NZ373694

DISCOUNTED ATTRACTIONS: **NORTH EAST**

Use your membership to get exclusive discounts at these independent attractions in the North East. Please remember to show your card as proof of membership.

Discount applies to:

| KEY | ▦ MEMBERS | OVP OVP HOLDERS | 👪? NO. OF MEMBER'S CHILDREN |

Terms and conditions may apply, so make sure you check the individual pages on our website or call the individual property for more details.

▦

ALNWICK CASTLE
Northumberland NE66 1NQ
Home to the Duke of Northumberland's family for over 700 years, Alnwick boasts State Rooms filled with one of the country's finest private art and furniture collections.
www.alnwickcastle.com
Tel. 01665 511100

▦ OVP 👪2

BAMBURGH CASTLE
Northumberland NE69 7DF
The King of Castles, Bamburgh has 14 rooms and over 3000 artefacts, including weapons, porcelain, paintings and furniture. Separate aviation artefacts museum, café and battlements.
www.bamburghcastle.com
Tel. 01668 214515

▦ 👪4

THE BOWES MUSEUM
County Durham DL12 8NP
An inspirational day out for all the family, with fascinating collections, stunning galleries, a romantic history, acclaimed Café Bowes and shop, all set in beautiful parkland and gardens.
www.thebowesmuseum.org.uk
Tel. 01833 690606

▦ OVP 👪6

KILLHOPE – THE NORTH OF ENGLAND LEAD MINING MUSEUM
Durham DL13 1AR
A multi-award winning Victorian Museum and a grand day out. Accompany a guide on an unforgettable mine tour.
www.killhope.org.uk
Tel. 01388 537 505

▦ 👪2

TANFIELD RAILWAY
County Durham NE16 5ET
The world's oldest railway. Six mile round trip behind locally built steam engines in vintage coaches. Stop and see historic Causey Arch. We run Sundays etc. Timetable and details at
www.tanfield-railway.co.uk
Tel. 0845 463 4938

GIVE THE GIFT OF MEMBERSHIP

Give friends and family the opportunity to enjoy these fantastic discounts too!

- Free entry to over 400 historic properties
- Kids go free (up to six per adult in a family group)
- Free or discounted entry to hundreds of events
- Free handbook worth £10.95
- Exclusive Members' Magazine

See page 355 for full details.

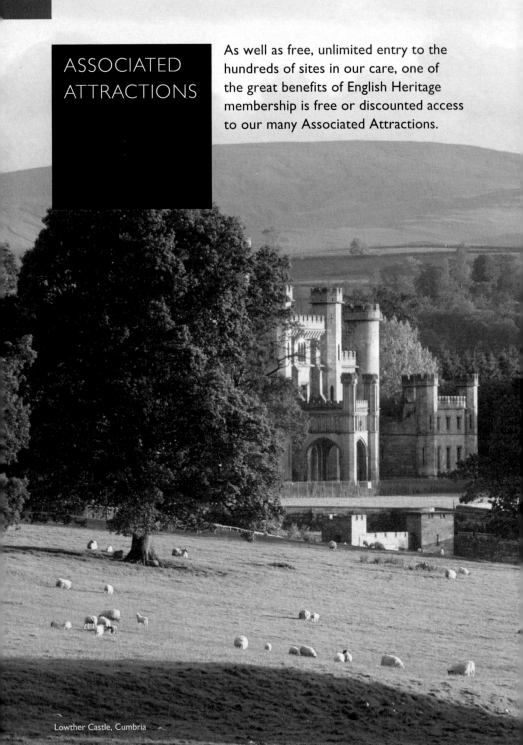

ASSOCIATED ATTRACTIONS

As well as free, unlimited entry to the hundreds of sites in our care, one of the great benefits of English Heritage membership is free or discounted access to our many Associated Attractions.

Lowther Castle, Cumbria

SCOTLAND, WALES AND ISLE OF MAN

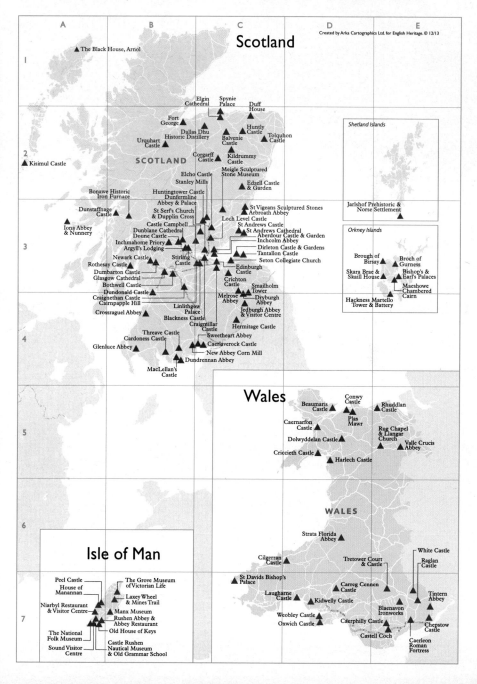

Scotland

Created by Arka Cartographics Ltd. for English Heritage. © 12/13

The Black House, Arnol

Elgin Cathedral
Spynie Palace
Duff House
Fort George
Dallas Dhu Historic Distillery
Huntly Castle
Tolquhon Castle
Urquhart Castle
Balvenie Castle
SCOTLAND
Corgarff Castle
Kildrummy Castle
Kisimul Castle
Meigle Sculptured Stone Museum
Elcho Castle
Stanley Mills
Edzell Castle & Garden
Bonawe Historic Iron Furnace
Huntingtower Castle
Dunfermline Abbey & Palace
Dunstaffnage Castle
Castle Campbell
St Serf's Church & Dupplin Cross
St Vigeans Sculptured Stones
Arbroath Abbey
Jarlshof Prehistoric & Norse Settlement
Iona Abbey & Nunnery
Dunblane Cathedral
Doune Castle
Loch Level Castle
St Andrews Castle
Aberdour Castle & Garden
Inchcolm Abbey
Inchmahome Priory
Argyll's Lodging
Dirleton Castle & Gardens
Tantallon Castle
Seton Collegiate Church
Newark Castle
Stirling Castle
Rothesay Castle
Edinburgh Castle
Dumbarton Castle
Glasgow Cathedral
Crichton Castle
Smailholm Tower
Bothwell Castle
Dundonald Castle
Craignethan Castle
Cairnpapple Hill
Melrose Abbey
Dryburgh Abbey
Linlithgow Palace
Crossraguel Abbey
Blackness Castle
Jedburgh Abbey & Visitor Centre
Craigmillar Castle
Hermitage Castle
Threave Castle
Cardoness Castle
Sweetheart Abbey
Caerlaverock Castle
Glenluce Abbey
New Abbey Corn Mill
Dundrennan Abbey
MacLellan's Castle

Shetland Islands

Orkney Islands
Brough of Birsay
Broch of Gurness
Skara Brae & Skaill House
Bishop's & Earl's Palaces
Maeshowe Chambered Cairn
Hackness Martello Tower & Battery

Wales

Beaumaris Castle
Conwy Castle
Rhuddlan Castle
Caernarfon Castle
Plas Mawr
Dolwyddelan Castle
Rug Chapel & Llangar Church
Valle Crucis Abbey
Criccieth Castle
Harlech Castle

WALES

Strata Florida Abbey

White Castle
Cilgerran Castle
Tretower Court & Castle
Raglan Castle

Isle of Man

St Davids Bishop's Palace
Carreg Cennen Castle
Peel Castle
House of Mananann
The Grove Museum of Victorian Life
Laxey Wheel & Mines Trail
Laugharne Castle
Tintern Abbey
Niarbyl Restaurant & Visitor Centre
Manx Museum
Rushen Abbey & Abbey Restaurant
Kidwelly Castle
Blaenavon Ironworks
The National Folk Museum
Old House of Keys
Weobley Castle
Oxwich Castle
Caerphilly Castle
Chepstow Castle
Sound Visitor Centre
Castle Rushen
Nautical Museum & Old Grammar School
Castell Coch
Caerleon Roman Fortress

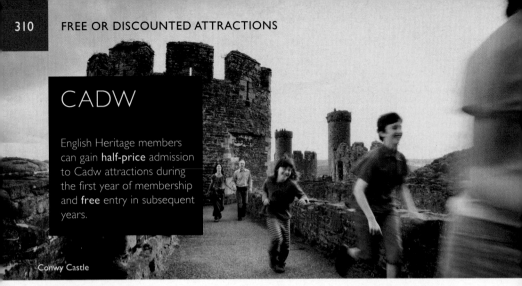

CADW

English Heritage members can gain **half-price** admission to Cadw attractions during the first year of membership and **free** entry in subsequent years.

Conwy Castle

Beaumaris Castle, Anglesey LL58 8AP **T.** 01248 810361

Blaenavon Ironworks, Nr Pontypool, Torfaen NP4 9RN **T.** 01495 792615

Caerleon Roman Fortress, Caerleon, Newport NP18 1AE **T.** 01633 422518

Caernarfon Castle, Caernarfon, Gwynedd LL55 2AY **T.** 01286 677617

Caerphilly Castle, Caerphilly CF83 1JD **T.** 029 2088 3143

Carreg Cennen Castle, Nr Trapp, Carmarthenshire SA19 6TS **T.** 01558 822291

Castell Coch, Cardiff CF15 7JS **T.** 029 2081 0101

Chepstow Castle, Chepstow, Monmouthshire NP16 5EY **T.** 01291 624065

Cilgerran Castle, Nr Cardigan, Pembrokeshire SA43 2SF **T.** 01239 621339

Conwy Castle, Conwy LL32 8AY **T.** 01492 592358

Criccieth Castle, Criccieth, Gwynedd LL52 0DP **T.** 01766 522227

Denbigh Castle, Denbigh LL16 3NB **T.** 01745 813385

Dolwyddelan Castle, Dolwyddelan, Gwynedd LL25 0JD **T.** 01690 750366

Harlech Castle, Harlech, Gwynedd LL46 2YH **T.** 01766 780552

Kidwelly Castle, Kidwelly, Carmarthenshire SA17 5BQ **T.** 01554 890104

Lamphey Bishop's Palace, Lamphey, Pembroke SA71 5NT **T.** 01646 672224

Laugharne Castle, Laugharne, Carmarthenshire SA33 4SA **T.** 01994 427906

Margam Stones Museum, Margam, Port Talbot SA13 2TA **T.** 01639 871184

Oxwich Castle, Oxwich, Swansea SA3 1ND **T.** 01792 390359

Plas Mawr, Conwy LL32 8DE **T.** 01492 580167

Raglan Castle, Raglan, Monmouthshire NP15 2BT **T.** 01291 690228

Rhuddlan Castle, Rhuddlan, Denbighshire LL18 5AD **T.** 01745 590777

Rug Chapel and Llangar Church, Corwen, Denbighshire LL21 9BT **T.** 01490 412025

St Davids Bishop's Palace, St Davids, Pembrokeshire SA62 6PE **T.** 01437 720517

Strata Florida Abbey, Pontrhydfendigaid, Ceredigion SY25 6ES **T.** 01974 831261

Tintern Abbey, Tintern, Monmouthshire NP16 6SE **T.** 01291 689251

Tretower Court and Castle, Tretower, Powys NP8 1RD **T.** 01874 730279

Valle Crucis Abbey, Nr Llangollen, Denbighshire LL20 8DD **T.** 01978 860326

Weobley Castle, Nr Llanrhidian, Swansea SA3 1HB **T.** 01792 390012

White Castle, Nr Abergavenny, Monmouthshire NP7 8UD **T.** 01600 780380

PLAS CAREW Unit 5/7 Cefn Coed, Parc Nantgarw, Cardiff CF15 7QQ **T.** 01443 336000 **W.** www.cadw.wales.gov.uk

MANX NATIONAL HERITAGE

Rushen Abbey

English Heritage members can gain **half-price** admission to Manx National Heritage attractions during the first year of membership and **free** entry in subsequent years.

Members must present a valid membership card on admission (Manx National Heritage permit free admission to the member only and children aged 4 years and under). Admission charges apply for special events. Travel connections between the Isle of Man's heritage sites are available through the Victorian Steam Railway, Manx Electric Railway, Horse Tram and Bus Vannin. **To book travel visit www.visitisleofman.com**

ISLE OF MAN

Castle Rushen – Castletown

The National Folk Museum – Cregneash

The Grove – Museum of Victorian Life – Ramsey

House of Manannan – Peel

Laxey Wheel and Mines Trail – Laxey

Manx Museum – Douglas

Nautical Museum – Castletown

Niarbyl Restaurant & Visitor Centre – Dalby

Old Grammar School – Castletown

Old House of Keys – Castletown

Peel Castle – Peel

Rushen Abbey & Abbey Restaurant – Ballasalla

The Sound Café and Visitor Centre – near Cregneash

Portcullis at Castle Rushen

Laxey Wheel

All images © Manx National Heritage

MANX NATIONAL HERITAGE Kingswood Grove, Douglas, Isle of Man IM1 3LY
T. 01624 648000 **W.** www.manxnationalheritage.im

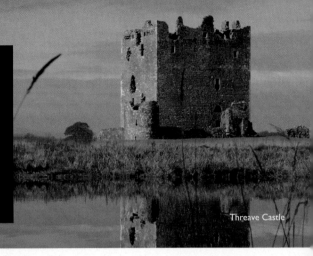

HISTORIC SCOTLAND

English Heritage members can gain **half-price** admission to Historic Scotland attractions during the first year of membership and **free** entry in subsequent years.

Threave Castle

Aberdour Castle and Garden, Aberdour, Fife **T.** 01383 860519

Arbroath Abbey, Angus **T.** 01241 878756

Argyll's Lodging, Stirling **T.** 01786 450000

Balvenie Castle, Dufftown, Grampian **T.** 01340 820121

Bishop's and Earl's Palaces, Kirkwall, Orkney **T.** 01856 871918

The Black House, Arnol, Lewis, Western Isles **T.** 01851 710395

Blackness Castle, Firth of Forth, Edinburgh and Lothians **T.** 01506 834807

Bonawe Historic Iron Furnace, Taynuilt, Argyll **T.** 01866 822432

Bothwell Castle, Bothwell, Greater Glasgow **T.** 01698 816894

Broch of Gurness, Aikerness, Orkney **T.** 01856 751414

Brough of Birsay, NW of Kirkwall, Orkney **T.** 01856 841815

Caerlaverock Castle, Nr Dumfries, Dumfries and Galloway **T.** 01387 770244

Cairnpapple Hill, Torphichen, Edinburgh and Lothians **T.** 01506 634622

Cardoness Castle, Nr Gatehouse of Fleet, Dumfries and Galloway **T.** 01557 814427

Castle Campbell and Gardens, Dollar Glen **T.** 01259 742408

Corgarff Castle, Nr Strathdon, Grampian **T.** 01975 651460

Craigmillar Castle, Edinburgh and Lothians **T.** 0131 661 4445

Craignethan Castle, Lanark, Greater Glasgow **T.** 01555 860364

Crichton Castle, Nr Pathhead, Edinburgh and Lothians **T.** 01875 320017

Crossraguel Abbey, Nr Maybole, Greater Glasgow **T.** 01655 883113

Dallas Dhu Historic Distillery, Nr Forres, Grampian **T.** 01309 676548

Dirleton Castle and Gardens, Dirleton, East Lothian **T.** 01620 850330

Doune Castle, Doune **T.** 01786 841742

Dryburgh Abbey, Nr Melrose, Borders **T.** 01835 822381

Duff House, Banff, Grampian **T.** 01261 818181

Dumbarton Castle, Dumbarton, Greater Glasgow **T.** 01389 732167

Dunblane Cathedral, Dunblane **T.** 01786 823 388

Dundonald Castle, Dundonald, Greater Glasgow **T.** 01563 851489

Dundrennan Abbey, Nr Kirkcudbright, Dumfries and Galloway **T.** 01557 500262

Dunfermline Abbey and Palace, Dunfermline, Fife **T.** 01383 739026

Dunstaffnage Castle, Nr Oban, Argyll **T.** 01631 562465

Edinburgh Castle, Edinburgh and Lothians **T.** 0131 225 9846

Edzell Castle and Garden, Edzell, Angus **T.** 01356 648631

Elcho Castle, Nr Bridge of Earn, Perthshire **T.** 01738 639998

Elgin Cathedral, Elgin, Highlands **T.** 01343 547171

Fort George, Nr Ardersier village, Highlands **T.** 01667 460232

Glasgow Cathedral, Glasgow **T.** 0141 552 6891

Glenluce Abbey, Nr Glenluce, Dumfries and Galloway **T.** 01581 300541

Hackness Martello Tower and Battery, Hoy, Orkney **T.** 01856 701727

Hermitage Castle, Nr Newcastleton, Borders **T.** 01387 376222

Huntingtower Castle, Nr Perth, Perthshire **T.** 01738 627231

Huntly Castle, Huntly, Grampian **T.** 01466 793191

Inchcolm Abbey, Firth of Forth, Fife **T.** 01383 823332

Inchmahome Priory, Lake of Menteith, Central **T.** 01877 385294

Iona Abbey and Nunnery, Island of Iona, Argyll **T.** 01681 700512

Jarlshof Prehistoric and Norse Settlement, Sumburgh Head, Shetland **T.** 01950 460112

Jedburgh Abbey and Visitor Centre, Jedburgh, Borders **T.** 01835 863925

Kildrummy Castle, Nr Alford, Grampian **T.** 01975 571331

Kisimul Castle, Isle of Barra, Western Isles **T.** 01871 810313

Linlithgow Palace, Linlithgow, West Lothian **T.** 01506 842896

Lochleven Castle, Lochleven, Perthshire **T.** 01577 862670

MacLellan's Castle, Kirkcudbright, Dumfries and Galloway **T.** 01557 331856

Maeshowe Chambered Cairn, Nr Kirkwall, Orkney **T.** 01856 761606

Meigle Sculptured Stone Museum, Meigle, Angus **T.** 01828 640612

Melrose Abbey, Melrose, Borders **T.** 01896 822562

New Abbey Corn Mill, New Abbey, Dumfries and Galloway **T.** 01387 850260

Newark Castle, Port Glasgow, Greater Glasgow **T.** 01475 741858

Rothesay Castle, Rothesay, Isle of Bute **T.** 01700 502691

St Andrews Castle, St Andrews, Fife **T.** 01334 477196

St Andrews Cathedral, St Andrews, Fife **T.** 01334 472563

St Serf's Church and Dupplin Cross, Dunning, Perthshire **T.** 01764 684497

St Vigeans Sculptured Stones, Nr Arbroath, Angus **T.** 01241 878756

Seton Collegiate Church, Nr Cockenzie, East Lothian **T.** 01875 813334

Skara Brae and Skaill House, Nr Kirkwall, Orkney **T.** 01856 841815

Smailholm Tower, Near Smailholm, Borders **T.** 01573 460365

Spynie Palace, Nr Elgin, Grampian **T.** 01343 546358

Stanley Mills, North of Perth **T.** 01738 828268

Stirling Castle, Stirling, Central **T.** 01786 450000

Sweetheart Abbey, New Abbey, Dumfries and Galloway **T.** 01387 850397

Tantallon Castle, Nr North Berwick, East Lothian **T.** 01620 892727

Threave Castle, Nr Castle Douglas, Dumfries and Galloway **T.** 07711 223101

Tolquhon Castle, Nr Aberdeen, Grampian **T.** 01651 851286

Urquhart Castle, Drumnadrochit, Highlands **T.** 01456 450551

HISTORIC SCOTLAND
Longmore House, Salisbury Place, Edinburgh EH9 1SH
T. 0131 668 8999
E. hs.members@scotland.gsi. gov.uk
W. www.historic-scotland. gov.uk

IRELAND

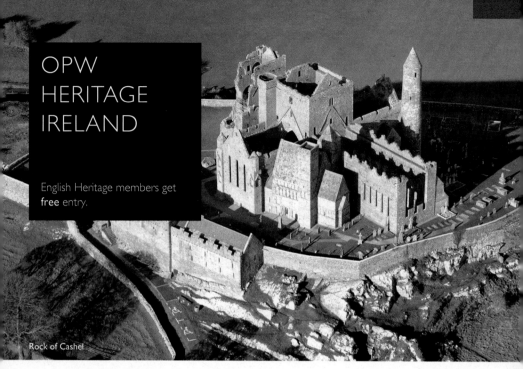

OPW HERITAGE IRELAND

English Heritage members get **free** entry.

Rock of Cashel

The Blasket Centrel,
an Bhlascaoid Mhóir,
Dún Chaoin, Baile an
Fheirtéaraigh, Trá Lí, Co Chiarraí
T. +353 (066) 915 6444/
(066) 915 6371

Ardfert Cathedral, Ardfert,
Tralee, Co Kerry
T. +353 (066) 713 4711

Athenry Castle, Athenry,
Co Galway
T. +353 (091) 844797

Aughnanure Castle,
Oughterard, Co Galway
T. +353 (091) 552214

Battle of the Boyne Visitor
Centre, Oldbridge, Co Meath
T. + 353 (041) 980 9950

Boyle Abbey, Boyle,
Co Roscommon
T. +353 (071) 966 2604

Brú na Bóinne Visitor Centre,
(Newgrange and Knowth),
Donore, Co Meath
T. +353 (041) 988 0300

Cahir Castle, Castle Street,
Cahir, Co Tipperary
T. +353 (52) 7441011

Carrowmore Megalithic
Cemetery, Carrowmore,
Co Sligo
T. +353 (071) 916 1534

Castletown, Celbridge,
Co Kildare
T. +353 (01) 628 8252

Céide Fields, Ballycastle,
Co Mayo
T. +353 (096) 43325

Charles Fort, Summer Cove,
Kinsale, Co Cork
T. +353 (021) 477 2263

Clonmacnoise, Shannonbridge,
Co Offaly
T. +353 (090) 967 4195

Derrynane House, National
Historic Park, Caherdaniel,
Co Kerry
T. +353 (066) 947 5113

Desmond Castle (French
Prison), Cork Street, Kinsale,
Co Cork
T. +353 (021) 477 4855

Donegal Castle, Donegal Town,
Co Donegal
T. +353 (074) 972 2405

Dublin Castle, Dame Street,
Dublin 2 **T.** +353 (01) 645 8813

Dún Aonghasa, Kilmurvey,
Inishmore, Aran Islands,
Co Galway
T. +353 (099) 61008

Left to right: Kilmainham Gaol, Dun Aonghasa, Ilnacullin (Garinish Island), Aughnanure Castle.

Dunmore Cave, Castlecomer
Road, Co Kilkenny
T. +353 (056) 776 7726

Emo Court, Emo, Co Laois
T. +353 (057) 862 6573

Ennis Friary, Abbey Street,
Ennis, Co Clare
T. +353 (065) 682 9100

Farmleigh, Phoenix Park,
Castleknock, Dublin 15
T. +353 (01) 815 5900/815 5981

Ilnacullin (Garinish Island),
Glengarriff, Bantry, Co Cork
T. +353 (027) 63040

Glebe House and Gallery,
Churchill, Letterkenny,
Co Donegal
T. +353 (074) 913 7071

Glendalough Visitor Centre,
Glendalough, Co Wicklow
T. +353 404 45352/25

Hill of Tara, Navan, Co Meath
T./F. +353 (046) 902 5903

JFK Arboretum, New Ross,
Co Wexford
T. +353 (051) 388171

Jerpoint Abbey, Thomastown,
Co Kilkenny
T. +353 (056) 772 4623

Kilkenny Castle, Kilkenny City,
Co Kilkenny
T. +353 (056) 770 4100

Kilmainham Gaol, Inchicore
Road, Kilmainham, Dublin 8
T. +353 (01) 453 5984

Old Mellifont Abbey, Tullyallen,
Drogheda, Co Louth
T. +353 (41) 982 6459

Parke's Castle, Fivemile Bourne,
Co Leitrim
T. +353 (071) 916 4149

Portumna Castle and Gardens,
Portumna, Co Galway
T. +353 (090) 974 1658

Reginald's Tower, The Quay,
Waterford
T./F. +353 (051) 304220

Rock of Cashel, Cashel,
Co Tipperary
T. +353 (062) 61437

Roscrea Heritage (Castle &
Damer House), Roscrea,
Co Tipperary
T. +353 (0505) 21850

Ross Castle, Killarney,
Co Kerry
T. +353 64 6635851

Sligo Abbey, Abbey Street,
Sligo, Co Sligo
T. +353 (071) 914 6406

Swiss Cottage, Kilcommon,
Cahir, Co Tipperary
T. +353 (052) 7441144

Teach an Phiarsaigh (Pearse's
Cottage), Inbhear, Ros Muc,
Co Galway
T. +353 (091) 574292

The Casino, Cherrymount
Crescent, off the Malahide Road,
Marino, Dublin 3
T. +353 (01) 833 1618

Trim Castle, Trim, Co Meath
T. +353 (046) 943 8619

We welcome visitors
from near and far and we
are particularly delighted
to welcome Members of
English Heritage and holders
of the Overseas Visitor
Pass – we look forward
to meeting you.

For more information about
our sites (including those
where admission is free)
please visit our website
www.heritageireland.ie

 Find us on Facebook

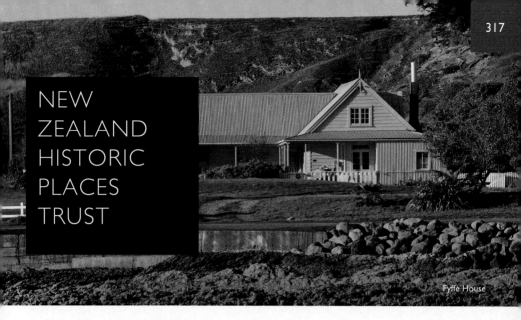

NEW ZEALAND HISTORIC PLACES TRUST

Fyffe House

New Zealand's built heritage may be considered young in world terms, but many of the properties cared for by the New Zealand Historic Places Trust (NZHPT) are physical reminders of the birth and development of this South Pacific nation and its enduring connection to Great Britain. From the Kerikeri Mission Station in Northland, New Zealand's oldest standing building dating from 1821-22, to Hayes Engineering Works in the gold mining region of Central Otago, NZHPT cares for 48 properties and sites where you can learn about the people and places that make New Zealand what it is today.

English Heritage Members get free entry to all our properties (charges may apply for special events and exhibitions).

OUR PROPERTIES RANGE FROM IMPRESSIVE HOMESTEADS, CENTRES OF INDUSTRY AND INNOVATION, BATTLE SITES AND SO MUCH MORE, INCLUDING:

Old St Paul's (Wellington) – where stunning stained glass windows help illuminate the glorious native timber interior of this 19th century Gothic Revival church, a home away from home for US servicemen during the Second World War.

The Kerikeri Mission Station and Stone Store (Northland) – the Mission Station is New Zealand's oldest standing building, built in 1821-22, while the nearby Stone Store is one of the country's most photographed buildings.

Fyffe House (Kaikoura) – where a whale of a time is guaranteed, the property built as part of the early whaling industry and partly on whale vertebrae foundations.

Alberton and Highwic (Auckland) – impressive dwellings that were home to two prominent colonial businessmen.

Totara Estate (South Canterbury) – British dinner tables have featured our finest cuts of meat over many years, and Totara Estate is where New Zealand's billion dollar frozen meat industry began.

More information on heritage sites to visit can be found on the NZHPT's website www.historicplaces.org.nz. Our staff look forward to welcoming you.

Left to right: Long Crichel, Dorset, where we repaired the tower in 2012 and Strachan glass at Brownshill (photos by Matthew Saunders).

THE FRIENDS OF FRIENDLESS CHURCHES

The Friends own redundant but beautiful places of worship that would otherwise have been demolished or left to ruin.

In the last two years we have taken a record number of new churches into care. One of them, the small Catholic chapel at Brownshill, Glos, contains the striking glass by Douglas Strachan, shown top right. We have just finished a major conservation campaign at the chapel of St John the Baptist, at Matlock Bath, Derbs by Guy Dawber, helped by a very generous EH grant.

We are a small, voluntary organisation that works in partnership, sharing an office and staff with the Ancient Monuments Society, a statutory consultee on listed building consent in England and Wales.

We warmly welcome visitors to our churches, but do not claim sophistication in terms of parking, toilets, attendants or shops, and access may require approach to a key-holder. Our churches are places for quiet study and contemplation, preserved for posterity as beautiful historic buildings.

FRIENDS
OF
FRIENDLESS
CHURCHES

St Ann's Vestry Hall, 2 Church Entry, London EC4V 5HB
T. 020 7236 3934 E. office@friendsoffriendlesschurches.org.uk
www.friendsoffriendlesschurches.org.uk Registered charity no: 1113097

Left to right: Walpole Old Chapel, Nr Halesworth, Suffolk; Wallasey Memorial Unitarian Church, Liscard Village, Wallasey, Merseyside; and Petre Chapel, Thorndon Park, near Brentwood, Essex.

HISTORIC CHAPELS TRUST

An Important Story of Dissent and Faith.

The Historic Chapels Trust rescues non-Anglican places of worship in England that are no longer in use by their congregations. We aim to hand them onto future generations in good condition, as the physical record of religious life and a vital strand of our history.

Since 1993 we have rescued a remarkable collection of Non-conformist chapels, meeting houses and Catholic churches. Together, they are the evidence of a remarkable story of dissent from the Established Church and of self-determination and autonomy by people of faith, courage and social vision.

VISIT OUR CHAPELS AND CHURCHES

All our sites are Listed Grade II* or Grade I. Some are important for their architecture, some as rare survivals, some for their history, some for what the architectural historian John Summerson described as 'endearing simplicity'. All of them are worth visiting.

To visit our chapels and churches please arrange a time with our local keyholders at the site first. Details of how to find the buildings and our keyholders are on our website.

EVENTS IN OUR CHAPELS

Many of our chapels can be hired for concerts or other events. Some provide interesting venues for marriages or commemorative events. If you are interested in using one of our buildings look for details on our website.

Historic Chapels Trust gratefully acknowledges financial support from English Heritage.

St George's German Lutheran Church, 55 Alie Street, London E1 8EB
T. 020 7481 0533 E. chapels@hct.org.uk www.hct.org.uk
UK Registered charity No 1017321

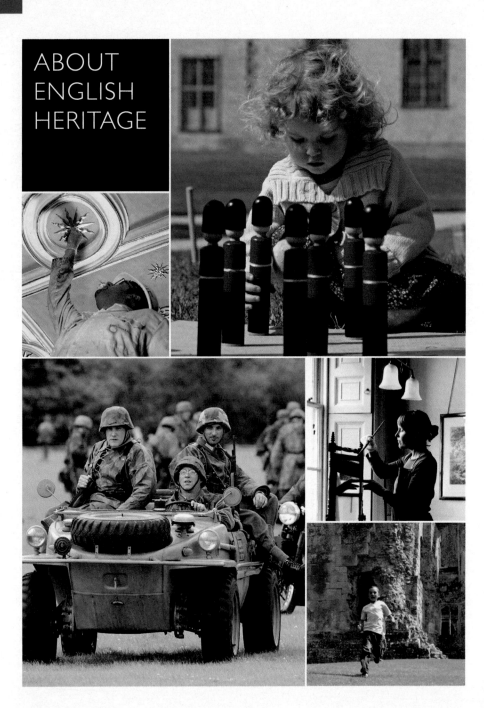

ABOUT
ENGLISH
HERITAGE

ENGLISH HERITAGE IS UNIQUE

We are the government's statutory adviser on the historic environment, but we are also a Members' organisation. This means our funding comes in part from the Department for Culture, Media & Sport (DCMS) and partly from memberships, donations and fundraising. Our remit is broad. We advise on what should be protected; we offer grants; provide training, education and information; we maintain the national archive and, crucially, we look after more than 400 sites – all of which are free to visit for all our Members and their families. We are a non-profit organisation, so every penny of your membership goes towards maintaining the properties in our care. As we move towards becoming an independent charity from 2015, the support we receive from you, our Members, supporters, donors and volunteers, becomes more important than ever.

We are overseen by a Commission of up to 17 Commissioners appointed by the Secretary of State. Day to day management is delegated to our Chief Executive, Dr Simon Thurley,

supported by an Executive Board comprising the Executive Directors of English Heritage's four operational groups.

HERITAGE GIVES US A SENSE OF BELONGING

The built environment has shaped our history and touches all of us – every day. We are convinced that our lives would be so much poorer if we allowed our heritage to ebb away on a tide of indifference. From stately homes to princely castles and from industrial buildings to modest terraced houses, shops and offices, our heritage belongs to us all, and we all have a responsibility to preserve and care for it for future generations to enjoy. We also know that England's historic environment is paramount to our tourist industry, contributing hugely to the country's prosperity.

DESIGNATION

Where possible we want to see historic buildings come to life, rather than being preserved as museum pieces. We also wish to ensure that any changes to buildings are in keeping with their historic roots. To this end, we work with local authorities on designating listed buildings. Most listed buildings date from before 1840, but we also designate some later buildings. There are three grades of listing: Grade I, Grade II* and Grade II.

We also designate monuments and landscapes, and help local authorities in establishing Conservation Areas. For more information on listing, visit **www.english-heritage.org.uk/listing**

Battlefields are important sources of archaeological and historic interest, and over 40 are on our Register of Historic Battlefields. We also oversee a similar Register of Parks and Gardens. Visit **www.english-heritage.org.uk/conservation**

OUR PARTNERSHIP WITH MEMBERS
We are determined to work closely with our members, and firmly believe we should join together to protect our nation's heritage. Please contact us on 0870 333 1182 or **members@english-heritage.org.uk** at any time if you have any comments or need our assistance. We endeavour to answer calls within 15 seconds, emails and letters within five working days, and will always protect your personal information.

INTERPRETATION
How we show our properties and the information we provide to visitors is essential. We use the latest technology to enhance your visit, but we do not want our properties only to be discovered through the prism of multi-media presentations. A large number of our sites now have audio guides and our new web resource, Portico, provides more comprehensive and scholarly information on properties curated by English Heritage. And our guidebooks, written by experts in their field, are renowned for their motivating content and illustration.

VOLUNTEERING
We welcome volunteers who are keen to share their passion and interest in the historic environment with others. Activities include room stewarding, gardening, curatorial cleaning and assisting with our education programme at selected properties. Find out more about this rewarding work by visiting **www.english-heritage.org.uk/volunteering**

OUR WIDER WORK
Supporting the heritage sector sits at the heart of everything we do, and our broad remit encompasses a range of initiatives connected to this.

We are responsible for the **blue plaques** scheme in London. To find out more, visit **www.english-heritage.org.uk/blueplaques**

English Heritage gives **grants** to individuals, local authorities and voluntary organisations to help conserve and enhance England's historic environment. These are targeted where there is greatest risk of loss of historic significance, as identified in our Heritage at Risk Register. We also advise the Heritage Lottery Fund. To find out more, visit **www.english-heritage.org.uk/grants**

We are the national archaeology service for England and we implement the statutory protection of England's 19,750 Scheduled Monuments. Visit **www.english-heritage.org.uk/archaeology**. We are also responsible for all **English maritime archaeological** sites up to 12 nautical miles off-shore. The seas and shores around England contain an immense wealth of important shipwreck sites – some of which are protected as they help contribute significantly to our understanding of the past. English Heritage administers a licensing scheme which enables free access to these sites for divers to enjoy and investigate. Designated Wrecks range from Bronze Age cargoes to early submarines. We advise the government on installations and extraction works at sea, which potentially can damage maritime archaeology.

Our **Research and Training** programmes increase understanding of the historic environment and help us guide its management in an informed and sustainable way. The pressures on capacity and skills are intense. We are working to address skills shortages within the traditional crafts and built heritage sector, to ensure there is a continuing source of craftspeople to care for England's half a million listed buildings.

As part of our **statutory remit**, we advise local authorities and owners on proposals to change historic sites, ensuring the impact on historic significance is managed constructively. To find out more, visit **www.english-heritage.org.uk/your-property/planning-advice**

Another key responsibility is to develop robust **policies** to protect and promote the historic environment. We publish the evidence to support these policies annually as Heritage Counts (**www.heritagecounts.org.uk**). We also work closely with **UNESCO**, advising on the designation and management of World Heritage Sites in England.

Then: 1891   Now: 2012

ENGLISH HERITAGE ARCHIVE

Discover the buildings, the places and the parts they played in the story of England with our free online archive. Search over one million historical photographs and documents, helping you paint a picture of where your ancestors lived, worked and played.

Bring local history to life, visit **www.englishheritagearchives.org.uk**

If you can't find what you're looking for online, you can either call, write or visit us. We want everyone to make the most of our collections. Contact us at:

Archive Services, The Engine House, Fire Fly Avenue, Swindon SN2 2EH
Tel: 01793 414600 Fax: 01793 414606
Email: **archive@english-heritage.org.uk**

If you share our passion for England's historic environment and want to help us make the past part of our future, view our current vacancies or register for our job alerts at **www.english-heritage.org.uk/jobs**

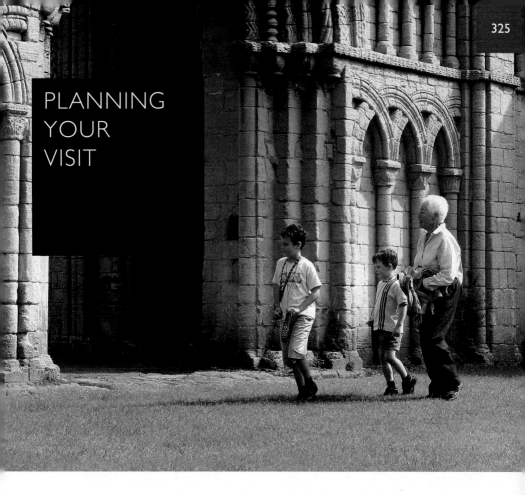

PLANNING YOUR VISIT

We want you to enjoy every moment of your visit. The following section contains important information about planning your visit, so please read it carefully. If you have any questions or need any further help, do not hesitate to call us on 0870 333 1181.

ADMISSIONS

Admission charges apply to non-members, and prices are given in this handbook as follows: Adult; Concession (senior citizens, jobseekers and students with relevant ID); Child (age 5-15, under 5s go free). Where available, Family tickets normally admit two adults and three children (may vary at properties not managed by us).

For groups of 11 or more visitors paying together, discounts of 15% (10% at Stonehenge) are available. We recommend that groups book in advance. Call 0870 333 1181 for a copy of our Group Visits Guide.

If you are a visitor from overseas and are planning to visit a number of properties, an **Overseas Visitors Pass** (OVP) may make financial sense. As well as other benefits, this allows unlimited free access to all English Heritage properties marked with the OVP symbol over a 9- or 16-day period. Call 0870 333 1181 or visit **www.english-heritage.org.uk/ovp**

CAR PARKING

There is free parking at most of our properties. In cases where parking charges apply, you will often be reimbursed on admission (exceptions apply. See individual property listings). Any revenue raised from car parking will be re-invested back into our properties. Disabled parking is available at many of our sites.

CATERING AND PICNICS

Many of our properties offer delicious home-made food and drink. Visitors are welcome to picnic in the grounds of most of our properties.

DOGS

Dogs on leads usually are welcome but please see individual property listings. No restrictions on assistance dogs.

EDUCATIONAL VISITS

There is nothing more inspiring or educational than visiting an English Heritage property. We believe that experiencing the local historic environment should be central to the national curriculum of every school in England. We actively encourage groups for this purpose, offering free self-led educational visits to over 400 historic sites in England, supporting the national curriculum across a range of subjects and all key stages. We also provide a wide range of free online teaching resources, and downloadable hazard information sheets for each of our sites. Book your school visit now and let us help bring the past to life **www.english-heritage.org.uk/education**

FAMILIES AND CHILDREN

Many of our properties are fascinating for children. We put on special exhibitions catering for children's needs, and at well over 50 properties we offer free activity sheets, back-packs, book boxes and Very Big Books. Our interactive Discovery Centres will keep younger visitors absorbed for hours. Please note that you will be responsible for the safety and supervision of your children at all times at our sites, so please ensure a sensible ratio of adults to children.

GUIDES AND TOURS

Guidebooks and audio tours help bring sites to life at more and more of our properties. We also provide audio-guides for children and people with learning difficulties, as well as in different languages. Specialist tours are available at certain sites for pre-booked groups of 11 or more. Many of our properties have dedicated guidebooks – including 50 or so in the 'Red Guide' series with their distinctive red spines. Written by leading experts, these feature a tour of the site together with a more in-depth history of the people who lived and worked there. Packed with plans, reconstruction drawings, eyewitness accounts and beautiful photography, they make essential reading as well as brilliant souvenirs of your visit. Short histories and descriptions of our free sites are also available online.

PHOTOGRAPHY

Taking pictures is not permitted in some properties, due to the sensitive nature of some materials. Non-commercial photography is welcome in the gardens and grounds of all our sites.

SAFETY AND SMOKING

Due to their historic nature, some of our sites have potentially hazardous features – please pay attention to all safety notices on site. If you have any doubts, our staff can always advise on safety issues. Please wear suitable footwear to avoid accidents, and do not climb on walls or monuments. In areas of woodland deer pasture there may be a slight risk of ticks, so keep vulnerable parts of your body covered and/or use insect repellent. Note that smoking is not permitted inside any of our properties.

TRAVEL AND TRANSPORT

Where possible in the property listings, we have provided public transport information, which has kindly been supplied by the Confederation of Passenger Transport (**cpt-uk.org**). These details were correct at time of going to press. For cycle routes, call 0845 113 0065 or visit sustrans.org.uk. OS LandRanger/Explorer map references have also been supplied for each property. A free Sat Nav download of our properties is available at **www.english-heritage.org.uk/satnav**

ACCESS

We want as many people as possible to enjoy a day out with English Heritage. The handbook listings indicate areas of properties accessible to disabled visitors and visitors with babies and younger children – with the use of the ♿ symbol. Remember that if you are disabled your carer is always admitted free, and many of our sites have parking spaces for the disabled.

For more detailed information, our free *Access Guide* offers an up-to-date and honest assessment about which properties and gardens are most suited to families and disabled people. There's information about parking and drop-off points, and about properties that have special features such as scented gardens or tactile objects for those with impaired sight.

For your free copy, call **0870 333 1181**, minicom **0800 015 0516**, or email customers@english-heritage.org.uk You can also download it from our website.

BOOKS & GIFTS

Complete your visit with a look in one of our on-site shops, where you'll find a huge range of fascinating books and unique gifts.

HOW TO ORDER

If you can't visit one of our properties, you can still see our range at our online shop, **www.english-heritageshop.org.uk** or call **01761 452 966**.

Products sold are subject to availability.

THANK YOU FOR YOUR SUPPORT

I Stonehenge visitor centre

English Heritage donors, members and volunteers make a significant difference to the work we do. The government funding English Heritage receives only goes some way towards the ongoing conservation of the properties in our care. In order to undertake our most significant projects – those which help us to tell England's story and make it more accessible to everybody – we rely on donations, gifts in wills and the support of volunteers.

Last year donations to English Heritage and the English Heritage Foundation, the charity which supports our properties and collections, made a huge difference to sites across the country.

The generosity of our donors meant that last year we were able to open the new **Stonehenge visitor centre** (1), providing exhibition spaces that will significantly improve public understanding of one of England's most recognisable but little understood landmarks. We were also able to complete the comprehensive conservation of the Grade I listed **Kenwood** (2) returning it to its former splendour and making it engaging and accessible for a much larger audience.

This year we will rely on donations to make other ambitious projects possible, including at the **Swiss Cottage** (3 & 4) – the retreat of the Victorian royal children at **Osborne**. We will bring it back to life by securing the buildings; re-displaying the collections; introducing a new

exhibition and better telling the stories of this little known part of history.

Without donations these projects simply would not happen. Please consider making a donation today and help to secure the sites which tell the story of England for future generations.

To find out more about the difference you can make, please contact the Fundraising Team at foundation@english-heritage. org.uk; visit **www.english-heritage.org.uk/supportus**; or call Customer Services on 0870 333 1181

The English Heritage Foundation is a registered charity, no. 1140351

EVENTS THAT BRING HISTORY TO LIFE

From family fun days and fighting knights to spectacular battle displays and exclusive Members' events, you'll find something for everyone to enjoy in our events calendar. In fact, we have the largest historical events programme in Europe, so you'll have hundreds of activities to choose from throughout the year.

HISTORY LIVE!

An action-packed weekend for the whole family to enjoy. Our showpiece event returns to Kelmarsh Hall, Northamptonshire on 19-20 July. Bringing the story of England to life, History Live! spans 2000 years of history and features over 50 shows each day. Special reduced rates for Members.

BIG SPECTACULAR EVENTS

If you enjoy huge historical re-enactments, then our 'tour de force' events could be just for you. St George's Day Festival, Wrest Park, 26-27 April; Second World War Weekend, Dover Castle, 24-26 May.

CASTLE SLEEPOVERS

A unique and special experience for children and adults alike! After enjoying a warming drink and enchanting supper, take part in games and activities before bedding down for the night in one of our castles. Check your Members' Magazine or our website for details.

PERFORMING ARTS

We've got a great variety of music and theatre events throughout the year – both indoors and out.

EXCLUSIVE MEMBERS' EVENTS

Go behind the scenes, learn a new skill and discover the secrets concealed by some of the most intriguing properties in England. We hold over 100 events throughout the year, which are available exclusively to Members. See your Members' Magazine for details.

SIGN UP FOR EVENTS UPDATES

Get regular updates of news and events direct to your inbox. Simply visit **www. english-heritage.org.uk/newsletter** to register. Alternatively, keep up to date with our events programme at **www. english-heritage.org.uk/events** or check the latest copy of your Members' Magazine.

STAY WITH US

Comfort. Atmosphere. A unique setting. Value for money. Then, add in direct access to some of the finest historic properties in Britain – and you end up with a compelling argument for staying at an English Heritage holiday cottage.

English Heritage offers 16 such cottages, available for rent at any time of the year. All have been given a stylish, contemporary 5-star makeover, all are equipped with the latest mod-cons and all are situated within, or with access to, the grounds of an English Heritage site. Choose from castles, abbeys and stately homes; when the crowds disperse and the car park is empty, you are left on your own to explore, allowing your imagination to wander where it pleases.

Not only do you have exclusive access to the property where you are staying: during your stay we will also give you free entry to all other English Heritage properties, discounts at our shops and cafés and complimentary tickets to most English Heritage events.

Choose between 13th-century towers and four-bedroom family homes, private gardens and roof terraces, beaches and woodland walks. Pick from three, four or seven night stays. Prices from £522 per week.

STAY WITH US, EAT WITH US, SHOP WITH US, EXPLORE WITH US.

BOOK NOW.

MAKE HISTORY
ON YOUR
HOLIDAY.

SOUTH EAST

BATTLE ABBEY South Lodge

CARISBROOKE CASTLE
The Bowling Green Apartment

DOVER CASTLE
The Sergeant Major's House and
Peverell's Tower

OSBORNE Pavilion Cottage

WALMER CASTLE
The Garden Cottage and The Greenhouse
Apartment

SOUTH WEST

PENDENNIS CASTLE
The Custodian's House and Callie's Cottage

ST MAWES CASTLE Fort House

EAST OF ENGLAND

AUDLEY END HOUSE Cambridge Lodge

EAST MIDLANDS

HARDWICK OLD HALL East Lodge

KIRBY HALL Peacock Cottage

WEST MIDLANDS

WITLEY COURT Pool House Cottage

YORKSHIRE

MOUNT GRACE PRIORY Prior's Lodge

RIEVAULX ABBEY Refectory Cottage

For a brochure or to make a booking
www.english-heritage.org.uk/
holidaycottages or call 0870 333 1187

SOUTH WEST

Bristol
Cornwall
Devon
Dorset
Gloucestershire
Isles of Scilly
Somerset
Wiltshire

🏰 English Heritage Sites
▲ Discounted Attractions
🛐 The Churches Conservation Trust

Isles of Scilly

King Charles's Castle
Cromwell's Castle
Old Blockhouse
Bant's Carn Burial Chamber & Halangy Down Ancient Village
Innisidgen Burial Chambers
Garrison Walls
Harry's Walls
Porth Hellick Down Burial Chamber

Cardigan
Cilgerran Castle ▲
Newcastle Emlyn
Fishguard
Newport (Pembs.)
Haverfordwest
Laugharne Castle ▲
St. Clears
Carmarthen
Carreg Cennen Castle ▲
Llandeilo
Llandovery
Kidwelly
Kidwelly Castle ▲
Pont Abraham
Milford Haven
Kilgetty
Saundersfoot
Pembroke
Tenby
Llanelli
Llandarcy
Carmarthen Bay
Weobley Castle ▲
Rhossili
Oxwich Castle ▲
Port Talbot
The Mumbles

Lundy Island
Hartland Point
Ilfracombe
Combe Martin
Lynton
Lynmouth
Woolacombe
Croyde
Braunton
Barnstaple
Bideford
South Molton
Great Torrington
Bude
Holsworthy
Hatherleigh
DEVON
Okehampton
Lydford Castle & Saxon Town
Okehampton Castle
Penhallam Manor
Grimspound
Tintagel Castle
Boscastle
Hound Tor Deserted Medieval Village
Launceston Castle
Launceston
The Arthurian Centre
Tintagel
Camelford
CORNWALL
Hurlers Stone Circles
Merrivale Prehistoric Settlement
Tavistock
Ashburton
Padstow
Wadebridge
King Doniert's Stone
Dupath Well
Upper Plym Valley
St Breock Downs Monolith
Trethevy Quoit
Bodmin
Liskeard
Restormel Castle
Totnes Castle
Totnes
Newquay
Ivybridge
PLYMOUTH
Perranporth
Wheal Martyn ▲
Eden Project ▲
Royal Citadel
Modbury
St Austell
Fowey
Looe
Talland Bay
Truro
St Catherine's Castle
Kingsbridge
St Ives
Redruth
St Mawes Castle
Salcombe
Chysauster Ancient Village
Falmouth
St. Mawes
Start Point
Ballowall Barrow
St Just
Penzance
Helston
National Maritime Museum Cornwall
Carn Euny Ancient Village
Pendennis Castle
Tregiffian Burial Chamber
Land's End
Halliggye Fogou
Lizard
Lizard Point

Llanwrtyd Wells
Hay-on-Wye
Queenswood
HEREFORDSHIRE
Arthur's Stone
Rotherwas Chapel
Hereford
Great Malvern
Pershore
Evesham
Broadway
M40
Banbury

Brecon
Longtown Castle
St Mary's Church Kempley
Ledbury
Upton-upon-Severn
Eastnor Castle
Tewkesbury
Belas Knap Long Barrow
Hailes Abbey
Winchcombe
Moreton-in-Marsh
Deddington Castle

Tretower Court & Castle
Tretower
Crickhowell
Church of St John the Baptist
St Michael's Church
Ross-on-Wye
Newent
Odda's Chapel
Over Bridge
CHELTENHAM
Sudeley Castle
Stow-on-the-Wold
Woodstock
Rollright Stones
Chipping Norton

Pen-y-Cae
Pont Nedd Fechan
Merthyr Tydfil
Abergavenny
White Castle
Monmouth
Goodrich Castle
St Nicholas Church
GLOUCESTER
Great Witcombe Roman Villa
Northleach
Minster Lovell Hall & Dovecote
North Leigh Roman Villa

Aberdare
Blaenavon Ironworks
Blaenafon
Raglan Castle
Coleford
Blackfriars & Greyfriars
Burford
Witney
North Hinksey Conduit House

Caerphilly Castle
Caerphilly
Tintern Abbey
Offa's Dyke
Nympsfield Long Barrow
Stroud
GLOUCESTERSHIRE
Cirencester Amphitheatre
Lechlade
Abingdon County Hall Museum

Pontypridd
Castell Coch
Caerleon
Chepstow
Kingswood Abbey Gatehouse
Windmill Tump Long Barrow
Faringdon
OXFORDSHIRE
Wantage

Castell Coch
Caerleon Roman Fortress
Magor
Chepstow Castle
Uley Long Barrow (Hetty Pegler's Tump)
Tetbury
Malmesbury
English Heritage Archive
SWINDON
Wayland's Smithy
Uffington Castle, White Horse

Bridgend
Porthcawl
Penarth
Avonmouth
Church of St Thomas the Martyr
S.GLOUCESTERSHIRE
Chipping Sodbury
Avebury Stone Circles & Alexander Keiller Museum
STEAM-Museum of the Great Western Railway
St Thomas' Church

Barry
Barry Island
BRISTOL
Temple Church
Sir Bevil Grenville's Monument
Chippenham
Windmill Hill
Avebury
Silbury Hill
Marlborough
Donnington Castle
Newbury
Hungerford

WESTON-SUPER-MARE
N SOMERSET
Bristol Channel
Bath Abbey
The American Museum
BATH
West Kennet Avenue & Long Barrow
Bradford-on-Avon Tithe Barn
Devizes
The Sanctuary
Chisbury Chapel

Stanton Drew Circles & Cove
Stoney Littleton Long Barrow
BATH & N.E. SOMERSET
Trowbridge
Hatfield Earthworks (Marden Henge)

Burnham-on-Sea
Cheddar
Farleigh Hungerford Castle
Westbury
Wiltshire Museum
Ludgershall Castle & Cross

Yarn Market & Butter Cross
Minehead
Cleeve Abbey
Wells
Nunney Castle
WILTSHIRE
Bratton Camp & White Horse
Netheravon Dovecote
Woodhenge
HAMPSHIRE

Gallox Bridge
St Martin of Tours
Bridgwater
Meare Fish House
Glastonbury Tribunal
Glastonbury
Warminster
Mere
St Andrew's Church
Stonehenge
Amesbury
Flowerdown Barrows

SOMERSET
Taunton
Wellington
All Saints' Church
Muchelney Abbey
Fleet Air Arm Museum
Sherborne Old Castle
Old Wardour Castle
Old Church St Mary's
Old Sarum
Salisbury
Stockbridge
Winchester
Wolvesey Castle
EASTLEIGH

Bampton
Church of St Mary the Virgin Working Wool Museum
Coldharbour Mill
Ilminster
Ilchester
Sherborne
Podimore
Yeovil
Old Castle
Shaftesbury
Salisbury & South Wilts Museum
Salisbury Cathedral & Magna Carta
Fordingbridge
Romsey
SOUTHAMPTON
Medieval Merchant's House
M27

Tiverton
Chard
Sherborne Castle
Fiddleford Manor
Knowlton Church & Earthworks
Lyndhurst
Netley Abbey

Crediton
Honiton
Blandford Forum
DORSET
Wimborne Minster
Ringwood
Christchurch Castle & Norman House
Lymington
Calshot Castle
Cowes

St Martin's Church
Otery St Mary
Axminster
Winterbourne Poor Lot Barrows
Bridport
The Nine Stones
Maiden Castle
Dorset County Museum
Dorchester
POOLE
Christchurch
Hurst Castle
Yarmouth Castle

EXETER
Blackbury Camp
Seaton
Lyme Regis
Kingston Russell Stone Circle
Abbotsbury
Whitcombe Church
Wareham
BOURNEMOUTH
Yarmouth
Carisbrooke Castle

Powderham Castle
Sidmouth
Budleigh Salterton
Exmouth
St Catherine's Chapel
Abbotsbury Abbey Remains
Jordan Hill Roman Temple
Weymouth
Lulworth Castle & Park
Swanage
ISLE OF WIGHT
St Catherine's Oratory

Newton Abbot
Dawlish
Teignmouth
Bill of Portland
Portland Castle
St George's Church

Berry Pomeroy Castle
Kents Cavern Prehistoric Caves
TORQUAY
Kirkham House
Brixham
Bayard's Cove Fort
Dartmouth
Dartmouth Castle

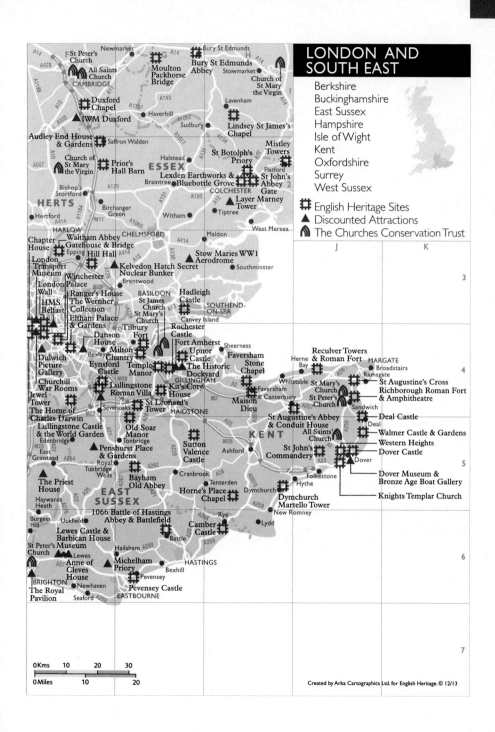

LONDON AND SOUTH EAST

Berkshire
Buckinghamshire
East Sussex
Hampshire
Isle of Wight
Kent
Oxfordshire
Surrey
West Sussex

⚏ English Heritage Sites
▲ Discounted Attractions
ᛟ The Churches Conservation Trust

0 Kms 10 20 30
0 Miles 10 20

Created by Arka Cartographics Ltd. for English Heritage. © 12/13

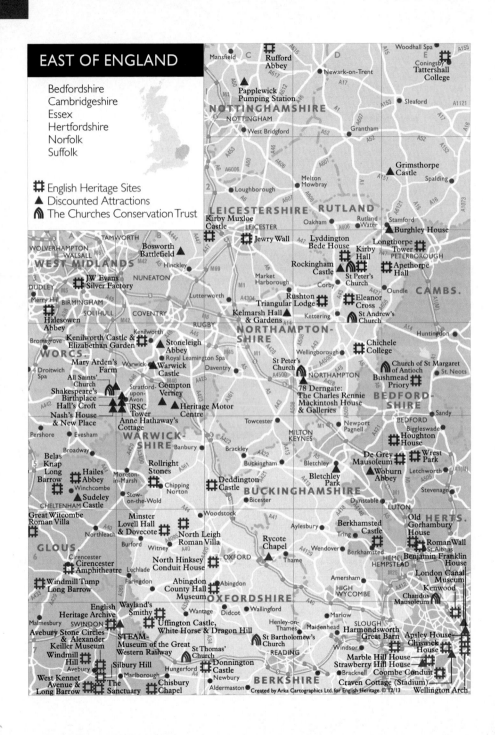

EAST OF ENGLAND

Bedfordshire
Cambridgeshire
Essex
Hertfordshire
Norfolk
Suffolk

English Heritage Sites
▲ Discounted Attractions
⋔ The Churches Conservation Trust

Sibsey Trader Windmill

Boston

Hunstanton

Holkham Hall

Wells-next-the-Sea

Blakeney Guildhall

Sheringham

Cromer

Holt

Creake Abbey

A149

Baconsthorpe Castle

Mundesley

The Wash

Binham Priory Binham Market Cross

Castle Rising Castle

Long Sutton

Holbeach

Fakenham

Aylsham

North Walsham

Hemsby

St Nicholas' Chapel

King's Lynn

Castle Acre Bailey Gate & Castle

North Elmham Chapel

RAF Air Defence Radar Museum

Wisbech

Downham Market

Castle Acre Priory

East Dereham

Church of St John

NORWICH

Norwich Castle Museum & Art Gallery

Caister Roman Fort

Great Yarmouth

March

Swaffham

St Mary's Church

Wymondham

Cow Tower

Berney Arms Windmill

Great Yarmouth Row Houses & Greyfriars' Cloisters

NORFOLK

Loddon

Burgh Castle

Grime's Graves

Attleborough

St Olave's Priory

LOWESTOFT

CAMBRIDGESHIRE

Weeting Castle

Thetford Warren Lodge

Thetford Priory

Bungay

Somerleyton Hall & Gardens

Beccles

Chatteris

Isleham Priory Church

Brandon

Thetford

Diss

Kessingland

Oliver Cromwell's House

Ely

Church of the Holy Sepulchre

A1066

Halesworth

Southwold

A1123

SUFFOLK

Denny Abbey & the Farmland Museum

Newmarket

Bury St Edmunds Abbey

Bury St Edmunds

Saxtead Green Post Mill

Framlingham Castle

St Peter's Church

Moulton Packhorse Bridge

Stowmarket

Church of St Mary the Virgin

Leiston Abbey

CAMBRIDGE

All Saints' Church

Aldeburgh

Duxford Chapel

Lavenham

St Peter's Church

Woodbridge

Orford Castle

IWM Duxford

Haverhill

Sudbury

Lindsey St James's Chapel

IPSWICH

Orford

Saffron Walden

Church of St Mary the Virgin

Audley End House & Gardens

Halstead

St Botolph's Priory

Mistley Towers

Felixstowe

Felixstowe Museum

Prior's Hall Barn

Braintree

Lexden Earthworks & Bluebottle Grove

Flatford

St John's Abbey Gate

Harwich

Landguard Fort

Bishop's Stortford

ESSEX

COLCHESTER

HERTS.

Birchanger Green

Witham

Layer Marney Tower

Tiptree

Frinton-on-Sea

Hertford

Chapter House

HARLOW

Waltham Abbey Gatehouse & Bridge

CHELMSFORD

Maldon

West Mersea

Clacton-on-Sea

Epping

London Transport Museum

Hill Hall

Kelvedon Hatch Secret Nuclear Bunker

Stow Maries Aerodrome

Southminster

London Wall

Winchester Palace

Brentwood

BASILDON

Hadleigh Castle

HMS Belfast

Ranger's House

The Wernher Collection

St James Church

SOUTHEND-ON-SEA

Eltham Palace & Gardens

St Mary's Church

Canvey Island

Churchill War Rooms

Milton Chantry

Tilbury Fort

Danson House

Rochester Castle

Jewel Tower

Temple Manor

Eynsford Castle

Upnor Castle

The Historic Dockyard

Fort Amherst

Sheerness

Herne Bay

Faversham Stone Chapel

Reculver Towers & Roman Fort

MARGATE

Broadstairs

Ramsgate

Whitstable

St Augustine's Cross

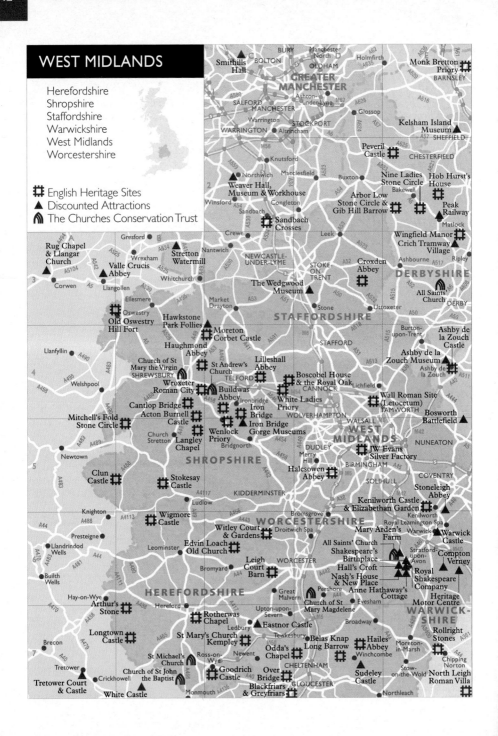

WEST MIDLANDS

Herefordshire
Shropshire
Staffordshire
Warwickshire
West Midlands
Worcestershire

⊞ English Heritage Sites
▲ Discounted Attractions
♠ The Churches Conservation Trust

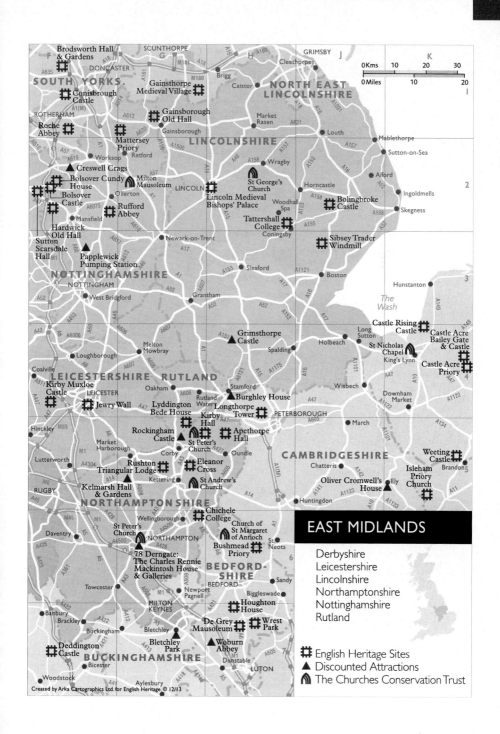

Brodsworth Hall & Gardens
SCUNTHORPE
DONCASTER
SOUTH YORKS.
A635
Conisbrough Castle
A1(M)
ROTHERHAM
Roche Abbey
A613
GRIMSBY
Cleethorpes
GAINSBOROUGH
Gainsthorpe Medieval Village
Brigg
M181
M180
A180
Caistor
NORTH EAST LINCOLNSHIRE
Market Rasen
Gainsborough Old Hall
Gainsborough
Mattersey Priory
A1500
LINCOLNSHIRE
A631
Louth
Mablethorpe
Sutton-on-Sea
Creswell Crags
Worksop
Retford
A158
Wragby
A157
Alford
Bolsover Cundy House
Milton Mausoleum
LINCOLN
Ollerton
Bolsover Castle
A6075
Rufford Abbey
St George's Church
Lincoln Medieval Bishops' Palace
Horncastle
A158
Bolingbroke Castle
Ingoldmells
Skegness
Mansfield
Woodhall Spa
Hardwick Old Hall
Sutton Scarsdale Hall
Newark-on-Trent
Tattershall College
Coningsby
Sibsey Trader Windmill
Papplewick Pumping Station
NOTTINGHAMSHIRE
A1
A17
A153
Sleaford
A1121
Boston
Hunstanton
NOTTINGHAM
West Bridgford
A52
Grantham
A52
A52
A52
The Wash
A149
Castle Rising Castle
Castle Acre Bailey Gate & Castle
Loughborough
Grimsthorpe Castle
Melton Mowbray
Spalding
Holbeach
Long Sutton
St Nicholas Chapel
King's Lynn
Castle Acre Priory
Coalville
LEICESTERSHIRE RUTLAND
Wisbech
Downham Market
A1122
Kirby Muxloe Castle
LEICESTER
Jewry Wall
Oakham
Rutland Water
Lyddington Bede House
Stamford
Burghley House
Longthorpe Tower
PETERBOROUGH
March
A134
Hinckley
Kirby Hall
Apethorpe Hall
Market Harborough
Rockingham Castle
St Peter's Church
Corby
Oundle
CAMBRIDGESHIRE
Weeting Castle
Lutterworth
Kettering
Rushton Triangular Lodge
Eleanor Cross
St Andrew's Church
Chatteris
Isleham Priory Church
Brandon
RUGBY
Kelmarsh Hall & Gardens
NORTHAMPTONSHIRE
Oliver Cromwell's House
Ely
Huntingdon
Chichele College
Wellingborough
St Peter's Church
Church of St Margaret of Antioch
St Neots
Daventry
NORTHAMPTON
Bushmead Priory
78 Derngate: The Charles Rennie Mackintosh House & Galleries
BEDFORD-SHIRE
BEDFORD
Sandy
Towcester
Newport Pagnell
Biggleswade
Banbury
MILTON KEYNES
Houghton House
Brackley
De Grey Mausoleum
Wrest Park
Buckingham
Bletchley
Deddington Castle
Bletchley Park
Woburn Abbey
BUCKINGHAMSHIRE
Dunstable
Bicester
LUTON
Woodstock
Aylesbury

Created by Arka Cartographics Ltd. for English Heritage. © 12/13

0Kms 10 20 30
0Miles 10 20

EAST MIDLANDS

Derbyshire
Leicestershire
Lincolnshire
Northamptonshire
Nottinghamshire
Rutland

English Heritage Sites
Discounted Attractions
The Churches Conservation Trust

NORTH WEST (South)

Cheshire
Greater Manchester
Lancashire
Merseyside

⌗ English Heritage Sites
▲ Discounted Attractions
♠ The Churches Conservation Trust

| 0 Kms | 10 | 20 | 30 |
| 0 Miles | 10 | 20 | |

Maryport
Cockermouth
Workington
A66
Mayburgh Henge
Penrith Castle
PENRITH
St Ninian's
Brougham Castle
Castlerigg Stone Circle
Clifton Hall
Countess Pillar
Keswick
Lowther Castle
Appleby-in-Westmorland
Barnard Castle
WHITEHAVEN
Ullswater
King Arthur's Round Table
Brough
Seatoller Barn
Shap Abbey
Egremont
CUMBRIA
Brough Castle
Bowes Castle
Bowes
Grasmere
Ambleside
Kirkby Stephen
Hardknott Roman Fort
Ambleside Roman Fort
Waterhead
Tebay
Reeth
Sellafield
Windermere
Ravenglass
Hawkshead
Coniston
Kendal
Sedbergh
Hawes
Aysgarth Falls
Ravenglass Roman Bath House
Broughton-in-Furness
Stott Park Bobbin Mill
Kirkby Lonsdale
Bootle
Millom
Ulverston
Grange-over-Sands
Horton-in-Ribblesdale
Furness Abbey
Warton Old Rectory
Ingleton
Clapham
Bow Bridge
BARROW-IN-FURNESS
Carnforth
High Bentham
Settle
Grassington
Morecambe
Morecambe
Lancaster
Piel Castle
Piel Island
Morecambe Bay
Malham
Skipton
Fleetwood
Garstang
LANCASHIRE
Sawley Abbey
Barnoldswick
Cleveleys
Clitheroe
Pendle Heritage Centre
Whalley Abbey Gatehouse
BLACKPOOL
BURNLEY
Hebden Bridge
Accrington
Lytham St. Anne's
PRESTON
BLACKBURN
Goodshaw Chapel
Todmorden
Oswaldtwistle
Rawtenstall
SOUTHPORT
Chorley
ROCHDALE
Ormskirk
BURY
Manchester North
Formby
Smithills Hall
BOLTON
OLDHAM
GREATER MANCHESTER
BOOTLE
KIRKBY
ST. HELENS
Ashton-under-Lyne
MERSEYSIDE
St Helens
SALFORD
MANCHESTER
Glossop
LIVERPOOL
Warrington
STOCKPORT
BIRKENHEAD
Runcorn
WARRINGTON
Altrincham
WIDNES
Llandudno
Rhos-on-Sea
Rhyl
Prestatyn
RUNCORN
Norton Priory Museum & Gardens
Knutsford
Conwy
Colwyn Bay
ELLESMERE PORT
Conwy Castle
Rhuddlan Castle
Neston
Northwich
Macclesfield
Plas Mawr
Flint
Chester Castle Agricola Tower & Castle Walls
Weaver Hall, Museum & Workhouse
Denbigh
Winsford
Mold
CHESTER
CHESHIRE
Sandbach
Congleton
Chester Roman Amphitheatre
Beeston Castle & Woodland Park
Sandbach Crosses
Leek
Ruthin
Gresford
Crewe
Betws-y-Coed
Wrexham
Nantwich
NEWCASTLE-UNDER-LYME
STOKE-ON-TRENT
Dolwyddelan Castle
Rug Chapel & Llangar Church
Stretton Watermill
Valle Crucis Abbey
Whitchurch
Blaenau Ffestiniog
The Wedgwood Museum
Corwen
Llangollen

Created by Arka Cartographics Ltd. for English Heritage. © 12/13

YORKSHIRE

East Riding of Yorkshire
North East Lincolnshire
North Lincolnshire
North Yorkshire
South Yorkshire
West Yorkshire

✠ English Heritage Sites
▲ Discounted Attractions
⋔ The Churches Conservation Trust

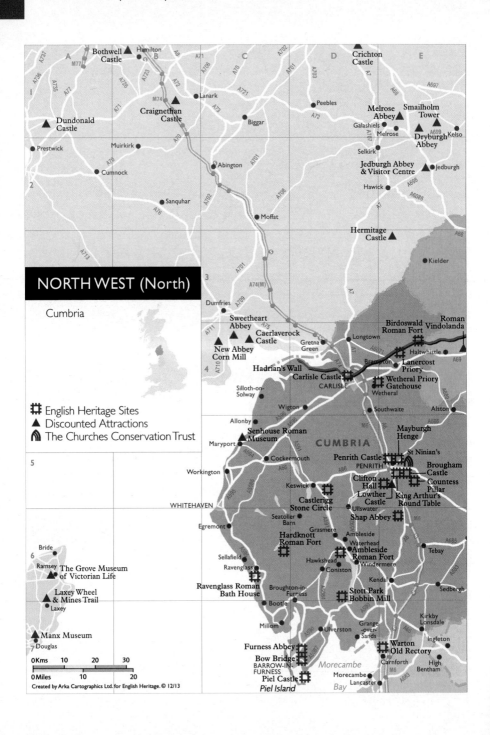

NORTH WEST (North)

Cumbria

🔳 English Heritage Sites
▲ Discounted Attractions
🄰 The Churches Conservation Trust

Bothwell Castle
Hamilton
Craignethan Castle
Lanark
Dundonald Castle
Prestwick
Muirkirk
Cumnock
Sanquhar
Abington
Biggar
Moffat
Dumfries
Sweetheart Abbey
New Abbey Corn Mill
Caerlaverock Castle
Hadrian's Wall
Carlisle Castle
CARLISLE
Silloth-on-Solway
Gretna Green
Longtown
Brampton
Wigton
Allonby
Maryport
Senhouse Roman Museum
Cockermouth
Workington
WHITEHAVEN
Keswick
Castlerigg Stone Circle
Seatoller Barn
Egremont
Grasmere
Hardknott Roman Fort
Ambleside
Waterhead
Ambleside Roman Fort
Windermere
Coniston
Hawkshead
Sellafield
Ravenglass
Ravenglass Roman Bath House
Broughton-in-Furness
Bootle
Millom
Ulverston
Grange-over-Sands
Furness Abbey
Bow Bridge
BARROW-IN-FURNESS
Piel Castle
Piel Island
Morecambe
Morecambe Bay
Lancaster

Crichton Castle
Peebles
Melrose Abbey
Smailholm Tower
Galashiels
Melrose
Dryburgh Abbey
Kelso
Selkirk
Jedburgh Abbey & Visitor Centre
Jedburgh
Hawick
Hermitage Castle
Kielder
Birdoswald Roman Fort
Roman Vindolanda
Haltwhistle
Lanercost Priory
Wetheral Priory Gatehouse
Wetheral
Southwaite
Alston
Mayburgh Henge
St Ninian's
Penrith Castle
PENRITH
Brougham Castle
Clifton Hall
Countess Pillar
Lowther Castle
King Arthur's Round Table
Ullswater
Shap Abbey
Tebay
Kendal
Sedbergh
Stott Park Bobbin Mill
Kirkby Lonsdale
Ingleton
Warton Old Rectory
Carnforth
High Bentham

CUMBRIA

Bride
Ramsey
The Grove Museum of Victorian Life
Laxey Wheel & Mines Trail
Laxey
Manx Museum
Douglas

0 Kms 10   20   30
0 Miles 10   20
Created by Arka Cartographics Ltd. for English Heritage. © 12/13

NORTH EAST

County Durham
Northumberland
Tyne & Wear
Tees Valley

English Heritage Sites
▲ **Discounted Attractions**
The Churches Conservation Trust

A6112
F
A6105 G
H
I
Berwick-upon-Tweed Barracks & Main Guard
Berwick-upon-Tweed Castle & Town Defences
Berwick-upon-Tweed
Norham Castle
Lindisfarne Priory
Coldstream
Etal Castle
Bamburgh Castle
Belford ● ● Seahouses
Adderstone ●
Wooler ●
Dunstanburgh Castle
Craster
2
Alnwick Castle ● Alnwick
Edlingham Castle
Warkworth Castle & Hermitage
Rothbury ● ● Amble
J
K
NORTHUMBERLAND
Black Middens Bastle House
Brinkburn Priory
● Otterburn
A1068
Morpeth
ASHINGTON
Newbiggin-by-the-Sea
3
Bellingham ●
Belsay Hall Castle & Gardens
● Blyth
Chesters Roman Fort & Museum
Bessie Surtees House
Whitley Bay
Chesters Bridge Abutment
NEWCASTLE UPON TYNE
Tynemouth Priory & Castle
Segedunum Roman Fort, Bath House & Museum
Housesteads Roman Fort
Aydon Castle
Prudhoe Castle
St Paul's Monastery
Haydon Bridge ●
Hexham ●
● Prudhoe
4
Hexham Old Gaol
Derwentcote Steel Furnace
TYNE & WEAR
SUNDERLAND
Corbridge Roman Town
St Andrew's Church
● Beamish
Hylton Castle
A19
Killhope - The North of England Lead Mining Museum
Consett
Tanfield Railway
Finchale Priory
● Stanhope
DURHAM
A1(M)
● Peterlee
5
DURHAM
● Spennymoor
A19
HARTLEPOOL
Auckland Castle Deer House
● Bishop Auckland
A177
● Billingham
● Redcar
The Bowes Museum
Piercebridge Roman Bridge
STOCKTON-ON-TEES
● Brotton
All Saints' Church
Gisborough Priory
Barnard Castle
TEES VALLEY
MIDDLES-BROUGH
● Guisborough
A174
● Pickering
Whitby Abbey
Brough
Bowes ● Bowes
DARLINGTON
Church of St John the Baptist
● Great Ayton
Whitby
St Stephen's Church
Brough Castle
Bowes Castle
Egglestone Abbey
Stanwick Iron Age Fortifications
A19
A172
● Danby
A169
Kirkby Stephen
Reeth ●
● Richmond
A167
6
Easby Abbey
A684
Mount Grace Priory
Wheeldale Roman Road
Richmond Castle
● Catterick
● Northallerton
Scarborough Castle
Hawes ●
Aysgarth Falls
A684
Leyburn ● Bedale ●
Leeming Bar
NORTH YORKSHIRE
Rievaulx Abbey
Helmsley
Helmsley Castle
Pickering Castle
SCARBOROUGH
Holy Trinity Church
Middleham Castle
Thirsk ●
A170
North Yorkshire Moors Railway
● Filey
Horton-in-Ribblesdale
Marmion Tower
Byland Abbey
Duncombe Park
B1257
A64
7
● Clapham
St Mary's Church, Studley Royal
● Ripon
Aldborough Roman Site
Castle Howard
Malton
St Peter's Church
Burton Agnes Manor House
Grassington ●
● Settle
Fountains Abbey & Studley Royal Water Garden
A61
Church of Christ the Consoler
Easingwold
● Boroughbridge
Kirkham Priory
Wharram Percy Deserted Medieval Village
A166
Malham ●

CELEBRATE WITH US

☉ PROPERTIES FOR HIRE

Properties available for hire are marked with a ☉ throughout the handbook. Those also licensed for civil ceremonies are marked with a ▣.

LONDON

▣ **Eltham Palace**
020 8294 2577

Kenwood
020 7973 3416

▣ **Marble Hill House**
020 7973 3416

▣ **Ranger's House**
020 8294 2577

Wellington Arch
020 7973 3416

SOUTH EAST

Osborne
Isle of Wight 01983 203055

EAST

▣ **Bolsover Castle**
Derbyshire 01246 856456

▣ **Wrest Park**
Bedfordshire 01525 863704

SOUTH WEST

▣ **Cleeve Abbey**
Somerset 01984 640377

▣ **Old Wardour Castle**
Wiltshire 01305 820868

▣ **Pendennis Castle**
Cornwall 01326 310106

▣ **Portland Castle**
Dorset 01305 820868

▣ **St Mawes Castle**
Cornwall 01326 310106

WEST

▣ **Kenilworth Castle and Elizabethan Garden**
Warwickshire 01926 857482

For more information on exclusive hire, please contact the Hospitality Managers on the property telephone numbers above, or visit **www.english-heritage.org. uk/hospitality**

Download the Aurasma App to view our short film

Simply follow these easy steps to download and activate the film:

1 If you have an iPhone or iPad, visit your App Store (for Android phones or tablets go to Google Play) and search for Aurasma. Follow the on-screen steps to download and install the app.

2 Open the app, search for and follow the English Heritage channel.

3 Hold your phone over the front cover where you will see the Aurasma logo.

4 The film will start automatically. To view full screen, double tap the screen. This will also allow you to move the phone away from the book. A single tap will pause and play the film.

Details of OS LandRanger and Explorer map references are provided for easy location of each property, with specific map numbers (LandRanger; Explorer) followed by the grid reference.

NB. All maps in this handbook are created using Ordnance Survey mapping. Unless otherwise credited, they are © Crown Copyright and database right 2012. All rights reserved. Ordnance Survey Licence number 100019088.

English Heritage Handbook 2014/15

For English Heritage:
Luke Whitcomb, Johanna Lovesey, Tersia Boorer, Charles Kightly, Alison Gilbert, Rebecca White, Peter D'Ambrosio.

Design and Publishing:
Ledgard Jepson Ltd.

For Ledgard Jepson Ltd:
David Exley, Bev Turbitt, Andrea Rollinson.

Print: Pindar plc.

Transport Information:
John Burch, CPT.

Images: All images in this handbook are © English Heritage unless otherwise stated.

All CCT images are © CCT unless otherwise stated.